Collins

Atlas of the Night Sky

Storm Dunlop

Illustrated by Wil Tirion and Antonín Rükl

HarperCollins*Publishers* Ltd.
77-85 Fulham Palace Road
London
W6 8JB

The Collins website address is:
www.collins.co.uk

Collins is a registered trademark of
HarperCollins*Publishers* Ltd.

First published in 2005

A catalogue record for this book is available from the British Library.

ISBN 0 00 717223 0

Designed by Colin Brown

Colour reproduction by Colourscan, Singapore
Printed and bound in Thailand by Imago

Photo credits: pp. 94, 95, 202, 203 and 204 – NASA/Space Telescope
Science Institute

Mars map, p. 202 – © Unione Astrofili Italiani (Planetary Section):
Paolo Tanga and Mario Frassati

Authors' acknowledgements
Storm and Wil would like to thank Steve Edberg and Steve O'Meara, together with Katie Piper (formerly at HarperCollins) for their
help in the initial stages, and Mary Chibnall and Peter Hingley (at the RAS Library), Peter Gill and Brian Marsden for assistance on
specific points. Thanks also go to Myles Archibald, Helen Brocklehurst and Emily Pitcher at HarperCollins for their patience in the
latter stages of the editorial process.
    Creating up-to-date charts of the Moon would not have been possible without the co-operation of prominent specialists, who
readily gave advice and enabled access to essential base materials. Foremost among these were: the late Dr Merton E. Davies, RAND
Corporation, USA; Mr. Ewen A. Whitaker, Lunar and Planetary Laboratory, Univ. of Arizona, USA; the late Dr Thomas W. Rackham,
Jodrell Bank, England and the late Professor Zdenek Kopal, Univ. of Manchester, England. Antonín Rükl would like to express his
gratitude to all of them for their friendly help, as well as to Storm for his significant suggestions and advice on the content and layout
of the lunar part of this atlas. Last but not least, he extends his thanks to his son, Michael, a computer specialist, for keeping father's
instrumentation operable, and to his wife, Sonja, for the patient moral support she gave him while he was working on this atlas.

Contents

Introduction

How to use this book

This atlas is intended to offer amateur astronomers all the information they need to navigate their way around the night sky with ease. It combines charts showing large areas of the sky with extensive and detailed coverage of each constellation, and has been split into four sections:

Section one contains 20 charts which cover the whole sky to a limiting magnitude of 6.5, accompanied by data detailing objects of particular interest within the relevant area. A master chart showing how these relate to each other is given on pages 216–217.

Section two covers all of the 88 constellations in detail, with descriptions of interesting objects. These objects have corresponding charts to a limiting magnitude of 7.5, which show fainter stars than the main charts. Complex or particularly interesting objects have additional charts at a larger scale and some are also complemented by photographs.

Section three provides extensive information on the Moon, with detailed, original maps created by Antonín Rükl. Each lunar map is accompanied by a smaller-scale reversed map, to help users of telescopes that have mirror-image reversal with orientation.

The final section gives details of Solar System objects, and also provides information on the positions of the major planets, on all four latitudes, for the next five years.

The index at the back of the book should help you to find quickly and easily all the lunar features and constellations you are looking for.

The celestial sphere and constellations

All astronomical objects appear to lie on a large sphere, centred on the observer. This celestial sphere is divided into 88 constellations, which are listed on pages 52–155 with their official Latin names.

An asterism is a prominent group of stars, usually with some popular name, that do not necessarily form a whole constellation. The group of seven stars known as 'The Plough' or 'The Big Dipper' is an asterism, and is just part of the large constellation of Ursa Major.

Positions on the sky are described in one of several different systems of coordinates. Two systems are commonly used, the first of these, known as the 'horizontal' or 'altitude-azimuth' (alt-az) system, being based on the observer's position and the horizon (Fig. 1). The position of any object is specified by its altitude, measured in degrees, above (+) or below (-) the horizon, and by its azimuth, the angle in degrees, measured around the horizon from north (through east, south, west, and back to north), to the vertical line beneath the object. Two points on the celestial sphere are

given specific names. These are the zenith, directly above the observer's head, and the nadir, directly below their feet. One line (a great circle) is particularly important. This is the meridian, which runs from the north point, through the zenith to the south point. The other common coordinate system resembles the system of latitude and longitude used on Earth (and on the Moon, other planets, and their satellites).

Celestial coordinates

Because of the rotation of the Earth, the celestial sphere appears to rotate once a day about an axis (an extension of the Earth's own axis), running through the North and South Celestial Poles (Fig. 2). The North Celestial Pole is very close to Polaris, the Pole Star, which is a convenient marker, but there is no bright star near the South Celestial Pole.

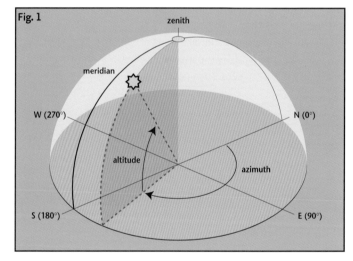

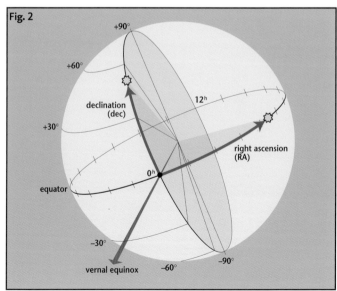

Halfway between the two poles, and in the same plane as the Earth's equator, is the celestial equator. During the course of a year, the Sun appears to travel along a path, known as the ecliptic, inclined at approximately 23.5° to the celestial equator, crossing it at the vernal (spring) and autumnal equinoxes. The ecliptic is shown as a red dashed line on the main star charts (pp. 12–51).

These points may be used to define a set of celestial coordinates, required for finding objects in the sky, and similar to the system of latitude and longitude used on Earth. The coordinate similar to latitude is declination (dec.), measured in degrees, minutes and seconds of arc north (+) or south (-) of the celestial equator. The coordinate similar to longitude is Right Ascension (RA). Because it is related to the rotation of the Earth, it is measured in hours, minutes and seconds of time, eastwards along the celestial equator. The starting (or zero) point is taken as the vernal equinox (otherwise known as the First Point of Aries), where the Sun, moving along the ecliptic, crosses the celestial equator from south to north (Fig. 3).

Astronomical positions are normally quoted in the order: RA, dec. The position of Sirius, the brightest star in the sky, for example, is RA = $06^h45^m19^s$, dec. = -16°43'01", generally given in this atlas in rounded, decimal form as $06^h45.3^m$, -16°43', the seconds of arc being omitted.

Because of the gravitational effects of the other bodies in the Solar System (particularly the Moon), the Earth's axis is not fixed in space, but slowly sweeps out a cone, taking about 25,800 years to complete one circle. This precession, as it is called, causes the intersection of the celestial equator and ecliptic to alter with time, so celestial coordinates are gradually changing. For most amateur purposes the effect is so small that it may be ignored, but it does affect charts, which are occasionally redrawn. The coordinate grid is given for one specific point in time, known as an epoch. For charts in this atlas the epoch is 2000.0, namely midnight (00:00 hours) on the night of 1999 December 31 to 2000 January 1. Older atlases may give charts for epoch 1950, 1900 or earlier.

Note that Right Ascension and declination apply for any observer, anywhere on Earth. They are not dependent on the observer's position. The stars that are visible to any observer, however, and the apparent paths of the Sun, Moon, planets, and stars across the sky are dependent on the observer's latitude. At one of the poles, half of the sky would always be visible, the other half being permanently hidden below the horizon. Stars' paths are circles parallel to the horizon (Fig. 4). At the equator, theoretically, the whole sky would be visible, and stars would rise at right-angles to the horizon (Fig. 5). At intermediate latitudes, the altitude of the respective pole is equal to the observer's latitude. At 50°N, for example, the North Celestial Pole is 50° above the northern horizon (Fig. 6). All stars within 50° of the Pole are permanently

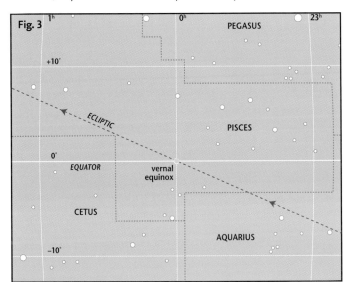

Fig. 3

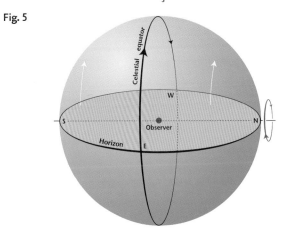

Fig. 4

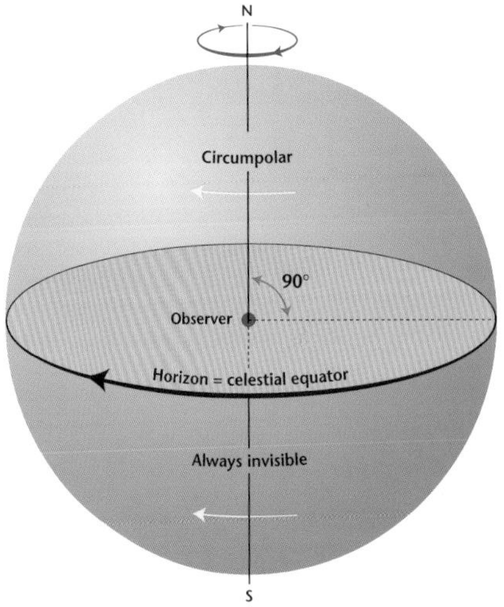

Fig. 5

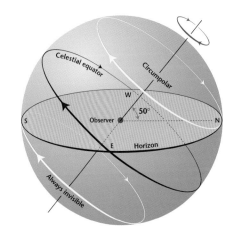

Fig. 6

above the horizon. Expressed differently, all stars with declinations greater than +43° (90°–47°) are above the horizon, and are said to be circumpolar. At the equator there are no circumpolar stars.

Because of the Earth's motion around the Sun, the constellations that are visible on any given night vary throughout the year. The best conditions for viewing any constellation are when it culminates (is highest in the sky), crossing the meridian (the north–south line) at local midnight. The descriptions of individual constellations include details of when they culminate at local midnight. (The dates apply to the centres of the constellations, so there may be a considerable period when parts of the constellation are readily visible.) Technically, stars and constellations that are circumpolar (i.e., always remain above the horizon at any one location) culminate twice, once below the pole (lower culmination) and once above it (upper culmination). Only upper culmination is given in these cases.

Every star moves in its own orbit around the centre of the Galaxy. Over a long period of time, all stars change their positions relative to one another. This proper motion may, in general, be neglected by amateurs because it is so slow. If neighbouring stars are found to possess identical proper motions, it is an indication that they probably belong to the same group or cluster. With double stars, this is a strong indication that they form a gravitationally bound system, even if no orbital motion is evident.

Other coordinate systems

Other coordinate systems exist, and two are occasionally used in general astronomy. The first, ecliptic coordinates, predates the use of right ascension and declination, and is used to specify the position of Solar System objects such as planets and comets. It is based upon the ecliptic, the Sun's apparent path across the sky, which is actually the plane of the Earth's orbit around the Sun. In the most commonly encountered form, the position of an object is given by its celestial latitude, north (+) or south (-) of the ecliptic, and its celestial longitude, measured in degrees (0–360°) from the vernal equinox (the First Point of Aries). The zodiac is the region of sky, 16° wide (± 8° celestial latitude), centred on the ecliptic, in which the Sun, Moon, and the major planets appear to move.

The other system of coordinates of particular interest is the system of galactic coordinates, which specifies the location of objects relative to the main plane of the galaxy, the galactic equator, which is highly inclined to both the celestial equator and the ecliptic. It is shown by a green dashed line on the main star charts (pp. 12–51). The North Galactic Pole is located in the constellation of Coma Berenices (Chart 5), and the South Galactic Pole in Sculptor (Chart 14). Again, galactic latitude is measured north (+) and south (-) of the galactic equator. Galactic longitude is measured in degrees (0–360°) from the centre of the galaxy, determined by radio methods, which lies in Sagittarius (RA 17^{h}46^m, dec. -28°56'), close to the borders of Ophiuchus and Scorpius.

Various classes of object show differing degrees of concentration towards the galactic equator, reflecting their distribution in the Galaxy. Objects such as open clusters, emission nebulae, and novae tend to lie close to the galactic equator, whereas globular clusters occupy a generally spherical region, centred on the galactic centre.

Relative positions on the sky

It is often necessary to specify the location of an object with reference to some other object, such as a bright star. Generally in this book, positions are given with reference to the standard compass points. Looking south in the northern hemisphere, for example, an object said to be northeast of a particular star will have a higher declination and greater right ascension, i.e., will be to the observer's left. In the southern hemisphere looking north, both declination and right ascension would still be greater, but the star would be to the observer's right. To prevent confusion, experienced observers often use the terms 'North preceding', 'North following', 'South preceding' and 'South following' (Fig. 7). These terms are particularly useful when using an undriven telescope because, whatever the orientation of the image, preceding objects will move

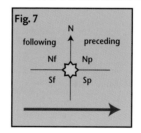

away from the centre of the field, while following ones will approach it. Relative positions may also be specified in terms of Position Angle and Separation (described later).

The names of stars

Many bright stars have individual names, such as Polaris, Sirius, and Arcturus. Most are of Arabic origin, but others come from Greek or Latin. Frequently, however, astronomers prefer to use the designations given by Johannes Bayer in the first star atlas, the *Uranometria*, published in 1603. He used Greek letters (see Table 1) for the brightest stars in each constellation. In some constellations he also used additional Roman letters. These designations are used with the genitive form of the constellation's name. Some examples are α Andromedae, β Orionis, and P Cygni.

Many fainter stars have numerical designations, sometimes preceded by a letter (or letters) indicating a specific catalogue. In this atlas the most common are Flamsteed numbers, assigned by the first Astronomer Royal, John Flamsteed, in his catalogue of 1725, generally in order of Right Ascension within a constellation. Examples are 61 Cygni, 16 and 17 Draconis, and 47 Ursae Majoris.

Specialized catalogues have been compiled for stars with specific characteristics. These numbers are often given without the constellation names. In this atlas the most common such designations are 'Σ' and 'OΣ', for 'Struve' and 'Otto Struve' (father and son), who compiled catalogues of double stars. An example is Σ 1785, a double star in Boötes. The designation 'β' indicates the

Table 1 Greek alphabet

α	alpha	ζ	zeta	λ	lambda	π	pi	φ	phi
β	beta	η	eta	μ	mu	ρ	rho	χ	chi
γ	gamma	ϑ	theta	ν	nu	σ	sigma	ψ	psi
δ	delta	ι	iota	ξ	xi	τ	tau	ω	omega
ε	epsilon	κ	kappa	ο	omicron	υ	upsilon		

catalogue compiled by S.W. Burnham and 'h' is used for a few southern objects described by J.F.W. Herschel.

Variable stars have their own designations. Where they have Greek-letter identifications, these are retained. For other variables, those first discovered in any constellation are given Roman-letter designations, from R to Z. (Bayer used letters as far as Q.) Then two letters are used: RR, RS ... YZ, ZZ. When these designations are exhausted, the sequence restarts: AA, AB ... AZ; BB, BC ... BZ; CC, CD ... CZ ... ZZ (J being omitted). This complicated scheme allows for the lettering of 334 variables in a constellation. When this number is exhausted, subsequent discoveries are designated with the letter 'V' followed by a number, beginning V335. Examples are: δ Cephei, P Cygni, R Aquilae, and V1500 Cygni.

The distances of stars and other objects

Astronomical distances have always been difficult to measure. Within the Solar System, triangulation may be used, and distances are normally expressed in astronomical units (AU), 1 AU being defined as 149,597,870 km, which is essentially the mean distance of the Earth from the Sun. The same unit is generally used in discussing the planetary systems existing round other stars.

The distances of stars and other objects in this atlas are generally given in light-years (l.y.): the distance light travels in one year. The closest known star, Proxima Centauri, lies at a distance of 4.22 light-years. Astronomers frequently use a different unit: the parsec (pc), a contraction of 'parallax second'. This is the distance at which the average radius of the Earth's orbit subtends an angle of one second of arc. It is equivalent to 3.2616 light-years, so all known stars lie at a greater distance than one parsec.

The distances to objects in the immediate neighbourhood of the Sun are now known with reasonable accuracy following the successful measurements made by the Hipparcos satellite. Distances within the Galaxy are often described in kiloparsecs (kpc): 1000 parsecs or 3261.6 l.y.; and distances of galaxies in megaparsecs (Mpc): 1 million parsecs or 3,261,600 l.y. Such great distances are determined by various methods, the most important of which rely upon the characteristics of certain variable stars, particularly Cepheid variables, where the period of the fluctuations is strictly related to their absolute (rather than apparent) luminosity. Another method relies upon certain supernovae, which have similarly well-defined amplitudes, and may be used for greater distance determinations.

The names of deep-sky objects

Deep-sky objects include the various types of nebulae, star clusters, and galaxies. A few star clusters were given names in antiquity, such as the Pleiades and Praesepe. Most are known by the numbers assigned in different catalogues, usually consisting of a letter (or letters) followed by a number. The designations most commonly encountered are those from the Messier catalogue, the New General Catalogue, and the Index Catalogue. These are abbreviated as M, NGC, and IC, respectively. For space considerations, the last is written as 'I.' on the charts. Examples are M45, NGC 404, and IC 2149 ('I.2149'). Because, unlike variable stars or most double stars, the names of such objects do not include the constellation name, the latter is shown separately in the lists accompanying the main charts.

The magnitudes of stars and other objects

The brightness of stars is measured in magnitudes, shown on the charts by dots of differing sizes. The scale was originally introduced by the Greek astronomer Hipparchos, who classified stars into six magnitude classes: the brightest being first magnitude, and the faintest visible to the naked eye, sixth magnitude. The scale now has a mathematical basis, and a first-magnitude star is defined as being precisely 100 times as bright as one of magnitude six. (The difference is logarithmic, each magnitude differing by a factor of 2.512 from the next.) The scale was defined by taking a particular star, Vega, α Lyrae, to have a magnitude of 0.0. Certain stars were found to be brighter than Vega, so negative magnitudes were introduced. Sirius has an apparent magnitude of -1.44, Venus and Jupiter may sometimes reach about magnitude -4.0, and the Full Moon is about -13.0.

Most of the magnitudes described in the detailed notes are apparent magnitudes (m) as they appear to the eye. However, stars' luminosities differ greatly: two stars of the same apparent brightness may actually be an extremely luminous star at a great distance and a much fainter one that is nearby. Astronomers therefore use a different form of magnitude, absolute magnitude (M), to describe a star's true luminosity. This is the magnitude that a star would have at a specific, fixed distance of 10 parsecs (32.616 light-years). Such absolute magnitudes are mentioned in a few cases in the descriptions of individual stars.

The majority of magnitudes given here are visual magnitudes, that is, the magnitudes that objects would appear to the human eye. In some cases, however, magnitudes may be followed by the letter 'p', indicating that the value is 'photographic'. Such photographic magnitudes are now obsolete, but may be given when no more recent or more accurate information is available. They generally differ slightly from visual magnitudes. It is also standard practice in astronomy for an approximate magnitude to be shown by a colon (:) following the value. When a star's magnitude is not known exactly, it might (for example) be shown as 'mag. 10.2:', meaning 'approximately magnitude 10.2'.

The brightness of other objects such as clusters and galaxies is also measured in magnitudes, but here the figures may be deceptive, because the magnitudes give the total brightness, (i.e., the brightness integrated over the whole area). Unlike stars, these objects may extend over a considerable area of sky, so they normally appear much fainter than the magnitude might imply. This should be taken into account when consulting the tables or descriptions. Experienced observers make use of 'averted vision' to see faint objects. In this technique, the observer does not look directly at the object concerned, but to one side. In doing so, the image falls on a part of the retina that is not sensitive to colour, but is more sensitive to faint light. Generally, the effect is greatest when the object is placed on the nose side, and towards the bottom of the field of view.

The colours and temperatures of stars

The most obvious feature of the brightest stars is that they differ in colour, ranging from blue-white stars, such as Rigel (β Orionis), to red stars, such as Antares (α Scorpii) or Betelgeuse (α Orionis). In fact, the colours reflect a range of surface temperatures, from the hottest, blue-white stars, through yellow stars (like the Sun), orange stars (such as Arcturus, α Boötis), to the coolest deep red stars, such as μ Cephei (the Garnet Star), and R Leporis (the Crimson Star). Stellar temperatures are normally given on the Kelvin scale, beginning at absolute zero (-273.16°C), and where 1 K = 1°C. Of the stars mentioned, Rigel has a surface temperature of about 11,500 K, and Betelgeuse, about 3450 K. The hottest stars may have temperatures as high as 50,000 K.

Colour is detectable by the human eye only above a certain level of brightness. For any given method of observation, whether naked-eye, binocular, or telescopic, there is a limit below which all stars appear white. This limit naturally varies slightly, depending on the observer's eyesight.

The spectra of stars

The spectrum of a star, obtained by passing the light through a prism or dispersing it with a diffraction grating, provides a great deal of information about the star's temperature and composition. Stars are often described by their spectral type. Omitting consideration of composition, which is shown by the presence or absence of bright or dark lines in the spectrum, the spectral sequence may be taken as a reflection of surface temperature.

Spectral classes, from hottest to coolest, follow the sequence O, B, A, F, G, K, M. (The standard mnemonic is 'Oh Be A Fine Girl, Kiss Me'.) Recently, classes L and T have been added at the cool end to characterize a group of stars with extremely low temperatures, and the objects known as brown dwarfs. Some additional classes are used to describe specific chemical compositions. These classes: R, N, S, and C (which are cool stars), and WN and WC (hot stars) may be mentioned occasionally. Most of the individual classes have 10 subdivisions, numbered 0–9

(hottest to coolest), although narrower subdivisions are sometimes used. The majority of stars fall between classes O5 and M8. The Sun, for example, is class G2, with a surface temperature of approximately 6000 K (Table 2).

Stellar sizes and luminosity classes

The sizes of stars vary widely, from gigantic objects such as μ Cephei, which if placed in the centre of the Solar System, would extend out beyond the orbit of Saturn, to white dwarf stars smaller

Table 2 Stellar colours, spectral classes, and temperatures

Star	Colour	Spectral class	Temperature
Regor (γ Vel)	Blue-white	WC8	50,000 K
Acrux (α Cru)	Blue-white	B0.5	28,000 K
Bellatrix (γ Ori)	Blue-white	B2	21,450 K
Regulus (α Leo)	Blue-white	B7	12,000 K
Rigel (β Ori)	Blue-white	B8	11,550 K
Merope (23 Tau)	Blue-white	B6	10,600 K
Vega (α Lyr)	White	A0	9,960 K
Sun	Yellow	G2	5,800 K
Arcturus (α Boo)	Orange	K1.5	4,420 K
μ Cephei	Deep Orange	M2	3,500 K
Betelgeuse (α Ori)	Red	M2	3,450 K
R Leporis	Deep Red	C7.6	3,000 K

than the Earth and, even smaller, to neutron stars just 10–20 km across. For historical reasons, stars are generally described as dwarfs (like the Sun), giants (such as Arcturus, α Tauri), and supergiants (Betelgeuse, α Orionis; Deneb, α Cygni; Antares, α Scorpii). Recently, some exceptionally large and luminous stars have been described as hypergiants.

An important property of stars is their luminosity. Large stars, such as Betelgeuse, may have low surface temperatures, but because they are gigantic, they may emit an enormous amount of energy. Depending on their size, therefore, stars with the same surface temperature may have widely different luminosities. Luminosity classes are occasionally mentioned in the descriptions and are shown in Table 3.

Variable stars

Many stars exhibit changes in brightness, and indeed all stars are variable at more than one stage in their evolution. The graph of magnitude against time is known as a light-curve, and the various classes tend to exhibit typical periods between maxima (or minima). The range of such periods is extreme: from flickering on a time-scale of minutes (or even seconds), to periods of many years. (The repeat period for certain eruptive variables is believed to be hundreds or even thousands of years.) Similarly, the range in brightness (the amplitude), although characteristic of the particular type of star, covers a wide span, from flickering of thousandths of a magnitude, to supernovae, where the change in brightness may be 20 magnitudes or more (i.e., an increase in luminosity of 100 million times, or more).

There are three broad classes of variables:

Eclipsing variables: stars in a binary system where one star periodically hides the second star, causing a decrease in brightness. Subdivided into the classes EA, EB, EW (and Ell), according to the shape of the light-curve.

Pulsating variables: stars that literally expand and contract, often on a very regular basis, and in doing so change their apparent brightness. This group includes the Cepheid variables (Cep, and CW); long-period variables (M); semiregular variables (SR); RV Tauri variables (RV); and irregular variables (Irr).

Eruptive or cataclysmic variables: stars that unexpectedly

brighten. These outbursts may range from small flares that are detectable only with sophisticated equipment, to supernovae, where whole stars are destroyed by the explosion. Eruptive variables include: supernovae (SN); novae and recurrent novae (N and NR); U Geminorum stars (UG); and Z Andromedae stars (ZAND). Shell stars of the γ Cassiopeiae type (GCAS), and R Coronae Borealis variables (RCB) may also be included in this group.

There are many different types of variables, not all of which are mentioned here, and many that may be studied only with large, professional telescopes. Brief details of some of the specific types included in the descriptions of individual constellations are given in Table 5.

Double stars

Close examination of individual stars reveals that many consist of more than one star, often too close to be separated without optical aid. Some such pairs consist of two stars at greatly differing distances that happen to lie close to the same line of sight. Such pairs are known as 'optical doubles' or 'visual doubles', and are, in fact, surprisingly rare.

Most stars exist in binary or multiple systems, where stars are gravitationally bound to one another. (The Sun is one of the

---

Table 3 Luminosity classes

Ia-0	Extreme supergiants (hypergiants)	II	Bright giants
		III	Giants
Ib	Bright supergiants	IV	Subgiants
Iab	Normal supergiants	V	Dwarfs
Ib	Supergiants		

Table 4 Variable stars

Abbr.	Name	Type of variation	Typical periods
Cep (or Cδ)	Classical Cepheids	pulsating	days
CW	W Virginis stars	pulsating	days
E	Eclipsing binaries	eclipses	hours to years
EA	Algol type	no variation outside eclipses	hours to years
EB	Beta Lyrae type	continuous variation, unequal minima	hours to days
EW	W Ursae Majoris type	continuous variation, similar minima	hours
GCAS	γ Cassiopeiae stars	brightening following ejection of a shell of material	unpredictable
Irr	Irregulars	pulsating, no obvious period	none
M	Mira (long-period) stars	pulsating, asymmetrical maxima	in excess of 100 days
N	Novae	sudden outburst	maximum lasts 10–100 days, recurrence period hundreds of years
NR	Recurrent novae	repeated outbursts	outburst interval of years (unpredictable)
RCB	R Coronae Borealis variables	occasional deep fades	unpredictable
RV	RV Tauri stars	semiregular, alternating deep and shallow minima; sub-type with longer, secondary period	10–100 days for principal variation; hundreds of days for secondary period
SDOR	S Doradûs variables	occasional brightenings	irregular, generally decades
SN	Supernovae	explosive disruption of star	–
SR	Semiregulars	pulsating, with intervals of irregularity	hundreds of days
UG	U Geminorum stars	outbursts of a few magnitudes	10–1000 days
UV	UV Ceti stars	flares of up to 6 magnitudes	rise in seconds or minutes; decay minutes to hours
ZAND	Z Andromedae stars (symbiotic stars)	irregular fluctuations	months or years

exceptions.) When the orbital plane coincides with the line of sight, binary systems may appear as eclipsing variables. In most cases, however, the orbital plane is inclined to our line of sight, and the stars may be resolved with suitable optical aid. In systems that consist of just two stars, the brighter is normally known as the primary and the fainter as the secondary. However, in multiple systems (of which there are many), the individual components are identified by the letters 'A', 'B', 'C', etc. Systems are known where there are five, six, or even more components. Occasionally, after the majority of components have been identified and lettered, one component may be found to consist of more than one star. In such cases, a second letter is used, so a system may (for example) contain components labelled 'A', 'Ba', 'Bb', 'C', and 'D'.

The positions of the components of double and multiple stars are described (Fig. 8) in terms of the position angle of the line joining the two stars (measured in degrees from north, through east), and their separation, usually specified in seconds of arc ("), but occasionally, for very wide doubles, given in minutes of arc ('). When just two stars are involved, the bright star (usually 'A') is normally taken as the reference point, but in multiple systems, position angle and separation may be measured from other components. In the tables and descriptions, it may be assumed that the measurements refer to the AB pair, unless otherwise stated. Generally, the information will be abbreviated to (for example) '(PA (BC) 219°, Sep. 10.2")', showing that the position angle for the BC pair is 219°, and their separation 10.2 seconds of arc. Where the orbital period (P) is known it will be shown as 'P = 107 yrs' (for example).

It is extremely difficult to obtain definitive values for the position angle and separation for many (if not most) double and multiple stars. Sources often differ greatly in the data for a specific object, frequently because measurements have been made in widely different years. Similarly, the orbital periods are often poorly known, so in many systems it is uncertain whether the apparent separation between stars is increasing or decreasing, and at what rate. Many systems have exceptionally long periods and have shown little change since first discovered in the 19th century. All such data should therefore be taken as guides to the true values.

The stars in some binary systems are so close that they cannot be separated optically. They are discovered by the appearance of specific features, such as doubled absorption lines in the spectrum, or when it is realized that the spectrum is a composite of more than one spectral type. Such systems are known as spectroscopic binaries, and may be mentioned as such in the constellation descriptions.

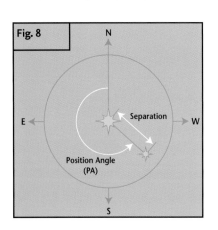

Fig. 8

N

E

W

Separation

Position Angle
(PA)

S

Open and globular clusters

Open clusters – also known as galactic clusters – are loose groups of stars, which are generally found close to the plane of the Milky Way (the galactic equator). They consist of young stars that have formed in the same region of space at approximately the same time. Over millions of years, open clusters tend to disperse, their stars becoming mixed with the general population of stars in the Galaxy. Members of the youngest clusters (like M45, the Pleiades, Chart 2) still form tight groups. In the lists, the quoted magnitude is the overall (integrated) magnitude. Very loose clusters may therefore be more difficult to detect than the magnitude suggests, as with M44, Praesepe (Chart 10). The column marked 'No.' gives the approximate number of members of each cluster.

Globular clusters are approximately spherical concentrations of many thousands of stars. The clusters themselves are found in an enormous spherical region of space surrounding the centre of the Galaxy, so although there is a concentration of clusters towards the galactic centre in Sagittarius and neighbouring constellations, they also appear far from the galactic plane. The stars themselves are (in contrast to those in open clusters) the oldest in the Galaxy, being some of the first to form. Again, in the lists, the quoted magnitude is the integrated magnitude over the whole cluster, but being fairly concentrated, globular clusters are often reasonably easy to detect.

Diffuse nebulae

Diffuse nebulae are concentrations of gas and dust, and frequently regions where stars are formed. Such nebulae are found close in the arms of spiral galaxies like our own, and are close to the galactic plane. They may take three different forms. In the lists, the approximate dimensions (length × width, in minutes of arc) of all diffuse nebulae, of whatever type, are given in the 'Diameter' column.

In emission nebulae (E), radiation from nearby hot stars (often blue-white) excites the interstellar gas and causes it to glow. The most common gas is hydrogen, which appears pink in photographs, but generally greenish to the human eye – although faint nebulae may show no colour at all. Some emission nebulae may be supernova remnants (shells of material ejected into space by supernova explosions), and glowing either because they are excited by radiation from the original star or by collision with interstellar material. The Crab Nebula (M1) in Taurus (Charts 3 & 9) is the most famous example.

Reflection nebulae (R) consist of dust that reflects light from neighbouring stars. Their colours are most commonly blue, because hot blue-white stars produce large amounts of radiation, but some reflection nebulae are illuminated by orange or red stars and appear in those colours. This is particularly noticeable in the reflection nebulae near Antares (α Scorpii), and ρ Ophiuchi. When there is a specific star illuminating either an emission or reflection nebula, its magnitude is shown in the 'Mag. star' column.

The other type of nebula consists of a dust cloud, which absorbs light from more distant stars and thus appears dark. The Great Rift in Cygnus (Chart 7), which extends towards the galactic centre, largely arises from such clouds of greater or lesser density. The Coalsack in Crux (Charts 17 & 20) is the most conspicuous example of an isolated dark nebula, but dark lanes are frequently observed silhoutted against the glowing gas of emission nebulae. A striking example is found in M20 (the Trifid Nebula) in Sagittarius (Charts 12 & 18).

Planetary nebulae

Planetary nebulae are of a completely different form. (They have no relationship with planets, but gained the name from the similarity some show to planetary disks.) These are shells of gas, shed by stars at a late evolutionary stage. As with emission nebulae, the gas is excited by radiation, in this case from the stellar remnant, either a hot, helium star or a white dwarf, which may be visible in the centre. Again, its magnitude is shown in the 'Mag. star' column. Some planetary nebulae have a bright core, and a fainter outer region, which may require a larger aperture telescope to be visible. In the lists, the dimensions are shown (in seconds of arc) under 'Diameter', with the larger, outer ones in parentheses. For example, the dimensions of NGC 6369 in Ophiuchus (Chart 18) are shown as '30 (66)'. M57 (the Ring Nebula) in Lyra and M27 (the Dumbbell Nebula) in Vulpecula (both Chart 6) are well-known examples of planetary nebulae.

Galaxies

There are various types of galaxy, and professional astronomers use a highly complex classification system. For the purposes of this atlas, an earlier, simple classification is used (Fig. 9), with four basic types: elliptical (E), spiral (S), barred spiral (SB), and irregular (Irr). Elliptical galaxies have no spiral arms, dust clouds, open clusters, or diffuse nebulae. They are systems where star formation has essentially ceased, so contain no young, bright, blue stars. They are subdivided by the degree of apparent flattening, ranging from E0 for essentially spherical systems to E7 (such as NGC 3384 in Leo) for lens-shaped systems.

Spiral galaxies have spiral arms, dust clouds, open clusters, and diffuse nebulae. They are subdivided by the degree to which the arms are open – Sa for tightly wound arms, to Sd for those with very open arms. (A subsidiary type, S0, known as lenticular galaxies, is applied to systems that show a central core surrounded by a disk.)

Barred spiral galaxies closely resemble spirals, but they exhibit a bar of stars across the centre. Our own galaxy is thought to be of this type. Like ordinary spirals, they are subdivided (SBa, SBb, SBc, and SBd) according to the degree to which the arms are open. Star formation is still occurring in both spirals and barred spirals.

Irregular galaxies show no particular, organized form. The Small Magellanic Cloud is possibly of this type, but the Large

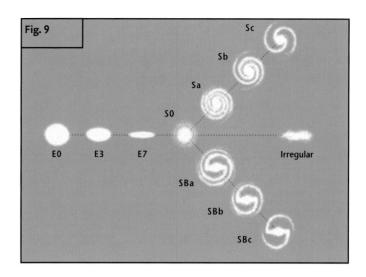

Fig. 9

Magellanic Cloud, which was once thought to be irregular, is now believed to show a barred-type structure. A few galaxies do not fit this classification scheme, and these are classified as 'Peculiar'. Some may be the result of collisions between two galaxies, which result in irregular, distorted shapes. Note that the arrangement of galaxies in the diagram should not be interpreted as showing the way galaxies evolve.

01 | North of Declination +65°

KEY TO VARIABLE STAR TYPES			
Cep Classical Cepheid	EB Beta Lyrae type	Irr Irregular	Rn Recurrent nova
CW Type II Cepheid	EW W Ursae Majoris type	RCB R Coronae Borealis type	N Nova
E Eclipsing Binary	M Mira (long-period) type	δ Sct Delta Scuti type	RV RV Tauri type
EA Algol Type	SR Semi-regular	ZA Z Andromedae type	SD S Dor type

VARIABLE STARS

Star	RA h m	Declination ° '	Range	Type	Period (days)	Spectrum	Notes
YZ Cas	00 45.7	+44 59	5.7 - 6.1	EA	4.47	A2 + F2	
RZ Cas	02 48.9	+69 38	6.2 - 7.7	EA	1.20	A3	
R UMa	10 44.6	+68 47	6.7 - 13.4	M	301.7	M	
VY UMa	10 45.1	+67 25	5.9 - 6.5	Irr	–	M	*
RY Dra	12 56.4	+66 00	6.0 - 8.0	SR	172.5:	K	
RR UMi	14 57.6	+65 56	6.1 - 6.5 p	SR	40:	M	
UX Dra	19 21.6	+76 34	5.9 - 7.1	SR	168:	C	

DOUBLE AND MULTIPLE STARS

Star	RA h m	Declination ° '	Magnitude	Position Angle °	Separation " (seconds of arc)	Notes
ψ Cas	01 25.9	+68 08	4.7 + 9.6	25	33.4	
48 Cas	02 02.0	+70 54	4.7 + 6.4	263	0.9	Binary, P = 60.4 yr
1 Cas	02 29.1	+67 24	8.4	230	2.5	AB, P = 840 yr
			8.4	114	7.2	AC
α UMi	02 31.8	+89 16	2.0 + 9.0	218	18.4	Polaris *
ψ¹ Dra	17 41.9	+72 09	4.8 + 5.8	15	30.3	
40 41 Dra	18 00.2	+80 00	5.7 + 6.1	232	19.3	*
ε Dra	19 48.2	+70 16	3.8 + 7.4	15	3.1	
κ Cep	20 08.9	+77 43	4.4 + 8.4	122	7.4	
β Cep	21 28.7	+70 34	3.2 + 7.9	249	13.3	Alfirk
π Cep	23 07.9	+75 23	4.6 + 6.6	357	1.2	P = 147 yr
o Cep	23 18.6	+68 07	4.9 + 7.1	223	2.8	P = 796.2 yr

OPEN CLUSTER

NGC/IC	Other desig.	Constellation	RA h m	Declination ° '	Magnitude	Diameter ' (minutes of arc)	No. of stars	Notes
188		Cep	00 44.4	+85 20	8.1	14	120	*

BRIGHT DIFFUSE NEBULAE

NGC/IC	Other desig.	Constellation	RA h m	Declination ° '	Type	Diameter '	Magnitude star	Notes
7822		Cep	00 03.6	+66 37	E	60 x 30	–	
–	Ced. 214	Cep	00 04.7	+67 10	E + R	50 x 40	1.7	
7023		Cep	21 01.8	+68 12	R	18 x 18	6.8	

PLANETARY NEBULAE

NGC/IC	Other desig.	Constellation	RA h m	Declination ° '	Magnitude	Diameter "	Magnitude star	Notes
40		Cep	00 13.0	+72 32	10.7	37	11.6	
IC 3568		Cam	12 32.9	+82 33	11.6	6	12.3	*
6543		Dra	17 58.6	+66 38	8.8	18 (350)	11.4	

GALAXIES See Fig. 9, p. 11

NGC/IC	Other desig.	Constellation	RA h m	Declination ° '	Magnitude	Size '	Type	Notes
IC 342		Cam	03 46.8	+68 06	9.1	17.8 × 17.4	Sc	
IC 356		Cam	04 07.8	+69 49	11.4	5.2 × 4.1	Sb	
IC 560		Cam	04 32.8	+71 53	11.5	9.8 × 2.8	Sd	
1961		Cam	05 42.1	+69 23	11.1	4.3 × 3.0	Sb	
2146		Cam	06 18.7	+78 21	18.5	6.0 × 3.8	SBb	
2336		Cam	07 27.1	+80 11	10.5	6.9 × 4.0	Sb	
2366		Cam	07 28.9	+69 13	10.9	7.6 × 3.5	Irr	
2403	U 4305	Cam	07 36.9	+65 36	8.4	17.8 × 11.0	Sc	*
–		UMa	08 18.9	+70 43	10.6	7.6 × 6.2	Irr	
2655		Cam	08 55.6	+78 13	10.1	5.1 × 4.1	SBa	
2715		Cam	09 08.1	+78 05	11.4	5.0 × 1.9	Sc	
2787		UMa	09 19.3	+69 12	10.8	3.4 × 2.3	Sa	
2976		UMa	09 47.3	+67 55	10.2	4.9 × 3.5	Sc	
2985		UMa	09 50.4	+72 17	10.5	4.3 × 3.4	Sb	
3031	M81	UMa	09 55.6	+69 04	6.9	25.7 × 14.1	Sb	
3034	M82	UMa	09 55.8	+69 41	8.4	11.2 × 4.6	Pec	
3077		UMa	10 03.3	+68 44	9.9	4.6 × 3.6	E1	
3147		Dra	10 16.9	+73 24	10.7	4.0 × 3.5	Sb	
IC2574		UMa	10 28.4	+68 25	10.6	12.3 × 5.9	S	
3348		UMa	10 47.2	+72 50	11.2	2.2 × 2.2	E1	
4125		Dra	12 08.1	+65 11	9.8	5.1 × 3.2	E5	
4236		Dra	12 16.7	+69 28	9.7	18.6 × 6.9	SB	
4589		Dra	12 37.4	+74 12	11.8	3.0 × 2.7	Sa	
4750		Dra	12 50.1	+72 52	11.9	2.3 × 2.1	Sa	
6503		Dra	17 49.4	+70 09	10.2	6.2 × 2.3	Sb	

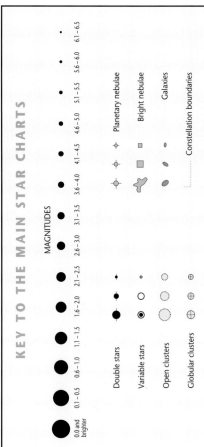

KEY TO THE MAIN STAR CHARTS

MAGNITUDES: 0.0 and brighter | 0.1 - 0.5 | 0.6 - 1.0 | 1.1 - 1.5 | 1.6 - 2.0 | 2.1 - 2.5 | 2.6 - 3.0 | 3.1 - 3.5 | 3.6 - 4.0 | 4.1 - 4.5 | 4.6 - 5.0 | 5.1 - 5.5 | 5.6 - 6.0 | 6.1 - 6.5

Double stars — Variable stars — Open clusters — Globular clusters — Planetary nebulae — Bright nebulae — Galaxies — Constellation boundaries

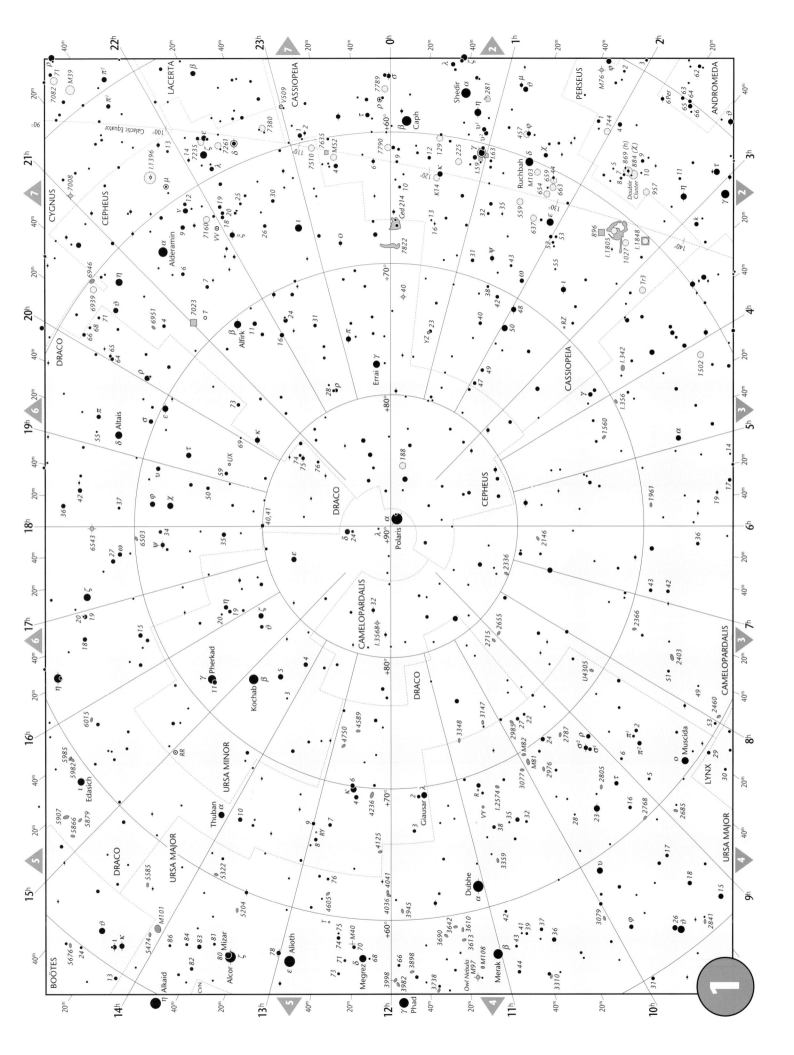

02 | Right Ascension 0ʰ to 4ʰ, Declination +65° to +20°

VARIABLE STARS

Star	RA h m	Declination ° '	Range	Type	Period (days)	Spectrum	Notes
R And	00 24.0	+38 35	5.8–14.9	M	409.3	M	
γ Cas	00 56.7	+60 43	1.6–3.0	Irr	–	B0	*
R Tri	02 37.0	+34 16	5.4–12.6	M	266.5	M	*
ρ Per	03 05.2	+38 50	3.3–4.0	EA	50:	M	*
β Per	03 08.2	+40 57	2.1–3.4	EA	2.87	B+G	Algol *
X Per	03 55.4	+31 03	6.1–7.0	Irr	–	O	*

DOUBLE AND MULTIPLE STARS

Star	RA h m	Declination ° '	Magnitude	Position Angle °	Sep. "	Notes
π And	00 36.9	+33 43	4.4+8.6	173	35.9	
η Cas	00 49.1	+57 49	3.4+7.5	317	12.9	P=480 yr *
γ Cas	00 56.7	+60 43	1.6v+11.2	248	2.1	Variable *
ψ¹ Psc	01 05.6	+21 28	5.6+5.8	159	30.0	
35 Cas	01 21.1	+64 40	6.3+8.7	344	55.5	AB, Almaak *
γ And	02 03.9	+42 20	2.3+5.1	103	9.8	BaBb: P=61.1 yr
6 Tri	02 12.4	+30 18	5.3+6.9	71	3.9	*
30 Ari	02 37.0	+24 39	6.6+7.4	274	38.6	
33 Ari	02 40.7	+27 04	5.5+6.4	0	28.6	
ε Ari	02 59.2	+21 20	5.2+5.5	203	1.5	*
θ Per	02 44.2	+49 14	4.1+9.9	305	20.0	P=2720 yr
η Per	02 50.7	+55 54	3.8+8.5	300	28.3	AB
			9.8	268	66.6	AC
40 Per	03 42.4	+33 58	5.0+9.5	238	20.0	
o Per	03 44.3	+32 17	3.8+8.3	37	10	
ζ Per	03 54.1	+31 53	2.9+9.5	208	12.9	Atik: AB *
			11.3	286	32.8	AC
			9.5	195	94.2	AD
ε Per	03 57.9	+40 01	2.9+6.1	185	120.3	AE
			10.2	10	8.8	

OPEN CLUSTERS

NGC/IC	Other desig.	Constellation	RA h m	Declination ° '	Magnitude	Diameter '	No.	Notes
129		Cas	00 29.9	+60 14	6.5	21	35	
–	K14	Cas	00 31.9	+63 10	8.5	7	20	
225		Cas	00 43.4	+61 47	7.0	12	15	
457		Cas	01 19.1	+58 20	6.4	13	80	
559		Cas	01 29.5	+63 18	9.5	4.4	60	
581	M103	Cas	01 33.2	+60 42	7.4	6	25	
637		Cas	01 42.9	+64 00	8.2	3.5	20	
654		Cas	01 44.1	+61 53	6.5	5	60	
659		Cas	01 44.2	+60 42	7.9	5	40	
663		Cas	01 46.0	+61 15	7.1	16	80	
752		And	01 57.8	+37 41	5.7	50	60	
744		Per	01 58.4	+55 29	7.9	11	20	*
869	h	Per	02 19.0	+57 09	4.3 p	30	200	Double Cluster *
884	χ	Per	02 22.4	+57 07	4.4 p	30	150	Double Cluster *
IC1805		Cas	02 32.7	+61 27	6.5	22	40	In nebulosity
957		Per	02 33.6	+57 32	7.6	11	30	
1039	M34	Per	02 42.0	+42 47	5.2	35	60	*
1027		Cas	02 42.7	+61 33	6.7	20	40	
IC1848		Cas	02 51.2	+60 26	6.5	12	10	
–	Tr3	Cas	03 11.8	+63 15	7.0 p	23	30	
1245		Per	03 14.7	+47 15	8.4	10	200	
1342		Per	03 31.6	+37 20	6.7	14	40	
–	M45	Tau	03 47.0	+24 07	1.2	110	100	Pleiades *
1444		Per	03 49.4	+52 40	6.6	4.0		

BRIGHT DIFFUSE NEBULAE

NGC/IC	Other desig.	Constellation	RA h m	Declination ° '	Type	Diameter '	Magnitude star	Notes
281		Cas	00 52.8	+56 36	E	35 × 30	7.8	
IC 59		Cas	00 56.7	+61 04	E+R	10 × 5	2.5	γ Cas *
IC 63		Cas	00 59.5	+60 49	E+R	10 × 3	2.5	γ Cas *
896		Cas	02 24.8	+61 54	E	27 ×13	10.5	
IC 1805		Cas	02 33.4	+61 26	E	60 × 60	–	
IC 1848		Cas	02 51.3	+60 25	E	60 × 30	–	

PLANETARY NEBULA

NGC/IC	Other desig.	Constellation	RA h m	Declination ° '	Magnitude	Diameter "	Magnitude star	Notes
650, 651	M76	Per	01 42.4	+51 34	12.2	65 (290)	17.0:	Little Dumbbell

GALAXIES

NGC/IC	Other desig.	Constellation	RA h m	Declination ° '	Magnitude	Size '	Type	Notes
23		Peg	00 09.9	+25 55	11.9	2.3 × 1.6	So	
147		Cas	00 33.2	+48 30	9.3	12.9 × 8.1	dE4	
185		Cas	00 39.0	+48 20	9.2	11.5 × 9.8	dE0	
205	M110	And	00 40.4	+41 41	8.0	17.4 × 9.8	E6	Satellite of M31 *
221	M32	And	00 42.7	+40 52	8.2	7.6 × 5.8	E2	Satellite of M31 *
224	M31	And	00 42.7	+41 16	3.5	178 × 63	Sb	Andromeda Galaxy *
278		Cas	00 52.1	+47 33	10.9	2.2 × 2.1	E0	
404		And	01 09.4	+35 43	10.1	4.4 × 4.2	E0	6.5' NW of β And *
598	M33	Tri	01 33.9	+30 39	5.7	62 × 39	Sc	Triangulum Galaxy *
IC1727		Tri	01 47.5	+27 20	11.6	6.2 × 2.9	SB	
672		Tri	01 47.9	+27 26	10.8	6.6 × 2.7	SB	
784		Tri	02 01.3	+28 50	11.8	6.2 × 1.7	Sb	
891		And	02 22.6	+42 21	10.0	13.5 × 2.8	Sb	
IC 239		And	02 36.5	+38 58	11.2	4.6 × 4.3	SBc	
1003		Per	02 39.3	+40 52	11.5	5.4 × 2.1	Sc	
1023		Per	02 40.4	+39 04	9.5	8.7 × 3.3	E7	

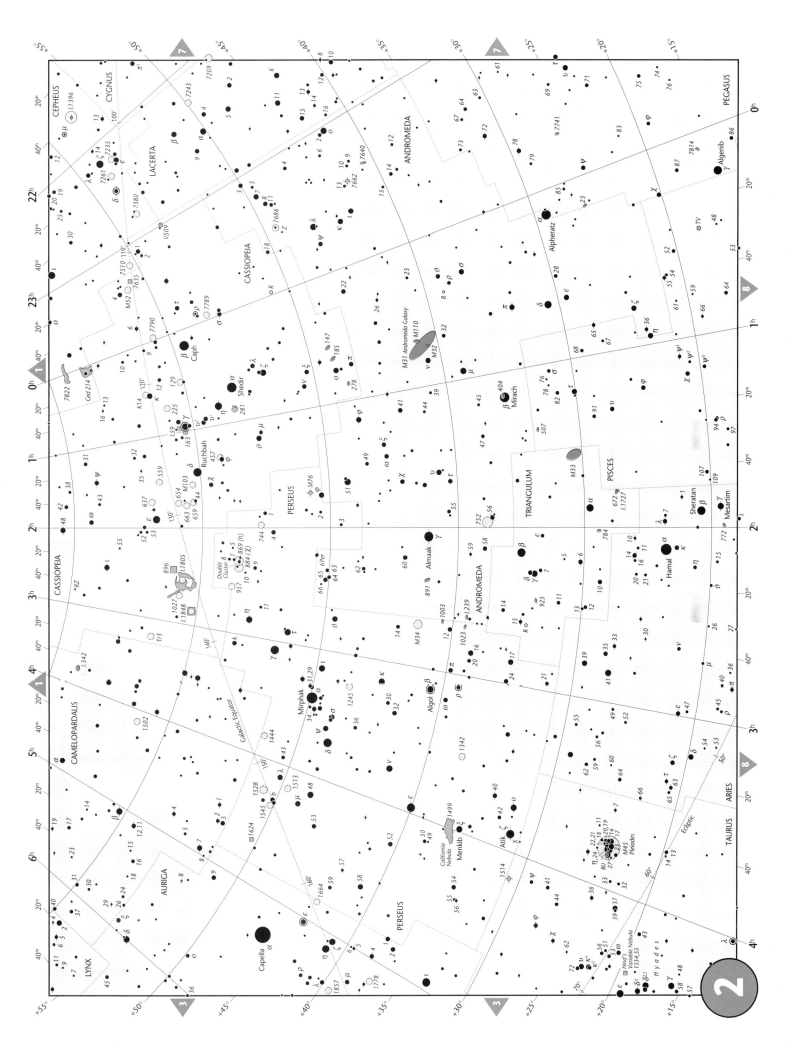

03 | Right Ascension 4ʰ to 8ʰ, Declination +65° to +20°

VARIABLE STARS

Star	RA h m	Declination ° '	Range	Type	Period (days)	Spectrum	Notes
HU Tau	04 38.3	+20 41	5.9–6.7	EA	2.06	A	*
ε Aur	05 02.0	+43 49	2.9–3.8	EA	9892	A–F	*
R Aur	05 17.3	+53 35	6.7–13.7	M	457.5	M	
AR Aur	05 18.3	+33 46	6.2–6.8	EA	4.13	A+B	
U Ori	05 55.8	+20 10	4.8–12.6	M	372.4	M	
TV Gem	06 11.8	+21 52	8.7–9.5 p	SR	182	M	
BU Gem	06 12.3	+22 54	5.7–7.5	Irr	–	M	
η Gem	06 14.9	+22 30	3.2–3.9	SR	232.9	M	Propus *
RT Aur	06 28.6	+30 30	5.0–5.8	Cep	3.72	F–G	
WW Aur	06 32.5	+32 27	5.8–6.5	EA	2.53	A	
UU Aur	06 36.5	+38 27	7.8–10.0	SR	234	C	*
ζ Gem	07 04.1	+20 34	3.7–4.2	Cep	10.15	F–G	Mekbuda
R Gem	07 07.4	+22 42	6.0–14.0	M	369.8	S	

DOUBLE AND MULTIPLE STARS

Star	RA h m	Declination ° '	Magnitude	Position Angle °	Separation "	Notes
φ Tau	04 20.4	+27 21	5.0+8.0	250	52.1	
χ Tau	04 22.6	+25 38	5.5+7.6	24	19.4	
56 Per	04 24.6	+33 58	5.9+8.7	22	4.2	
k¹,k² Tau	04 25.4	+22 18	4.2+5.3	173	339	
4 Aur	04 59.3	+37 53	5.0+8.0	359	5.4	
14 Aur	05 15.4	+32 41	5.1+11.1	352	11.1	
			7.4	226	14.6	Variable
			10.4	321	184.0	
R Aur	05 17.3	+53 35	6.9v+8.6	339	47.5	
118 Tau	05 29.3	+25 09	5.8+6.6	204	4.8	
26 Aur	05 38.6	+30 30	6.0+6.3	3	0.2	AB, P=53.2 yr
			8.0	267	12.4	BC
V Aur	05 51.5	+39 09	4.0+9.3	206	54.6	
δ Aur	05 59.5	+54 17	3.7+9.5	271	115.4	
			9.5	67	197.1	
θ Aur	05 59.7	+37 13	2.6+7.1	313	3.6	*
			10.6	297	50.0	
η Gem	06 14.9	+22 30	3.3v+6.5	257	1.6	Propus: var; P=473.7 yr *
μ Gem	06 22.9	+22 31	3.2+9.4	141	121.7	
ν Gem	06 29.0	+20 13	4.2+8.7	329	112.5	
ε Gem	06 43.9	+25 08	3.0+9.0	94	110.3	Mebsuta
12 Lyn	06 46.2	+59 27	5.4+6.0	70	1.7	P=699 yr
			7.3	308	8.7	
ζ Gem	07 04.1	+20 34	3.7v+10.5	84	87.0	Variable, AB *
			8.0	350	96.5	AC
δ Gem	07 20.1	+21 59	3.5+8.2	226	5.8	Wasat: P=1200 yr
19 Lyn	07 22.9	+55 17	5.6+6.5	315	14.8	AB
			8.9	3	214.9	AD
α Gem	07 34.6	+31 53	1.9+2.9	68	4.0	Castor: AB, P=420 yr *
			10.9	288	74.2	BC
24 Lyn	07 43.0	+58 43	5.0+9.5	163	72.5	AC
			8.8	320	54.7	

OPEN CLUSTERS

NGC/IC	Other desig.	Constellation	RA h m	Declination ° '	Magnitude	Diameter '	No.	Notes
1502		Cam	04 07.7	+62 20	5.7	8	45	*
1513		Per	04 10.0	+49 31	8.4	9	50	
1528		Per	04 15.4	+51 14	6.4	24	40	
1545		Per	04 20.9	+50 15	6.2	18	28	
1664		Aur	04 51.1	+43 42	7.6	18	–	
1746		Tau	05 03.6	+23 49	6.1	42	20	
1778		Aur	05 08.1	+37 03	7.7	7	25	
1857		Aur	05 20.2	+39 21	7.0	6	40	
1893		Aur	05 22.7	+33 24	7.5	11	60	
1907		Aur	05 28.0	+35 19	8.2	7	30	
1912	M38	Aur	05 28.7	+35 50	6.4	21	100	*
1960	M36	Aur	05 36.1	+34 08	6.0	12	60	*
2099	M37	Aur	05 52.4	+32 33	5.6	24	150	*
2129		Gem	06 01.0	+23 18	6.7	7	40	
IC 2157		Gem	06 05.0	+24 00	8.4	7	20	
2158	M35	Gem	06 07.5	+24 06	8.6	5	–	
2168		Gem	06 08.9	+24 20	5.1	28	200	*
2175		Ori	06 09.8	+20 19	6.8	18	60	In neb. NGC 2174 *
2281		Aur	06 49.3	+41 04	5.4	15	30	
2331		Gem	07 07.2	+27 21	8.5	18	30	
2420		Gem	07 38.5	+21 34	8.3	10	100	

GLOBULAR CLUSTER

NGC/IC	Other desig.	Constellation	RA h m	Declination ° '	Magnitude	Diameter '	Notes
2419		Lyn	07 38.1	+38 53	10.4	4.1	

BRIGHT DIFFUSE NEBULAE

NGC/IC	Other desig.	Constellation	RA h m	Declination ° '	Type	Diameter '	Magnitude star	Notes
1499		Per	04 00.7	+36 37	E	145×40	4.0	California Nebula
1624		Per	04 40.5	+50 27	E	5×5		
1931		Aur	05 31.4	+34 15	E+R	3×3		
1952	M1	Tau	05 34.5	+22 01	E	6×4	16	Crab Nebula, SNR *
2174		Gem	06 09.7	+20 30	E	40×30	7.6	Contains cluster 2175 *
IC 443		Gem	06 16.9	+22 47	E	50⊻40	8.8	SNR

PLANETARY NEBULAE

NGC/IC	Other desig.	Constellation	RA h m	Declination ° '	Magnitude	Diameter "	Magnitude Star	Notes
1514		Tau	04 09.2	+30 47	10.0	114	9.4	
2392		Gem	07 29.2	+20 55	9.9	13 (44)	10.5	Eskimo Nebula *

GALAXY

NGC/IC	Other desig.	Constellation	RA h m	Declination ° '	Magnitude	Size '	Type	Notes
2460		Cam	07 56.9	+60 21	11.7	2.9×2.2	Sb	

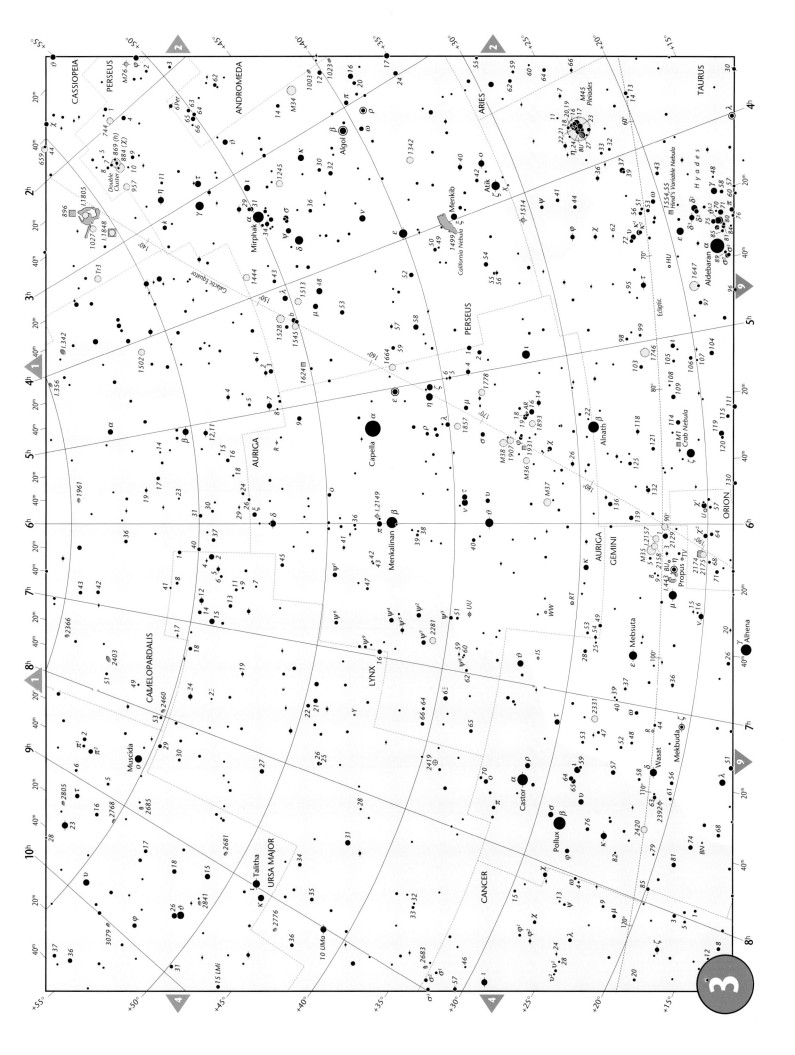

04 | Right Ascension 8ʰ to 12ʰ, Declination +65° to +20°

VARIABLE STARS

Star	RA h m	Declination ° '	Range	Type	Period (days)	Spectrum	Notes
RS Cnc	09 10.6	+30 58	5.1–7.0	SR	120:	M	
R LMi	09 45.6	+34 31	6.3–13.2	M	371.9	M	
ST UMa	11 27.8	+45 11	7.7–9.5	SR	81	M	

DOUBLE AND MULTIPLE STARS

Star	RA h m	Declination ° '	Magnitude	Position Angle °	Separation "	Notes
ι Cnc	08 46.7	+28 46	4.2 + 6.6	307	30.5	*
ι UMa	08 59.2	+48 02	3.1 + 10.2	177	2.0	
38 Lyn	09 18.8	+36 48	3.9 + 6.6	229	2.7	Talitha: P = 817.9 yr
23 UMa	09 31.5	+63 04	3.7 + 8.9	270	22.7	
54 Leo	10 55.6	+24 45	4.5 + 6.3	110	6.5	
α UMa	11 03.7	+61 45	1.9 + 4.8	223	0.6	Dubhe: P = 44.7 yr *
ξ UMa	11 18.2	+31 32	4.3 + 4.8	273	1.8	P = 59.8 yr *
ν UMa	11 18.5	+33 06	3.5 + 9.9	147	7.2	
57 UMa	11 29.1	+39 20	5.3 + 8.3	359	5.4	*

PLANETARY NEBULA

NGC/IC	Other desig.	Constellation	RA h m	Declination ° '	Magnitude	Diameter	Magnitude star	Notes
3587	M97	UMa	11 14.8	+55 01	12.0	194	15.9	Owl Nebula

GALAXIES

NGC/IC	Other desig.	Constellation	RA h m	Declination ° '	Magnitude	Size '	Type	Notes
2683		Lyn	08 52.7	+33 25	9.7	9.3 × 2.5	Sb	*
2681		UMa	08 53.5	+51 19	10.3	3.8 × 3.5	Sa	
2685		UMa	08 55.6	+58 44	11.1	5.2 × 3.0	Sb	
2770		Lyn	09 09.6	+33 07	12.1	3.7 × 1.3	Sa	
2768		UMa	09 11.6	+60 02	10.0	6.3 × 2.8	E5	
2776		Lyn	09 12.2	+44 57	11.6	2.9 × 2.7	Sc	
2805		UMa	09 20.3	+64 06	11.3	6.3 × 5.0	SBd	
2841		UMa	09 22.0	+50 58	9.3	8.1 × 3.8	Sb	
2903		Leo	09 32.2	+21 30	8.9	12.6 × 6.6	Sb	
3079		UMa	10 02.0	+55 41	10.7	7.6 × 1.7	Sb	
3190		Leo	10 18.1	+21 50	11.0	4.6 × 1.5	Sb	
3184		UMa	10 18.3	+41 25	9.8	6.9 × 6.8	Sc	
3193		Leo	10 18.4	+21 54	10.9	2.8 × 2.6	E0	
3198		UMa	10 19.9	+45 33	10.4	8.3 × 3.7	Sc	
3245		LMi	10 27.3	+28 30	10.8	3.2 × 1.9	E5	
3294		LMi	10 36.3	+37 20	11.7	3.3 × 1.8	Sc	
3310		UMa	10 38.7	+53 30	10.9	3.6 × 3.0	So	
3319		UMa	10 39.2	+41 41	11.3	6.8 × 3.9	SBc	
3344		UMa	10 43.5	+24 55	10.0	6.9 × 6.5	Sc	
3359		UMa	10 46.6	+63 13	10.5	6.8 × 4.3	SBc	
3430		LMi	10 52.2	+32 57	11.5	3.9 × 2.3	Sc	
3432		LMi	10 52.5	+36 37	11.3	6.2 × 1.5	SB	
3486		LMi	11 00.4	+28 58	10.3	6.9 × 5.4	Sb	
3504		LMi	11 03.2	+27 58	11.1	2.7 × 2.2	Sb	
3556	M108	UMa	11 11.5	+55 40	10.1	8.3 × 2.5	Sc	*
—	U 6253	Leo	11 13.5	+22 10	11.5	14.5 × 12.9	dE0	Leo II
3583		UMa	11 14.2	+48 19	11.7	2.8 × 2.0	Sc	
3610		UMa	11 18.4	+58 47	10.8	3.2 × 2.5	E2	
3613		UMa	11 18.6	+58 00	11.6	3.6 × 2.0	E5	
3631		UMa	11 21.0	+53 10	10.4	4.6 × 4.1	Sc	
3646		Leo	11 21.7	+20 10	11.2	3.9 × 2.6	Sc	
3642		UMa	11 22.3	+59 05	11.1	5.8 × 4.9	Sc	
3665		UMa	11 24.7	+38 46	10.8	3.2 × 2.6	E2	
3675		UMa	11 26.1	+43 35	10.9	5.9 × 3.2	Sb	
3690		UMa	11 28.5	+58 33	12.0	2.4 × 1.9	S	
3718		UMa	11 32.6	+53 04	10.5	8.7 × 4.5	SBa	
3726		UMa	11 33.3	+47 02	10.4	6.0 × 4.5	So	
3738		UMa	11 35.8	+54 31	11.7	2.6 × 2.0	Pec	
3769		UMa	11 37.7	+47 54	11.8	3.20 × 1.1	Sb	
3877		UMa	11 46.1	+47 30	11.6	5.4 × 1.5	Sb	
3893		UMa	11 48.6	+48 43	11.1	4.4 × 2.8	Sc	
3898		UMa	11 49.2	+56 05	10.8	4.4 × 2.6	Sb	
3941		UMa	11 52.9	+36 59	11.4	3.8 × 2.5	E3	
3945		UMa	11 53.2	+60 41	10.6	5.5 × 3.6	SBa	
3949		UMa	11 53.7	+47 52	11.0	3.0 × 1.8	Sb	
3953		UMa	11 53.8	+52 20	10.1	6.6 × 3.6	Sb	
3982		UMa	11 56.5	+55 08	11.7	2.5 × 2.2	Sb	
3992	M109	UMa	11 57.6	+53 23	9.8	7.6 × 4.9	SBb	*
3998		UMa	11 57.9	+55 27	10.6	3.1 × 2.5	E2	
IC 700		UMa	11 58.9	+42 43	11.8	2.9 × 1.4	Sb	
4026		UMa	11 59.4	+50 50	11.7	5.1 × 1.4	S0	

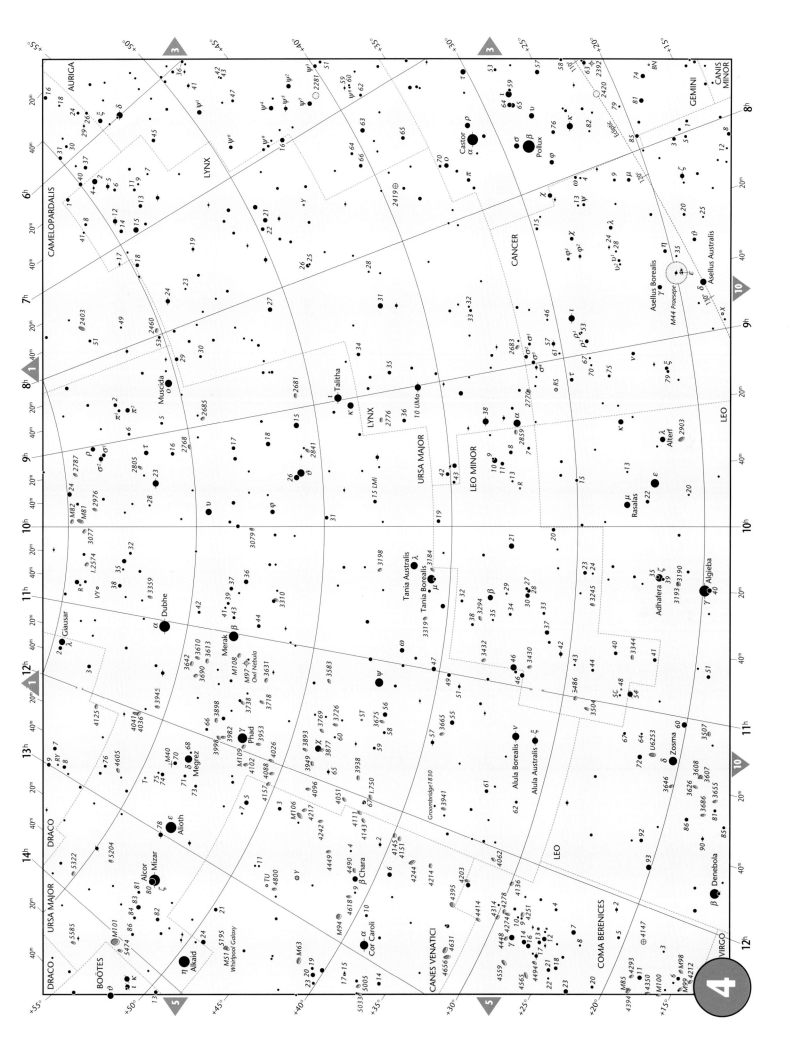

05 | Right Ascension 12ʰ to 16ʰ, Declination +65° to +20°

VARIABLE STARS

Star	RA h m	Declination ° '	Range	Type	Period (days)	Spectrum	Notes
T UMa	12 36.4	+59 29	6.6–13.4	M	256.5	M	
Y CVn	12 45.1	+45 26	5.2–6.6	SR	257:	K	La Superba
TU CVn	12 54.9	+47 12	5.6–6.6	SR	50	M	
FS Com	13 06.4	+22 37	5.3–6.1	SR	58:	M	
R CVn	13 49.0	+39 33	6.5–12.9	M	328.53	M	
ZZ Boo	13 56.2	+25 55	5.8–6.4	EW	4.99	G	
V Boo	14 29.8	+38 52	7.0–12.0	SR	258	M	
R Boo	14 37.2	+26 44	6.2–13.1	M	233.4	M	
W Boo	14 43.4	+26 32	4.7–5.4	SR	450:	M	
44 Boo	15 03.8	+47 39	5.8–6.4	EW	0.27	G+G	i Boo
S CrB	15 21.4	+31 22	5.8–14.1	M	360.3	M	
R CrB	15 48.6	+28 09	5.7–14.8	RCB	–	G	*
T CrB	15 59.5	+25 55	2.0–10.8	NR	29000:	M	*

DOUBLE AND MULTIPLE STARS

Star	RA h m	Declination ° '	Magnitude	Position Angle °	Separation "	Notes
2 CVn	12 16.1	+40 40	5.8 + 8.1	260	11.4	
α CVn	12 56.0	+38 19	2.9 + 5.6	229	19.4	Cor Caroli *
78 UMa	13 00.7	+56 22	5.0 + 7.4	69	1.5	P = 115.7 yr
ζ UMa	13 23.9	+54 56	2.3 + 4.0	152	14.4	Mizar *
			4.0		708.7	80 UMa, Alcor *
κ Boo	14 13.5	+51 47	4.6 + 6.6	236	13.4	
ε Boo	14 45.0	+27 04	2.5 + 4.9	339	2.8	Izar *
39 Boo	14 49.7	+48 43	6.2 + 6.9	45	2.9	
44 Boo	15 03.8	+47 39	5.3 + 6.2 v	53	2.2	P = 225 yr; variable *
η CrB	15 23.2	+30 17	5.6 + 5.9	63	0.8	P = 41.6 yr
μ¹, μ² Boo	15 24.5	+37 23	4.3 + 6.5 d	171	108.3	Alkalurops *
μ² Boo	15 24.5	+37 21	7.0 + 7.6	8	2.3	P = 260.1 yr *

GLOBULAR CLUSTERS

NGC/IC	Other desig.	Constellation	RA h m	Declination ° '	Magnitude	Diameter '	Notes
5272	M3	CVn	13 42.2	+28 23	6.4	16.2	*
5466		Boo	14 05.5	+28 32	9.1	11.0	*

GALAXIES

NGC/IC	Other desig.	Constellation	RA h m	Declination ° '	Magnitude	Size '	Type	Notes
4036		UMa	12 01.4	+61 54	10.6	4.5×2.0	E6	
4041		UMa	12 02.2	+62 08	11.1	2.8×2.7	Sc	
4051		UMa	12 03.2	+44 32	10.3	5.0×4.0	Sc	
4062		UMa	12 04.1	+31 54	11.2	4.3×2.0	Sb	
4080		UMa	12 05.6	+50 33	10.5	5.8×2.5	Sc	
4096		UMa	12 06.0	+47 29	10.6	6.5×2.0	Sc	
4102		UMa	12 06.4	+52 43	12.3	3.2×1.9	Sc	
4111		CVn	12 07.1	+43 04	10.8	4.8×1.1	S0	
4136		Com	12 09.3	+29 56	11.4	4.1×3.9	Sc	
4143		CVn	12 09.6	+42 32	12.1	2.9×1.8	E4	
4145		CVn	12 10.0	+39 53	11.0	5.8×4.4	Sc	
4151		CVn	12 10.5	+39 24	10.4	5.9×4.4	Sc	
4157		UMa	12 11.1	+50 29	11.7	6.9×1.7	Sb	
4214		CVn	12 15.6	+36 20	9.7	7.9×6.3	Irr	
4217		CVn	12 15.8	+47 06	11.9	5.5×1.8	Sb	
4242		CVn	12 17.5	+45 37	11.0	4.8×3.8	S	
4244		CVn	12 17.5	+37 49	10.2	16.2×2.5	S	
4251	M106	Com	12 18.1	+28 10	11.6	4.2×1.9	E7	*
4258		CVn	12 19.0	+47 18	8.3	18.2×7.9	Sb	
4274		Com	12 19.8	+29 37	10.4	6.9×2.8	Sb	
4278		Com	12 20.1	+29 17	10.2	3.6×3.5	E1	
4314		Com	12 22.6	+29 53	10.5	4.8×4.3	SBa	
4395		CVn	12 25.8	+33 33	10.2	12.9×11.0	S	
4414		Com	12 26.4	+31 13	10.3	3.6×2.2	Sc	
4448		Com	12 28.2	+28 37	11.1	4.0×1.6	Sb	
4449		CVn	12 28.2	+44 06	9.4	5.1×3.7	Irr	
4490		Com	12 30.6	+41 38	9.8	5.9×3.1	Sc	
4494		Com	12 31.4	+25 47	9.7	4.8×3.8	E1	
4559		Com	12 36.0	+27 58	9.9	10.5×4.9	Sc	
4565		Com	12 36.3	+25 59	9.6	16.2×2.8	SBc	
4605		UMa	12 40.0	+61 37	11.0	5.5×2.3	Sc	
4618		CVn	12 41.5	+41 09	10.8	4.4×3.8	Sc	
4631		Com	12 42.1	+32 32	9.3	15.1×3.3	Sc	
4656		Com	12 44.0	+32 10	10.4	13.8×3.3	Sc	
4725		Com	12 50.4	+25 30	9.2	11.0×7.9	SBb	
4736	M94	CVn	12 50.9	+41 07	8.2	11.0×9.1	Sb	*
4800		CVn	12 54.6	+46 32	12.3	1.8×1.4	Sb	
4826	M64	Com	12 56.7	+21 41	8.5	9.3×5.4	Sb	Black-Eye Galaxy *
5005		CVn	13 10.9	+37 03	9.8	5.4×2.7	Sb	
5033		CVn	13 13.4	+36 36	10.1	10.5×5.6	Sb	
5055	M63	CVn	13 15.8	+42 02	8.6	12.3×7.6	Sb	
5112		CVn	13 21.9	+38 44	11.9	3.9×2.9	Sc	
5204		UMa	13 29.6	+58 25	11.3	4.8×3.0	Irr	
5194	M51	CVn	13 29.9	+47 12	8.4	11.0×7.8	Sc	Whirlpool Galaxy *
5195		CVn	13 30.0	+47 16	9.6	5.4×4.3	Pec	Companion to M51
5322		UMa	13 49.3	+60 12	10.0	5.5×3.9	E2	
5371		CVn	13 55.7	+40 28	10.8	4.4×3.6	Sb	
5377		UMa	13 56.3	+47 14	11.2	4.6×2.7	Sb	
5457	M101	UMa	14 03.2	+54 21	7.7	26.9×26.3	Sc	Pinwheel Galaxy *
5474		UMa	14 05.0	+53 40	10.9	4.5×4.2	Sc	
5585		UMa	14 19.8	+56 44	10.9	5.5×3.7	S	
5676		Boo	14 32.8	+49 28	10.9	3.9×2.0	Sc	
5866		Dra	15 06.5	+55 46	10.0	5.2×2.3	E6	
5879		Dra	15 09.8	+57 00	11.5	4.4×1.7	So	
5907		Dra	15 15.9	+56 19	10.4	12.3×1.8	Sb	
5982		Dra	15 38.7	+59 21	11.1	2.9×2.2	E3	
5985		Dra	15 39.6	+59 20	11.0	5.5×3.2	Sb	
6015		Dra	15 51.4	+62 19	11.2	5.4×2.3	Sc	

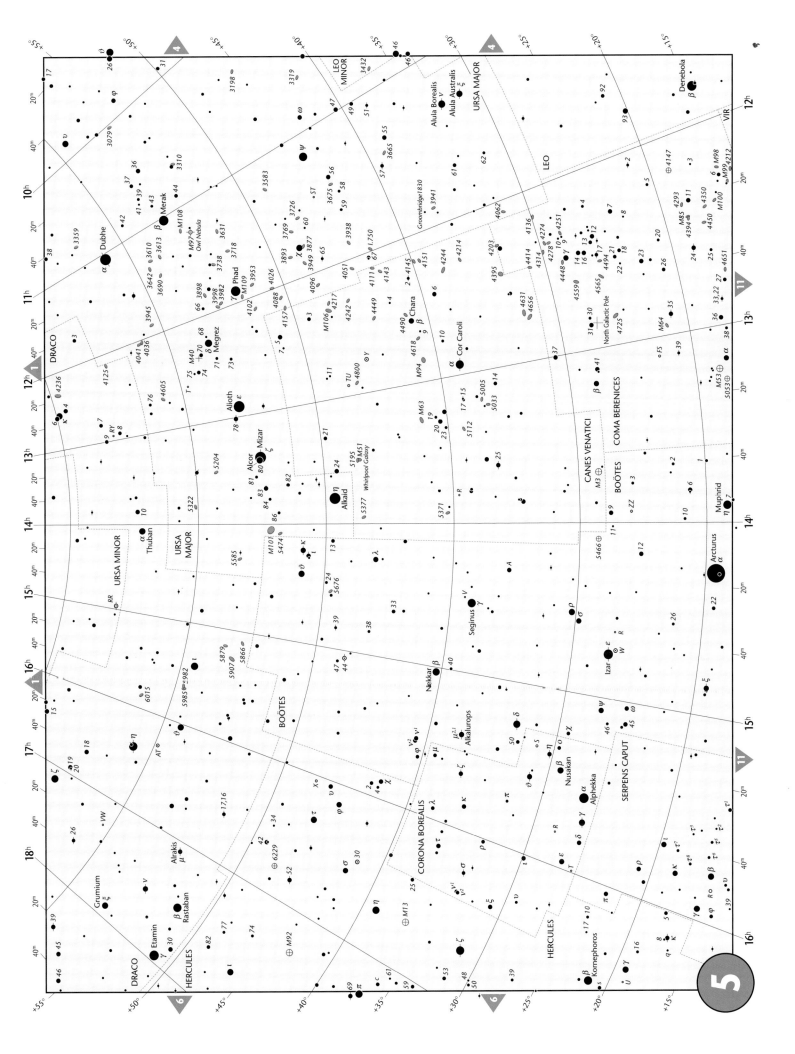

06 | Right Ascension 16^h to 20^h, Declination +65° to +20°

VARIABLE STARS

Star	RA h m	Declination ° '	Range	Type	Period (days)	Spectrum	Notes
X Her	16 02.7	+47 14	6.3–7.4	SR	95.0	M	
AT Dra	16 17.3	+59 45	5.3–6.0	Irr	–	M	
30 Her	16 28.6	+41 53	4.3–6.3	SR	70:	M	g Her
VW Dra	17 16.5	+60 40	6.0–6.5	SR	170	K	
68 Her	17 17.3	+33 06	4.7–5.4	EB	205	B	u Her
OP Her	17 56.8	+45 21	5.9–6.7	Irr	–	M	
XY Lyr	18 38.1	+39 40	5.8–6.4	Irr	–	M	
β Lyr	18 50.1	+33 22	3.3–4.3	EB	12.94	B+A	Sheliak
R Lyr	18 55.3	+43 57	3.9–5.0	SR	46.0	M	
AF Cyg	19 30.2	+46 09	6.4–8.4	SR	94.1	M	
U Vul	19 36.6	+20 20	6.8–7.5	Cep	7.99	F-G	
R Cyg	19 36.8	+50 12	6.1–14.2	M	426.4	S	
V1143 Cyg	19 38.7	+54 58	5.9–6.4	EA	7.64	F	
RT Cyg	19 43.6	+48 47	6.4–12.7	M	190.3	M	
V973 Cyg	19 44.8	+40 43	6.1–6.6	SR	40	M	
SU Cyg	19 44.8	+29 16	6.5–7.2	Cep	3.85	F	
χ Cyg	19 50.6	+32 55	3.3–14.2	M	406.9	S	
V449 Cyg	19 53.3	+33 57	7.4–9.0p	Irr	–	M	

DOUBLE AND MULTIPLE STARS

Star	RA h m	Declination ° '	Magnitude	Position Angle °	Separation "	Notes
η Dra	16 24.0	+61 31	2.7 + 8.7	142	5.2	
17 Dra	16 36.2	+52 55	5.4 + 6.4	108	3.4	
			5.5	194	90.3	16 Dra
ζ Her	16 41.3	+31 36	2.9 + 5.5	12	0.8	P = 34.5 yr
μ Dra	17 05.3	+54 28	5.7 + 5.7	1.9	8	P = 482 yr
ρ Her	17 23.7	+37 09	4.6 + 5.6	316	4.1	
ν Dra	17 32.2	+55 11	4.9 + 4.9	312	61.9	
μ Her	17 46.5	+27 42	3.4 + 10.1	247	33.8	
90 Her	17 53.3	+40 00	5.2 + 8.5	116	1.6	
95 Her	18 01.5	+21 36	5.0 + 5.1	258	6.3	
100 Her	18 07.8	+26 06	5.9 + 6.0	183	14.2	
39 Dra	18 23.9	+58 48	5.0 + 8.0	351	3.1	
			7.4	21	88.9	AB
ε Lyr	18 44.3	+39 40	4.7 + 4.6	207.7	173	AC; 4 more components
			5.0 + 6.1	350	2.6	ε¹; P = 1165 yr
			5.2 + 5.5	82	2.3	ε²; P = 585 yr
ζ Lyr	18 44.8	+37 36	4.3 + 5.9	150	43.7	ζ¹; ζ²*
β Lyr	18 50.1	+33 22	3.4 + 8.6	149	45.7	Sheliak: variable *
ο Dra	18 51.2	+59 23	4.8 + 7.8	326	34.2	
η Lyr	19 13.8	+39 09	4.4 + 9.1	82	28.1	
2 Vul	19 17.7	+23 02	5.4 + 9.2	127	1.8	ES Vul
α, 8 Vul	19 28.7	+24 40	4.4 + 5.8	28	413.7	
β Cyg	19 30.9	+27 58	3.1 + 5.1	54	34.4	Albireo *
δ Cyg	19 45.0	+45 08	2.9 + 6.3	221	2.5	P = 827.6 yr
17 Cyg	19 46.4	+33 44	5.0 + 9.2	69	26.0	
ψ Cyg	19 55.6	+52 26	4.9 + 7.4	178	3.2	

OPEN CLUSTERS

NGC/IC	Other desig.	Constellation	RA h m	Declination ° '	Magnitude	Diameter '	No.	Notes
–	Steph 1	Lyr	18 53.5	+36 55	3.8	20	15	δ Lyrae Cluster
–	Cr 399	Vul	19 25.4	+20 11	3.6	60	40	Brocchi's Cluster
6811		Cyg	19 38.2	+46 34	6.8	13	70	
6819		Cyg	19 41.3	+40 11	7.3	5		
6823		Vul	19 43.1	+23 18	7.1	12	30	In neb. NGC 6820
6830		Vul	19 51.0	+23 04	7.9	12	20	
6834		Cyg	19 52.2	+29 25	7.8	5	50	

GLOBULAR CLUSTERS

NGC/IC	Other desig.	Constellation	RA h m	Declination ° '	Magnitude	Diameter '	Notes
6205	M13	Her	16 41.7	+36 28	5.9	16.6	Hercules Cluster *
6229		Her	16 47.0	+47 32	9.4	4.5	
6249		Her	17 17.1	+43 08	6.5	11.2	*
6779	M56	Lyr	19 16.6	+30 11	8.2	7.1	*

PLANETARY NEBULAE

NGC/IC	Other desig.	Constellation	RA h m	Declination ° '	Magnitude	Diameter '	Magnitude star	Notes
6210		Her	16 44.5	+23 49	9.3	14	12.9	
–	PK+51+9.1	Her	18 49.7	+20 51	12.2	3	13.0	
6720	M57	Lyr	18 53.6	+33 02	9.7	70 (150)	14.8	Ring Nebula *
–	PK+64-5.1	Cyg	19 34.8	+30 31	9.6	8	10.0	
6826		Cyg	19 44.8	+50 31	9.8	30 (140)	10.4	Blinking Planetary
6853	M27	Vul	19 59.6	+22 43	7.6	350 (910)	13.9	Dumbbell Nebula *

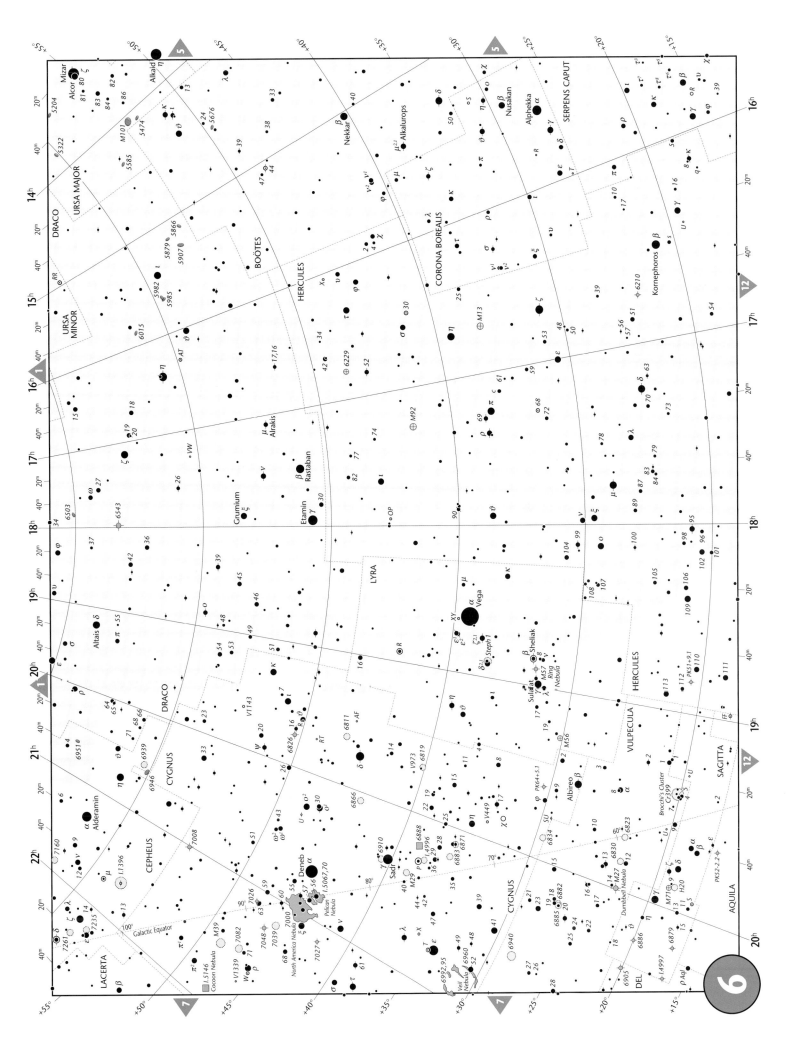

07 | Right Ascension 20ʰ to 0ʰ, Declination +65° to +20°

VARIABLE STARS

Star	RA h m	Declination ° '	Range	Type	Period (days)	Spectrum	Notes
P Cyg	20 17.8	+38 02	3.0–6.0	SD	–	B	*
U Cyg	20 19.6	+47 54	5.9–12.1	M	462.4	M	
X Cyg	20 43.4	+35 35	5.9–6.7	Cep	16.39	F–G	
T Cyg	20 47.2	+34 22	5.0–5.5	Irr	–	K	
T Vul	20 51.5	+28 15	5.4–6.1	Cep	4.43	F–G	
W Cyg	21 36.0	+45 22	5.0–7.6	SR	126.3	M	*
V460 Cyg	21 42.0	+35 31	5.6–7.0	Irr	–	M	
V1339 Cyg	21 42.1	+45 46	5.9–7.1	SR	35:	M	
μ Cep	21 43.5	+58 47	3.4–5.1	SR	730	M	*
VV Cep	21 56.7	+63 38	4.8–5.4	EA	7430	M	*
AR Lac	22 08.7	+45 45	6.1–6.8	EA	1.98	G, K	
δ Cep	22 29.2	+58 25	3.9–4.4	Cep	5.37	F–G	*
V509 Cas	23 00.1	+56 57	4.8–5.5	SR	–	F–K	
β Peg	23 03.8	+28 05	2.3–2.7	SR	–	M	Scheat *
Z And	23 33.7	+48 49	8.0–12.4p	ZA	–	M	*
ρ Cas	23 54.4	+57 30	4.1–6.2	SR	320	F–K	
R Cas	23 58.4	+51 24	4.7–13.5	M	430.5	M	

DOUBLE AND MULTIPLE STARS

Star	RA h m	Declination ° '	Magnitude	Position Angle °	Separation "	Notes
52 Cyg	20 45.7	+30 43	4.2 + 6.4	67	6.0	In NGC 6920
61 Cyg	21 06.9	+38 45	5.2 + 6.0	150	30.3	P = 653.3 yr *
τ Cyg	21 14.8	+38 03	3.8 + 6.4	306	0.8	P = 49.9 yr
ν Cyg	21 17.9	+34 54	4.4 + 10.0	220	15.1	
λ Cyg	21 44.1	+28 45	4.8 + 6.1	320	1.2	P = 507.5 yr
ξ Cep	22 03.8	+64 38	4.4 + 6.5	274	8.2	Variable *
δ Cep	22 29.2	+58 25	3.9 + 7.5	191	41.0	AB, multiple system
8 Lac	22 35.9	+39 38	5.7 + 6.5	186	22.4	
72 Peg	23 34.0	+31 20	5.7 + 5.8	97	0.5	P = 241.2 years
78 Peg	23 44.0	+29 22	5.0 + 8.1	235	1.0	
6 Cas	23 48.8	+62 13	5.5 + 8.0	193	1.6	
σ Cas	23 59.0	+55 45	5.0 + 7.1	326	3.0	

OPEN CLUSTERS

NGC/IC	Other desig.	RA h m	Declination ° '	Constellation	Magnitude	Diameter '	No.	Notes
6866		20 03.7	+44 00	Cyg	7.6	7	80	
6871		20 05.9	+35 47	Cyg	5.2	20	15	
6883		20 11.3	+35 51	Cyg	8.0	35	30	
6882		20 11.7	+26 33	Vul	8.1	18	–	
6885		20 12.0	+26 29	Vul	5.7	7	30	Near cluster NGC 6885
IC4996		20 16.5	+37 38	Cyg	7.3	6	15	Contains 20 Vul
6910		20 23.1	+40 47	Cyg	7.4	8	50	
6913	M29	20 23.9	+38 32	Cyg	6.6	7	50	*
6939		20 31.4	+60 38	Ceph	7.8	8	80	*
6940		20 34.6	+28 18	Vul	6.3	31	60	
7039		21 11.2	+45 39	Cyg	7.6	25	50	
7063		21 24.4	+36 30	Cyg	7.0	8	12	
7082		21 29.4	+47 05	Cyg	7.2	25	–	
7092	M39	21 32.2	+48 26	Cyg	4.6	32	30	*
IC1396		21 39.1	+57 30	Cep	3.5	50	50	*
7160		21 53.7	+62 36	Cep	6.1	7	12	
7209		22 05.2	+46 30	Lac	6.7	25	25	
7235		22 12.6	+57 17	Cep	7.7	4	30	
724:		22 15.3	+49 53	Lac	6.4	21	40	
7261		22 20.4	+58 05	Cep	8.4	6	30	
738C		22 47.0	+58 06	Cep	7.2	12	40	
7510		23 11.5	+60 34	Cep	7.9	4	60	
7654	M52	23 24.2	+61 35	Cas	6.9	13	100	*
7686		23 30.2	+49 08	And	5.6	15	20	
7789		23 57.0	+56 44	Cas	6.7	16	300	
7790		23 58.4	+61 13	Cas	8.5	17	40	

BRIGHT DIFFUSE NEBULAE

NGC/IC	Other desig.	RA h m	Declination ° '	Constellation	Type	Diameter '	Magnitude star	Notes
6888		20 12.0	+38 21	Cyg	E	20 × 10	7.4	Veil Nebula (SNR)
6960		20 45.7	+30 43	Cyg	E	70 × 6		Veil Nebula (SNR)
IC5067,70		20 50.8	+44 21	Cyg	E	45 × 30		Pelican Nebula
6992		20 56.4	+31 43	Cyg	E	80 × 70		Veil Nebula (SNR)
6995		20 57.1	+31 13	Cyg	E	60 × 8		Veil Nebula (SNR)
7000		20 58.8	+44 20	Cyg	E	120 × 100	6.0	North America Nebula
IC5146		21 53.5	+47 16	Cyg	E	12 × 12	10.0	Cocoon Nebula
7635		23 20.7	+61 12	Cas	E	15 × 8	6.9	Bubble Nebula

PLANETARY NEBULAE

NGC/IC	Other desig.	RA h m	Declination ° '	Constellation	Magnitude	Diameter "	Magnitude star	Notes
6905		20 22.4	+20 07	Del	11.9	46 (100)	13.5	
7008		21 00.6	+54 33	Cyg	13.3	83	13.2	
7026		21 06.3	+47 51	Cyg	12.7	21	14.5	
7027		21 07.1	+42 14	Cyg	10.4	15	11.3	
7048		21 14.2	+46 16	Cyg	11.3	61	18.3	
7662		23 25.9	+42 33	And	9.2	20 (130)	13.2	Blue Snowball *

GALAXIES

NGC/IC	Other desig.	RA h m	Declination ° '	Constellation	Magnitude	Size '	Type	Notes
6946		20 34.8	+60 09	Cep	8.9	11.0 × 9.8	Sc	
7217		22 07.9	+31 22	Peg	10.2	3.7 × 3.2	Sb	
7331		22 37.1	+34 25	Peg	9.5	10.7 × 4.0	Sb	*
7332		22 37.4	+23 48	Peg	11.0	4.2 × 1.3	E7	
7457		23 01.0	+30 09	Peg	10.8	4.4 × 2.5	E	*
7640		23 22.1	+40 51	And	10.9	10.7 × 2.5	SBb	
7741		23 43.9	+26 05	Peg	11.4	4.0 × 2.8	SBc	

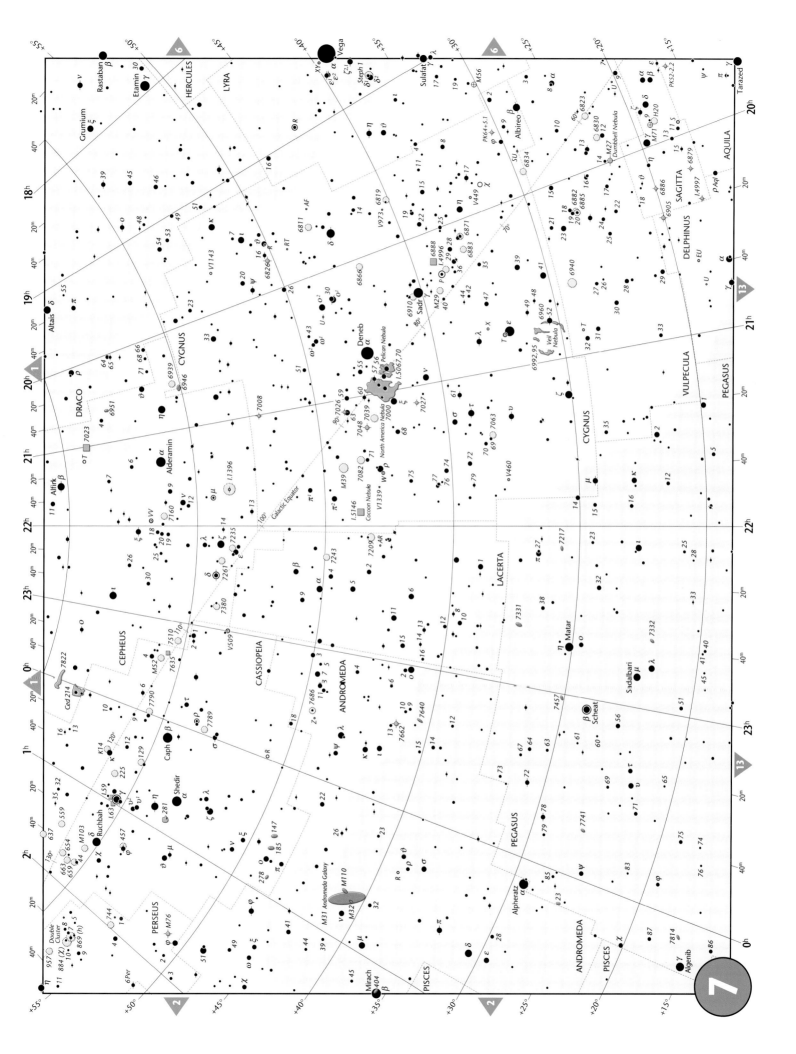

08 | Right Ascension 0ʰ to 4ʰ, Declination +20° to -20°

VARIABLE STARS

Star	RA h m	Declination ° '	Range	Type	Period (days)	Spectrum	Notes
TV Psc	00 28.0	+17 54	4.7-5.4	SR	70	M	
o Cet	02 19.3	-02 59	2.0-10.1	M	332.0	M	Mira *
U Cet	02 33.7	-13 09	6.8-13.4	M	234.8	M	
Z Eri	02 47.9	-12 28	5.6-7.2	SR	80	M	
RR Eri	02 52.2	-08 16	6.3-8.1	SR	97	M	

DOUBLE AND MULTIPLE STARS

Star	RA h m	Declination ° '	Magnitude	Position Angle °	Separation "	Notes
51 Psc	00 32.4	+06 57	5.7 + 9.5	83	27.5	
26 Cet	01 03.8	+01 22	6.2 + 8.6	253	16.0	
ζ Psc	01 13.7	+07 35	5.6 + 6.5	63	23.0	
37 Cet	01 14.4	-07 55	5.2 + 8.7	331	49.7	
χ Cet	01 49.6	-10 41	4.9 + 6.9	250	183.8	
γ Ari	01 53.5	+19 18	4.6 + 4.7	1	7.6	Mesartim *
α Psc	02 02.0	+02 46	4.2 + 5.1	272	1.8	P = 933.1 yr
66 Cet	02 12.8	-02 24	5.7 + 7.5	234	16.5	
84 Cet	02 41.2	-00 42	5.8 + 9.0	310	4.0	
γ Cet	02 43.3	+03 14	3.5 + 6.2	294	2.8	*
π Ari	02 49.3	+17 28	5.2 + 8.7	118	3.3	*
ρ³ Eri	03 02.7	-07 41	5.3 + 9.5	75	1.8	
95 Cet	03 18.4	-00 56	5.6 + 7.5	250	1.1	P = 217.2 yr

PLANETARY NEBULA

NGC/IC	Other desig.	Constellation	RA h m	Declination ° '	Magnitude	Diameter	Magnitude star	Notes
246		Cet	00 47.0	-11 53	8.0	225	11.9	*

GALAXIES

NGC/IC	Other desig.	Constellation	RA h m	Declination ° '	Magnitude	Size '	Type	Notes
7814		Peg	00 03.3	+16 09	10.5	6.3 × 2.6	Sb	
128		Psc	00 29.3	+02 52	11.6	3.4 × 1.0	S0	
157		Cet	00 34.8	-08 24	10.4	4.3 × 2.9	Sc	
210		Cet	00 40.6	-13 52	10.9	5.4 × 3.7	Sb	
255		Cet	00 47.8	-11 28	11.8	3.1 × 2.8	Sb	
309		Cet	00 56.7	-09 55	11.8	3.1 × 2.7	Sc	
337		Cet	00 59.8	-07 35	11.6	2.8 × 2.0	Sc	
IC1613		Cet	01 04.8	+02 07	9.3	12.0 × 11.2	Irr	
428		Cet	01 12.9	-00 59	11.4	4.1 × 3.2	Sc	
474		Psc	01 20.1	+03 25	11.1	7.9 × 7.2	S0	
488		Psc	01 21.8	+05 15	10.3	5.2 × 4.1	Sb	
524		Cet	01 24.8	+09 32	10.6	3.2 × 3.2	E1	
584		Cet	01 31.1	-06 52	10.4	3.8 × 2.4	E4	
628	M74	Psc	01 36.7	+15 47	9.2	10.2 × 9.5	Sc	*
676		Psc	01 49.0	-05 54	11.0	4.3 × 1.5	Sa	
720		Cet	01 53.0	-13 44	10.2	4.4 × 2.8	E3	
772		Ari	01 59.3	+19 01	10.3	7.1 × 4.5	Sb	*
779		Cet	01 59.7	-05 58	11.1	4.1 × 4.5	Sb	
864		Cet	02 15.5	+06 00	11.0	4.6 × 3.5	Sc	
895		Cet	02 21.6	-05 31	11.8	3.6 × 2.8	SBa	
936		Cet	02 27.6	-01 09	10.1	5.2 × 4.4	SBc	
988		Cet	02 35.4	-09 21	11:	4.7 × 2.7	Sc	
1042		Cet	02 41.4	-08 26	10.9	4.7 × 3.9	Sc	
1052		Cet	02 41.1	-08 15	10.6	2.9 × 2.0	E2	
1055		Cet	02 41.8	+00 26	10.6	7.6 × 3.0	Sb	
1068	M77	Cet	02 42.7	-00 01	8.8	6.9 × 5.9	Sb	*
1073		Cet	02 43.7	+01 23	11.0	4.9 × 4.6	SBc	
1084		Eri	02 46.0	-07 35	10.6	2.9 × 1.5	Sc	
1087		Cet	02 46.4	-00 30	11.1	3.5 × 2.3	Sc	
1179		Eri	03 02.6	-18 54	11.8	4.6 × 3.9	S	
1300		Eri	03 19.7	-19 25	10.4	6.5 × 4.3	SBb	
1337		Eri	03 28.1	-08 23	11.7	6.8 × 2.0	S	
1407		Eri	03 40.2	-18 35	9.8	2.5 × 2.5	E0	

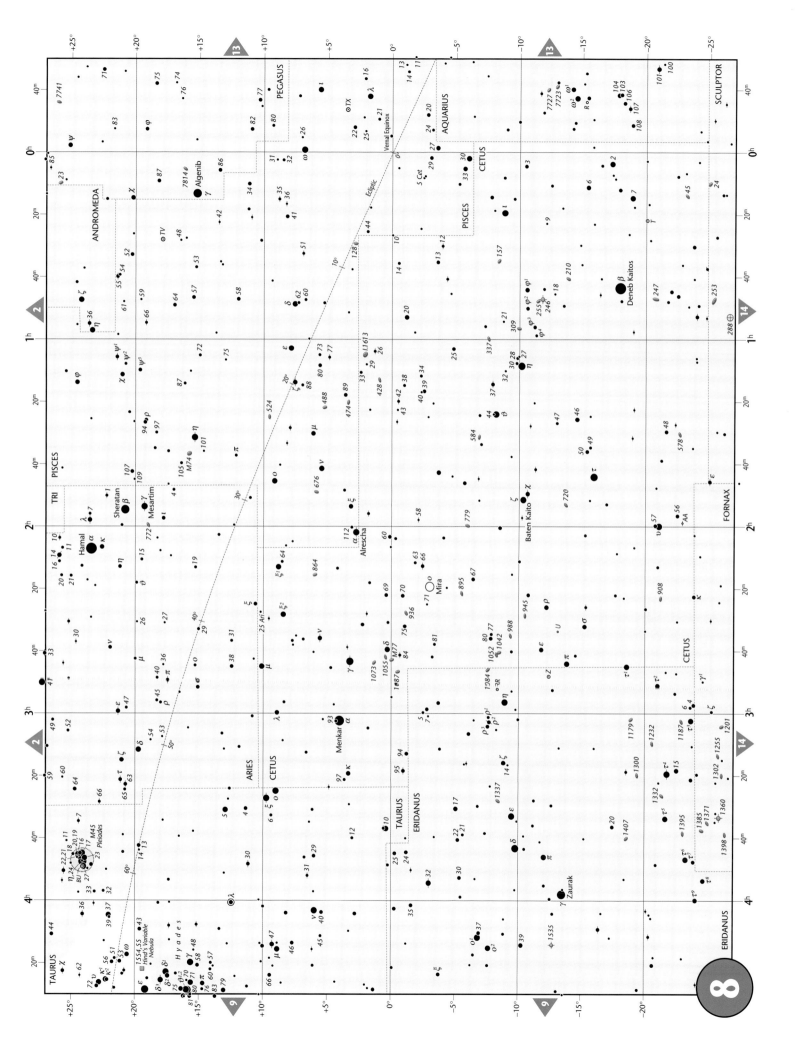

09 | Right Ascension 4ʰ to 8ʰ, Declination +20° to -20°

VARIABLE STARS

Star	RA h m	Declination ° '	Type	Range	Period (days)	Spectrum	Notes
λ Tau	04 00.7	+12 29	EA	3.3–3.8	3.95	B+A	*
R Lep	04 59.6	-14 18	M	5.5–11.7	432.1	M	*
W Ori	05 05.4	+01 11	SR	5.9–7.7	212	B	
RX Lep	05 11.4	-11 51	Irr	5.0–7.0	–	B	
CK Ori	05 30.3	+04 12	SR	5.9–7.1	120:	M	
α Ori	05 55.2	+07 24	SR	0.4–1.3	2110	M	Betelgeuse *
V Mon	06 22.7	-02 12	M	6.0–13.7	333.8	M	
T Mon	06 25.2	+07 05	Cep	5.6–6.6	27.02	F-K	
BL Ori	06 25.5	+14 43	Irr	6.3–6.9	–	M	
R CMa	07 19.5	-16 24	EA	5.7–6.3	1.14	F	
L Mon	07 30.8	-09 47	RV	5.9–7.8	92.26	F-K	*
BN Gem	07 37.1	+16 54	Irr	6.0–6.6 p	–	O	

DOUBLE AND MULTIPLE STARS

Star	RA h m	Declination ° '	Magnitude	Position Angle °	Separation "	Notes
47 Tau	04 13.9	+09 16	4.9+7.4	351	1.1	*
θ¹, θ² Tau	04 28.7	+15 52	3.4+3.8	346	337.4	
σ¹, σ² Tau	04 39.3	+15 55	4.7+5.1	193	431.2	
55 Eri	04 43.6	-08 48	6.7+6.8	317	92	*
14 Ori	05 07.9	+08 30	5.8+6.5	322	0.8	P = 198.9 years
κ Lep	05 13.2	-12 56	4.5+7.4	358	2.6	
π Ori	05 13.3	+02 52	4.5+8.3	64	7.0	
β Ori	05 14.5	-08 12	0.2+6.8	202	9.5	Rigel *
η Ori	05 24.5	-02 24	3.8+4.5	80	1.5	
θ¹ Ori	05 35.3	-05 23	6.7+7.9	31	8.8	Trapezium: in Orion Nebula; AB *
			5.1	132	12.8	AC
			6.7	96	21.5	AD
θ² Ori	05 35.4	-05 25	5.2+6.5	92	52.5	In Orion Nebula *
ι Ori	05 35.4	-05 55	2.8+6.9	141	11.3	*
ζ Ori	05 40.8	-01 57	1.9+4.0	165	2.3	Alnitak; P = 1509 yr
75 Ori	06 17.1	+09 57	5.4+9.5	258	62.7	AB
			8.5	159	117.3	AC
8 Mon	06 23.8	+04 36	4.5+6.5	27	13.4	=ε Mon *
β Mon	06 28.8	-07 02	4.7+5.2	132	7.3	AB
			6.1	124	10.0	AC
ν¹ CMa	06 36.4	-18 40	5.8+8.5	262	17.5	*
15 Mon	06 41.0	+09 54	4.7+7.5	213	2.8	S Mon; AB *
			9.8	13	16.6	AC
			9.6	308	41.3	AD; In cluster 2264
			9.9	139	73.9	AE
			7.7	222	156.0	AF
α CMa	06 45.2	-16 43	-1.4+8.5	150	4.6	Sirius; P = 50.1 years *
38 Gem	06 54.6	+13 11	4.7+7.7	145	7.1	P = 3,190 years
μ CMa	06 56.1	-14 03	5.3+8.6	340	3.0	

OPEN CLUSTERS

NGC/IC	Other desig.	Constellation	RA h m	Declination ° '	Magnitude	Diameter '	No.	Notes
1647		Tau	04 46.0	+19 04	6.4	45	200	*
1662		Ori	04 48.5	+10 56	6.4	20	35	
1807		Tau	05 10.7	+16 32	7.0	17	20	
1817		Tau	05 12.1	+16 42	7.7	16	60	
1981		Ori	05 35.2	-04 26	4.6	25	20	
2169		Ori	06 08.4	+13 57	5.9	7	30	
2194		Ori	06 13.8	+12 48	8.5	10	80	
2204		CMa	06 15.7	-18 39	8.6	13	80	
2215		Mon	06 21.0	-07 17	8.4	11	40	Contains 10 Mon
2232		Mon	06 26.6	-04 45	3.9	30	20	In Rosette Nebula
2244		Mon	06 32.4	+04 52	4.80	24	100	In Rosette Nebula
2252		Mon	06 35.0	+05 23	7.7	20	30	
2286		Mon	06 47.6	-03 10	7.5	15	50	
2301		Mon	06 51.8	+00 28	6.0	12	80	
2323	M50	Mon	07 03.2	-08 20	5.9	16	80	*
2335		Mon	07 06.6	-10 05	7.2	12	35	
2343		Mon	07 08.3	-10 39	6.7	7	20	
2345		CMa	07 08.3	-13 10	7.7	12	70	
2353		Mon	07 14.6	-10 18	7.1	20	30	
2360		CMa	07 17.8	-15 37	7.2	13	80	
2374		CMa	07 24.0	-13 16	8.0	19	25	
2395		Gem	07 27.1	+13 35	8.0	12	30	
2414		Pup	07 33.3	-15 27	7.9	4	35	
2422	M47	Pup	07 36.6	-14 30	4.4	30	30	*
2423		Pup	07 37.1	-13 52	6.7	19	40	
–	Mel 71	Pup	07 37.5	-12 04	7.1	9	80	
2437	M46	Pup	07 41.8	-14 49	6.1	27	100	Contains pl. neb. NGC 2438 *

BRIGHT DIFFUSE NEBULAE

NGC/IC	Other desig.	Constellation	RA h m	Declination ° '	Type	Diameter '	Magnitude star	Notes
1554, 1555		Tau	04 21.8	+19 32	R	Var	9.4	Hind's Variable Nebula
1973		Ori	05 35.1	-04 44	E+R	5×5	7.4	
1975		Ori	05 35.4	-04 41	E+R	10×5	10.9	
1976	M42	Ori	05 35.4	-05 27	E+R	66×60	2.9	Orion Nebula *
1977		Ori	05 35.5	-04 52	E+R	20×10	4.6	
1982	M43	Ori	05 35.6	-05 16	E+R	20×15	6.9	Extension of M42 *
IC434		Ori	05 41.0	-02 24	E	60×10	2.1	Contains Horse-Head Nebula (B33)
2024		Ori	05 41.9	-01 51	E	30×30	2.1	ζ Ori *
2068	M78	Ori	05 46.7	+00 03	R	8×6	10.5	*
2237-2239		Mon	06 32.3	+05 03	E	80×60	–	Rosette Nebula *
2261	R Mon	Mon	06 39.2	+08 44	E+R	2×1	10.0	Hubble's Variable Nebula
2264	S Mon	Mon	06 40.9	+09 54	E	60×30	4.5	Includes Cone Nebula *
IC2177		Mon	07 05.1	-10 42	E	120×40	6.2	

PLANETARY NEBULAE

NGC/IC	Other desig.	Constellation	RA h m	Declination ° '	Magnitude	Diameter "	Magnitude star	Notes
1535		Eri	04 14.2	-12 44	9.6	18 (44)	12.2	
IC418		Lep	05 27.5	-12 42	10.7	12	10.6	
2438		Pup	07 41.8	-14 44	10.1	66	17.7	In open cluster NGC 2437
2440		Pup	07 41.9	-18 13	10.8	14 (32)	14.3	

GALAXIES

NGC/IC	Other desig.	Constellation	RA h m	Declination ° '	Magnitude	Size '	Type	Notes
1637		Eri	04 41.5	-02 51	10.9	3.3×2.9	Sc	
1723		Eri	04 59.4	-10 59	12:	3.7×2.3	SB	

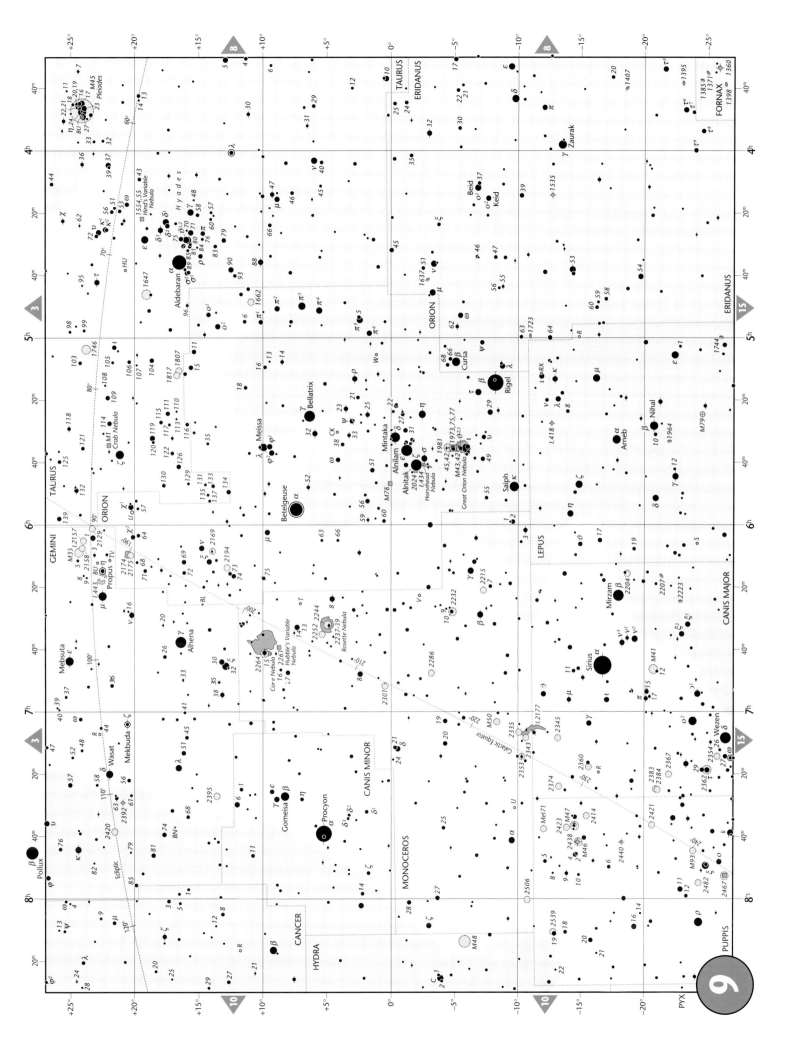

10 | Right Ascension 8ʰ to 12ʰ, Declination +20° to -20°

VARIABLE STARS

Star	RA h m	Declination ° '	Range	Type	Period (days)	Spectrum	Notes
R Cnc	08 16.6	+11 44	6.1-11.8	M	361.6	M	*
AK Hya	08 39.9	-17 18	6.3-6.9	SR	112:	M	
X Cnc	08 55.4	+17 14	5.6-7.5	SR	195:	K	
R Leo	09 47.6	+11 26	4.4-11.3	M	312.4	M	
U Hya	10 37.6	-13 23	4.3-6.5	SR	450:	B	*

DOUBLE AND MULTIPLE STARS

Star	RA h m	Declination ° '	Magnitude	Position Angle °	Separation "	Notes
ζ Cnc	08 12.2	+17 39	5.6 + 6.2	72	6.0	AC: P = 1150 yrs
			6.0	86	0.8	AB: P=59.7 yrs
ε Hya	08 46.8	-06 25	3.8 + 4.7	302	2.7	P = 890 yrs
27 Hya	09 20.5	-09 33	5.0 + 6.9	211	229.4	
ω Leo	09 28.5	+09 03	5.9 + 6.5	84	0.6	P = 118.2 yrs *
6 Leo	09 32.0	+09 43	5.2 + 8.2	75	37.4	
γ Sex	09 52.5	-08 06	5.6 + 6.1	56	0.6	P = 75.6 yrs
α Leo	10 08.4	+11 58	1.4 + 7.7	307	176.9	Regulus *
γ Leo	10 20.0	+19 51	2.2 + 3.5	125	4.4	Algieba; AB: P = 618.6 yrs *
			9.2	291	259.9	AC
			9.6	302	333.0	AD
46 Leo	10 35.0	+08 39	5.8 + 8.5	157	2.4	TX Leo
ι Crt	11 23.9	+10 32	4.0 + 6.7	117	1.7	P = 192 yrs
γ Crt	11 24.9	-17 41	4.1 + 9.6	96	5.2	
90 Leo	11 34.7	+16 48	6.0 + 7.3	209	3.3	AB
			8.7	234	63.1	AC

OPEN CLUSTERS

NGC/IC	Other desig.	RA h m	Declination ° '	Magnitude	Diameter '	No.	Notes
2506		08 00.2	-10 47	7.6	7	150	
2539		08 10.7	-12 50	6.5	22	50	
2548	M48	08 13.8	-05 48	5.8	54	80	*
2632	M44	08 40.1	+19 59	3.1	95	50	Praesepe / Beehive *
2682	M67	08 50.4	+11 49	6.9	30	200	*

PLANETARY NEBULA

NGC/IC	Other desig.	Constellation	RA h m	Declination ° '	Magnitude	Diameter "	Magnitude star	Notes
3242		Hya	10 24.8	-18 38	5.6	26 (40)	12.0	Ghost of Jupiter *

GALAXIES

NGC/IC	Other desig.	Constellation	RA h m	Declination ° '	Magnitude	Size '	Type	Notes
2775		Cnc	09 10.3	+07 02	10.3	4.5 × 3.5	Sc	
2967		Sex	09 42.1	-00 20	11.6	3.0 × 2.9	Sc	
2974		Sex	09 42.6	-03 42	10.8	3.4 × 2.1	Sa	
–		Sex	10 00.0	-05 20	11.4	4.6 × 3.3	Irr	
3115	U 5373	Sex	10 05.2	-07 43	9.2	8.3 × 3.2	E6	*
–	U 5470	Leo	10 08.4	+12 18	9.8	10.7 × 8.3	dE3	Leo I *
3166		Sex	10 13.8	+03 26	10.6	5.2 × 2.7	SBa	*
3169		Sex	10 14.2	+03 28	10.5	4.8 × 3.2	Sb	
3351	M95	Leo	10 44.0	+11 42	9.7	7.4 × 5.1	SBb	*
3367		Leo	10 46.6	+13 45	11.5	2.3 × 2.1	Sc	*
3368	M96	Leo	10 46.8	+11 49	9.2	7.1 × 5.1	Sb	*
3377		Leo	10 47.7	+13 59	10.2	4.4 × 2.7	E5	*
3379	M105	Leo	10 47.8	+12 35	9.3	4.5 × 4.0	E1	
3384		Leo	10 48.3	+12 38	10.0	5.9 × 2.6	E7	
3412		Leo	10 50.9	+13 25	10.6	3.6 × 2.0	E5	
3489		Leo	11 00.3	+13 54	10.3	3.7 × 2.1	E6	
3507		Leo	11 03.5	+18 08	11.4	3.5 × 3.0	SBb	
3521		Leo	11 05.8	-00 02	8.9	9.5 × 5.0	Sb	
3593		Leo	11 14.6	+12 49	11.0	5.8 × 2.5	Sb	
3596		Leo	11 15.1	+14 47	11.6	4.2 × 4.1	Sc	
3607		Leo	11 16.9	+18 03	10.0	3.7 × 3.2	E1	
3623	M65	Leo	11 18.9	+13 05	9.3	10.0 × 3.3	Sb	*
3626		Leo	11 20.1	+18 21	10.9	3.1 × 2.2	Sb	
3627	M66	Leo	11 20.2	+12 59	9.0	8.7 × 4.4	Sb	*
3628		Leo	11 20.3	+13 36	9.5	14.8 × 3.6	Sb	
3640		Leo	11 21.1	+03 14	10.3	4.1 × 3.4	E1	
3655		Leo	11 22.9	+16 35	11.6	1.6 × 1.1	S:	
3672		Crt	11 25.0	-09 48	11.5	4.1 × 2.1	Sb	
3686		Leo	11 27.7	+17 13	11.4	3.3 × 2.6	Sc	
3810		Leo	11 41.0	+11 28	10.8	4.3 × 3.1	Sc	
3818		Vir	11 42.0	-06 09	11.8	2.1 × 1.4	E2	
3887		Crt	11 47.1	-16 51	11.0	3.3 × 2.7	Sc	
3962		Crt	11 54.7	-13 58	10.6	2.9 × 2.6	E2	
4027		Crv	11 59.5	-19 16	11.1	3.0 × 2.3	Sc	

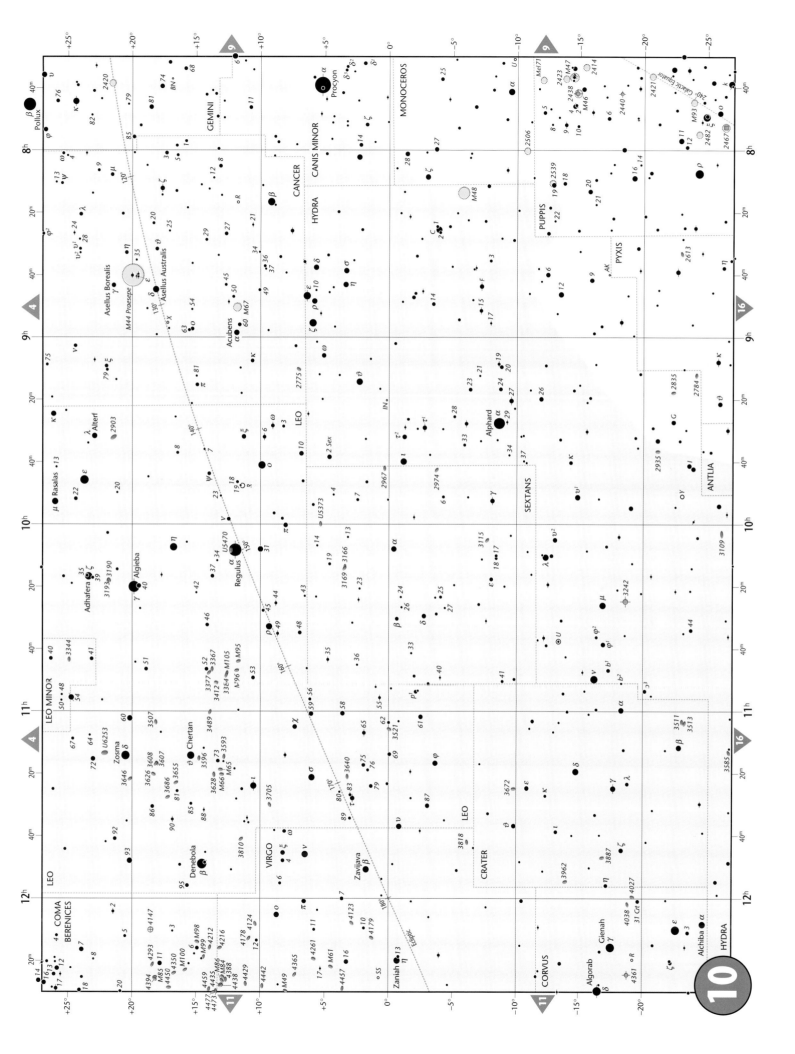

11 | Right Ascension 12ʰ to 16ʰ, Declination +20° to -20°

VARIABLE STARS

Star	RA h m	Declination ° '	Range	Type	Period (days)	Spectrum	Notes
R Crv	12 19.6	-19 15	6.7-14.4	M	317.0	M	
SS Vir	12 25.3	+00 48	6.0-9.6	M	354.7	K	
R Vir	12 38.5	+06 59	6.0-12.1	M	145.6	M	
S Vir	13 33.0	-07 12	6.3-13.2	M	377.4	M	
δ Lib	15 01.0	-08 31	4.9-5.9	EA	2.33	B	
R Ser	15 50.7	+15 08	5.2-14.4	M	356.4	M	*

DOUBLE AND MULTIPLE STARS

Star	RA h m	Declination ° '	Magnitude	Position Angle °	Separation "	Notes
24 Vir	12 22.5	+05 18	6.6 + 9.4	337	20.0	
δ Crv	12 29.9	-16 31	3.0 + 9.2	214	24.2	Algorab
24 Com	12 35.1	+18 23	5.2 + 6.7	271	20.3	
γ Vir	12 41.7	-01 27	3.5 + 3.5	267	1.8	Porrima; P = 171.4 yr *
θ Vir	13 09.9	-05 32	4.4 + 9.4	343	7.1	
84 Vir	13 43.1	+03 32	5.5 + 7.9	229	2.9	
π Boo	14 40.7	+16 25	4.9 + 5.8	108	5.6	
ζ Boo	14 41.1	+13 44	4.5 + 4.6	300	0.8	P = 123.4 yr
μ Lib	14 49.3	-14 09	5.8 + 6.7	355	1.8	
α¹, α² Lib	14 50.9	-16 02	2.8 + 5.2	314	231.0	Zubenelgenubi *
ι Lib	15 12.2	-19 47	5.1 + 9.4	106	60.0	P = 23.4 yr *
δ Ser	15 34.8	+10 32	4.2 + 5.2	176	4.4	P = 3168 yr
47 Lib	15 55.0	-19 23	6.1 + 8.1	129	0.5	

GLOBULAR CLUSTERS

NGC/IC	Other desig.	RA h m	Constellation	Declination ° '	Magnitude	Diameter '	Notes
4147		12 10.1	Com	+18 33	10.3	4.0	
5024	M53	13 12.9	Com	+18 10	7.7	12.6	
5353		13 16.4	Com	+17 42	9.8	10.5	
5534		14 29.6	Vir	-05 59	9.6	4.9	
5904	M5	15 18.6	Ser	+02 05	5.8	17.4	

PLANETARY NEBULA

NGC/IC	Other desig.	RA h m	Constellation	Declination ° '	Magnitude	Diameter "	Magnitude star	Notes
4361		12 24.5	Crv	+18 48	10.3	45 (110)	13.2	

GALAXIES

NGC/IC	Other desig.	RA h m	Constellation	Declination ° '	Magnitude	Type	Size '	Notes
4038		12 01.9	Crv	-18 52	10.7	Sc	2.6 × 1.8	
4123		12 08.2	Vir	+02 53	11.2	SBb	4.5 × 3.5	
4179		12 12.9	Vir	+01 18	10.9	S0	4.2 × 1.2	
4192	M98	12 13.8	Com	+14 54	10.1	Sb	9.5 × 3.2	*
4212		12 15.7	Com	+13 54	11.2	Sb	3.0 × 2.1	
4216		12 15.9	Com	+13 09	10.0	Sb	8.3 × 2.2	
4254	M99	12 18.8	Com	+14 25	9.8	Sc	5.4 × 4.8	*
4261		12 19.4	Vir	+05 49	10.3	E2	3.9 × 3.2	
4293		12 21.2	Com	+18 23	11.2	Sa	6.0 × 3.0	
4303	M61	12 21.9	Vir	+04 28	9.7	Sc	6.0 × 5.5	*
4321	M100	12 22.9	Com	+15 49	9.4	Sc	6 × 6.2	*
4350		12 24.0	Com	+16 42	11.1	E7	3.2 × 1.1	
4365		12 24.5	Vir	+07 19	10.5	E2	6.2 × 4.6	
4374	M84	Vir	12 25.1	+12 53	9.3	E1	5.0 × 4.4	*
4382	M85	Com	12 25.4	+18 11	9.2	E	7.1 × 5.2	*
4388		Vir	12 25.8	+12 40	11.1	SBb	5.1 × 1.4	
4394		Com	12 25.9	+18 13	10.9	SBb	3.9 × 3.5	
4406	M86	Vir	12 26.2	+12 57	9.2	E3	7.4 × 5.5	*
4429		Vir	12 27.4	+11 07	10.2	S0	5.5 × 2.6	
4435		Vir	12 27.7	+13 05	10.9	E4	3.0 × 1.0	
4438		Vir	12 27.8	+13 01	10.5	Sa	9.3 × 3.9	
4442		Vir	12 28.1	+09 48	10.5	ES	4.6 × 1.9	
4450		Com	12 28.5	+17 05	10.1	Sb	4.8 × 3.5	
4457		Vir	12 29.0	+03 33	10.8	SBa	3.0 × 2.5	
4459		Com	12 29.0	+13 59	10.4	E2	3.8 × 2.8	
4472	M49	Vir	12 29.8	+08 00	8.4	E4	8.9 × 7.4	*
4473		Com	12 29.8	+13 26	10.2	E4	4.5 × 2.6	
4477		Com	12 30.0	+13 38	10.4	SBa	4.0 × 3.5	
4486	M87	Vir	12 30.8	+12 24	8.6	E1	7.2 × 6.8	Virgo A; 3C274 *
4501	M88	Com	12 32.0	+14 25	9.5	Sb	6.9 × 3.9	*
4517		Vir	12 32.8	+00 07	10.5	Sc	10.2 × 1.9	
4526		Vir	12 34.0	+07 42	9.6	E7	7.2 × 2.3	
4535		Vir	12 34.3	+08 12	9.8	SBc	6.8 × 5.0	*
4548	M91	Com	12 35.4	+14 30	10.2	SBb	5.4 × 4.4	
4546		Vir	12 35.5	-03 48	10.3	E6	3.5 × 1.7	
4552	M89	Vir	12 35.7	+12 33	9.8	E0	4.2 × 4.2	*
4568		Vir	12 36.6	+11 14	9.8	Sc	4.6 × 2.1	
4569	M90	Vir	12 36.8	+13 10	9.5	Sb	9.5 × 4.7	*
4570		Vir	12 36.9	-07 15	10.9	S0	4.1 × 1.3	
4571		Vir	12 36.9	+14 13	11.3	Sc	3.8 × 3.4	
4579	M58	Vir	12 37.7	+11 49	9.8	SBb	5.4 × 4.4	*
4596		Vir	12 39.9	+10 11	10.5	Sb	3.9 × 2.8	
4594	M104	Vir	12 40.0	-11 37	8.3	SBa	8.9 × 4.1	Sombrero Galaxy *
4621	M59	Vir	12 42.0	+11 39	9.8	E3	5.1 × 3.4	*
4636		Vir	12 42.8	+02 41	9.6	E1	6.2 × 5.0	
4643		Vir	12 43.3	-01 59	10.6	SBa	3.4 × 2.7	*
4649	M60	Com	12 43.7	+11 33	8.8	E1	7.2 × 6.2	*
4651		Vir	12 44.0	+16 24	10.5	Sc	3.8 × 2.7	
4654		Vir	12 44.0	+13 08	10.5	Sc	4.7 × 3.0	
4665		Vir	12 45.1	+03 03	11.6	SBa	4.2 × 3.5	
4666		Vir	12 45.1	-00 28	10.8	Sc	4.5 × 1.5	
4689		Com	12 47.8	+13 46	10.9	Sc	4.0 × 3.5	
4691		Vir	12 48.2	-03 20	11.2	SBb	3.2 × 2.7	
4697		Vtr	12 48.6	-05 48	9.3	E4	6.0 × 3.8	
4698		Vir	12 48.4	-08 29	10.7	Sa	4.3 × 2.5	
4699		Vir	12 49.6	-08 40	9.6	S0	3.5 × 2.7	
4710		Vir	12 49.6	+15 10	11.0	SBc	5.1 × 1.4	
4731		Vir	12 51.0	-06 24	11.3	SBc	6.5 × 3.4	
4754		Vir	12 52.3	-11 19	10.6	SB0	4.7 × 2.6	
4753		Vir	12 52.4	-01 12	9.9	Pec	5.4 × 2.9	
4762		Vir	12 52.9	+11 14	10.2	SB0	8.7 × 1.6	
4856		Vir	12 59.3	-15 02	10.4	SBa	4.6 × 1.6	
4866		Vir	12 59.5	+14 10	11.0	Sb	6.5 × 1.5	
4902		Vir	13 01.0	-14 31	11.2	Sb	3.0 × 2.8	
4941		Vir	13 04.2	-05 33	11.1	Sb	3.7 × 2.1	
4958		Vir	13 05.8	-08 01	10.5	ES	4.1 × 1.4	
4995		Vir	13 09.7	-07 50	11.0	Sb	2.5 × 1.7	
5018		Vir	13 13.0	-19 31	10.8	Sa	2.6 × 2.1	
5044		Vir	13 15.4	-16 23	11.0	E0	2.6 × 2.6	
5054		Vir	13 17.0	-16 38	11.3	Sc	5.0 × 3.1	*
5247		Vir	13 38.1	-17 53	10.5	Sc	5.4 × 4.7	
5248		Boo	13 37.5	-08 53	10.2	SBb	6.5 × 4.9	
5363		Vir	13 56.1	+05 15	10.2	E	4.2 × 2.7	
5364		Vir	13 56.2	+05 01	10.4	Sb	7.1 × 5.0	
5566		Vir	14 20.3	+03 56	10.5	Sb	6.5 × 2.4	
5576		Vir	14 21.1	+03 16	10.9	E2	3.2 × 2.2	
5746		Vir	14 44.9	+01 57	10.6	Sb	7.9 × 1.7	
5813		Vir	15 01.2	+01 42	10.7	E1	3.6 × 2.8	
5838		Vir	15 05.4	-02 06	10.8	Sa	4.2 × 1.6	
5846		Vir	15 06.8	+01 36	10.2	E0	3.4 × 3.2	

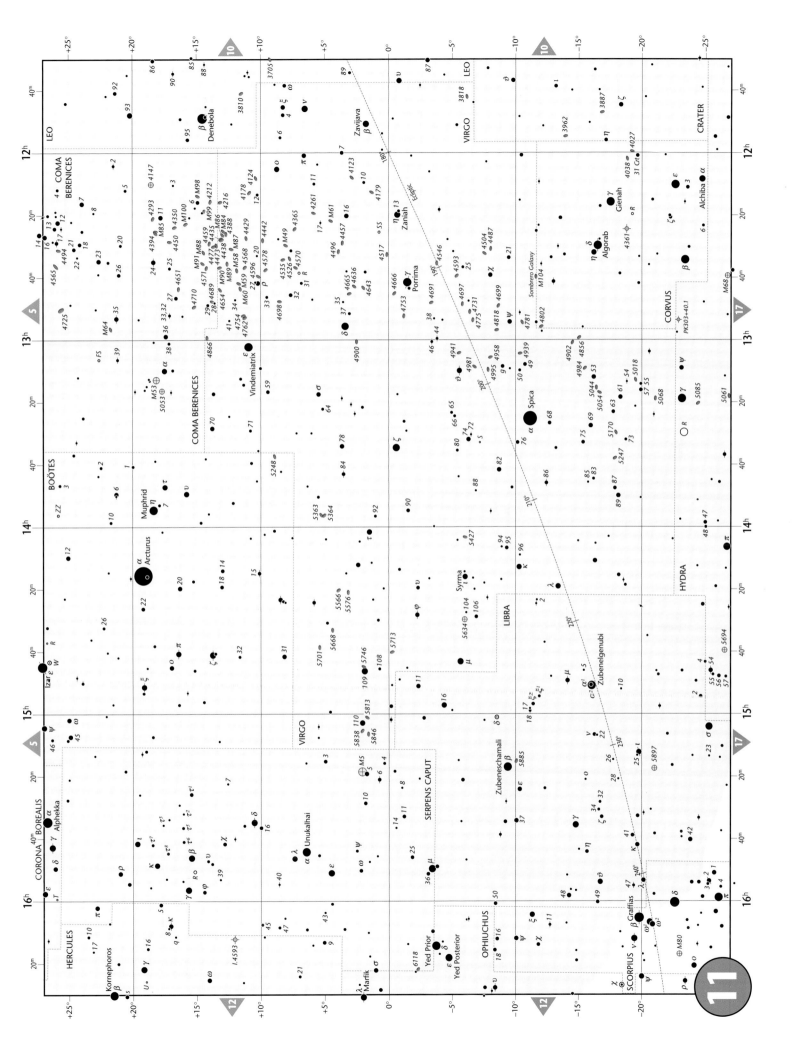

12 | Right Ascension 16ʰ to 20ʰ, Declination +20° to -20°

VARIABLE STARS

Star	RA h m	Declination ° '	Range	Type	Period (days)	Spectrum	Notes
U Her	16 25.8	+18 54	6.5-13.4	M	406.1	M	
χ Oph	16 27.0	-18 27	4.2-5.0	Irr	–	M	
V1010 Oph	16 49.5	-15 40	6.1-7.0	EB	0.66	A	
S Her	16 51.9	+14 56	6.4-13.8	M	307.4	M	
R Oph	17 07.8	-16 06	7.0-13.8	M	302.6	M	
α Her	17 14.6	+14 23	2.7-4.0	SR	–	M	
U Oph	17 16.5	+01 13	5.9-6.6	EA	1.68	B	
Y Sgr	18 21.4	-18 52	5.4-6.1	Cep	5.77	F	
59 Ser	18 27.2	+00 12	4.9-5.9	–	–	G+A	
U Sgr	18 31.9	-19 07	6.3-7.1	Cep	6.74	F-G	
X Oph	18 38.3	+08 50	5.9-9.2	M	334.4	M+K	
V3879 Sgr	18 42.9	-19 17	6.1-6.6	SR	50:	M	
R Sct	18 47.5	-05 42	4.5-8.2	RV	140.1	G-K	
FF Aql	18 58.2	+17 22	5.2-5.7	Cep	4.47	F	
V Aql	19 04.4	-05 41	6.6-8.4	SR	353	K	
R Aql	19 06.4	+08 14	5.5-12.0	M	284.2	M	*
U Sge	19 18.8	+19 37	6.6-9.2	EA	3.38	B+K	
U Aql	19 29.4	-07 03	6.1-6.9	Cep	7.02	F-G	
η Aql	19 52.5	+01 00	3.5-4.4	Cep	7.17	F-G	*
V505 Sgr	19 53.1	-14 36	6.5-7.5	EA	1.18	A+F	
S Sge	19 56.0	+16 38	5.3-6.0	Cep	8.38	F-G	

DOUBLE AND MULTIPLE STARS

Star	RA h m	Declination ° '	Magnitude	Position Angle °	Separation "	Notes
β Sco	16 05.4	-19 48	2.6+4.9	21	13.6	Graffias
11 Sco	16 07.6	-12 45	10.3	132	0.5	
κ Her	16 08.1	-17 03	5.6+9.9	257	3.3	
ν Sco	16 12.0	-19 28	5.3+6.5	12	28.4	AC
			4.3+6.8	337	41.1	AB
			6.8	3	0.9	CD
υ(upsilon) Oph	16 27.8	-08 22	7.8	51	2.3	
λ Oph	16 30.9	+01 59	4.6+7.8	95	1.0	P=129.9 yr
37, 36 Her	16 40.6	+04 13	4.2+5.2	30	69.8	
19 Oph	16 47.2	+02 04	5.8+7.0	230	23.4	
η Oph	17 10.4	-15 43	6.1+9.4	89	0.6	P=84.3 yr
α He	17 14.6	+14 23	3.0+3.5	237	4.6	Rasalgethi: var.; P=3600 yr
41 Oph	17 16.6	-00 27	2.9v+5.4	104	1.0	
V[nu] Ser	17 20.8	-12 51	4.8+7.8	346	46.3	
53 Oph	17 34.6	+09 35	4.3+8.3	28	41.2	AB, P=280 yr *
τ Oph	18 03.1	-08 11	5.8+8.5	191	1.7	AC
			5.2+5.9	283	100.3	
70 Oph	18 05.5	+02 30	9.3	127	3.8	P=88.1 yr
59 Ser	18 27.2	+00 12	4.2+6.0	148	3.8	
θ Ser	18 56.2	+04 12	5.3+7.6	318	22.3	
23 Aql	19 18.5	+01 05	4.5+5.4	104	3.1	
π Aql	19 48.7	+11 49	5.3+9.3	5	1.4	
57 Aql	19 54.6	-08 14	6.1+6.9	110	35.7	*
			5.8+6.5	170		

OPEN CLUSTERS

NGC/IC	Other desig.	Constellation	RA h m	Declination ° '	Magnitude	Diameter '	No.	Notes
IC4665		Oph	17 46.3	+05 43	4.2	41	30	*
6494	M23	Sgr	17 56.8	-19 01	5.5	27	150	*
6595		Sgr	18 17.0	-19 53	7.0	11	30	
–	M24	Sgr	18 17:	-18 40:	–	120:		Star Cloud *
6604		Ser	18 18.1	-12 14	6.5	2	30	
6613	M18	Sgr	18 19.9	-17 08	6.9	9	20	*
6633		Oph	18 27.7	+06 34	4.6	27	30	*
IC4725	M25	Sgr	18 31.6	-19 15	4.6	32	30	*
6645		Sgr	18 32.6	-16 54	8.5	10	40	
IC4756		Ser	18 39.0	+05 27	5.4	52	80	*
6694	M26	Sct	18 45.2	-09 24	8.0	15	30	
6705	M11	Sct	18 51.1	-06 16	5.8	14	500	Wild Duck Cluster *
6709		Aql	18 51.5	+10 21	6.7	13	40	*
6716		Sgr	18 54.6	-19 53	6.9	7	20	
6738		Aql	19 01.4	+11 36	8.3	15		
6755		Aql	19 07.8	+04 14	7.5	15	100	
–	I-20	Sge	19 53.1	+18 20	7.7	7	15	

GLOBULAR CLUSTERS

NGC/IC	Other desig.	Constellation	RA h m	Declination ° '	Magnitude	Diameter '	Notes
6171	M107	Oph	16 32.5	-13 03	8.1	10.0	*
6218	M12	Oph	16 47.2	-01 57	6.6	14.5	*
6254	M10	Oph	16 57.1	-04 06	6.6	15.1	*
6333	M9	Oph	17 19.2	-18 31	7.9	9.3	*
6342		Oph	17 21.2	-19 35	9.9	3.0	
6356		Oph	17 23.6	-17 49	8.4	7.2	
6366		Oph	17 27.7	-05 05	10.0	8.3	
6402	M14	Oph	17 37.6	-03 15	7.6	11.7	*
6517		Ser	18 01.8	-08 58	10.3	4.3	
6535		Ser	18 03.8	-00 18	10.6	3.6	
6539		Ser	18 04.8	-07 35	9.6	6.9	
IC1276		Ser	18 10.7	-07 12	10.3	7.1	*
6712		Sct	18 53.1	-08 42	8.2	7.2	*
6760		Aql	19 11.2	+01 02	9.1	6.6	
6838	M71	Sge	19 53.8	+18 47	8.3	7.2	*

BRIGHT DIFFUSE NEBULAE

NGC/IC	Other desig.	Constellation	RA h m	Declination ° '	Type	Diameter '	Notes
6611	M16	Ser	18 18.8	-13 47	E	35×28	Eagle Nebula: * & open cluster
6618	M17	Sgr	18 20.8	-16 11	E	46×37	Omega Nebula: * & open cluster

PLANETARY NEBULAE

NGC/IC	Other desig.	Constellation	RA h m	Declination ° '	Magnitude	Diameter "	Magnitude star	Notes
IC4593		Her	16 12.2	+12 04	10.9	12(120)	11.3	
6309		Oph	17 14.1	-12 55	10.8	14(66)	14.4	
6537		Sgr	18 05.2	-19 51	12.5	8		
6572		Aql	18 12.1	+06 51	9.0	8	13.6	*
6741		Aql	19 02.6	-00 27	10.8	6	14.7	
6751		Aql	19 05.9	-06 00	12.5	20	13.9	
6781		Aql	19 18.4	+06 33	11.8	109	5.0	
6790		Aql	19 23.2	+01 31	10.2	7	13.5	
6803		Aql	19 31.3	+10 03	11.3	6	15.2	
6818		Sgr	19 44.0	-14 09	9.9	17	13.1	

GALAXIES

NGC/IC	Other desig.	Constellation	RA h m	Declination ° '	Magnitude	Size '	Type
6384		Oph	17 32.4	+07 04	10.6	6.0×4.3	Sb
6822		Sgr	19 44.9	-14 48	9.4	10.2×9.5	Irr

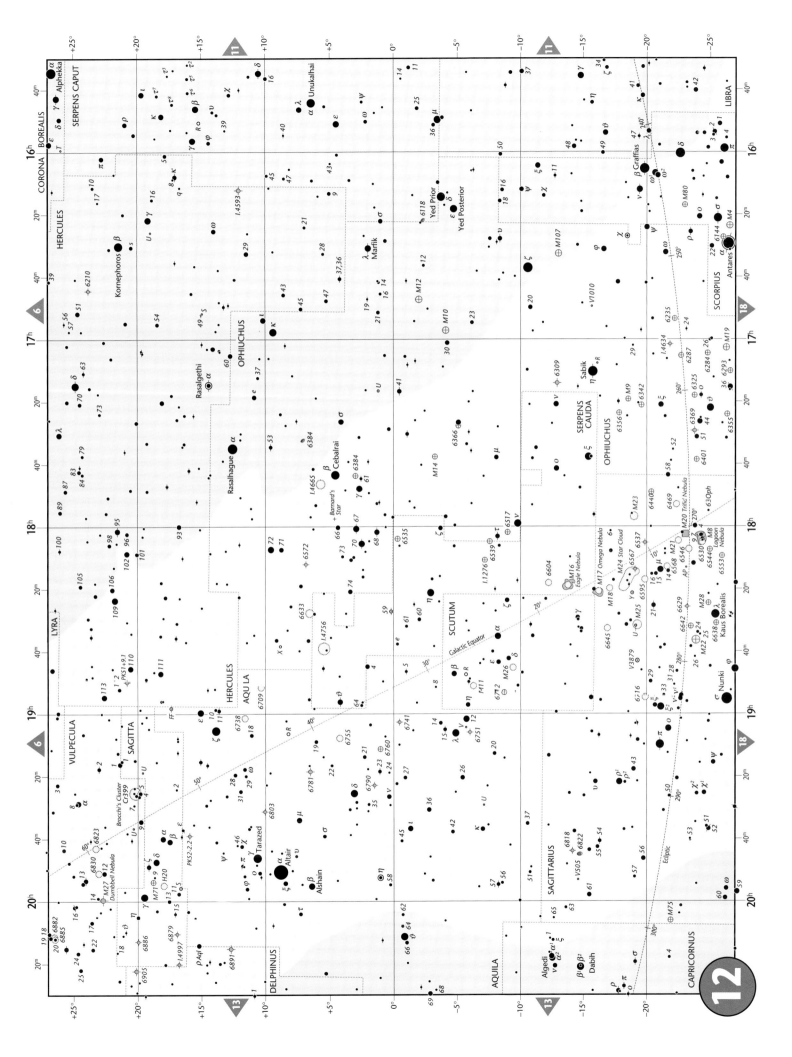

13 | Right Ascension 20ʰ to 0ʰ, Declination +20° to -20°

VARIABLE STARS

Star	RA h m	Declination ° '	Range	Type	Period (days)	Spectrum	Notes
EU Del	20 37.9	+18 16	5.8–6.9	SR	59.5	M	
U Del	20 45.5	-15 05	5.6–7.5	SR	110:	M	
EP Aqr	21 46.5	-02 13	6.4–6.8	SR	55:	M	
AG Peg	21 51.0	-12 38	6.0–9.4	ZA	830.1	M	*
R Aqr	23 43.8	-15 17	5.8–12.4	M	387.0	M	*
TX Psc	23 46.4	+03 29	4.8–5.2	Irr	–	M	

DOUBLE AND MULTIPLE STARS

Star	RA h m	Declination ° '	Magnitude	Position Angle °	Separation "	Notes
15 Sge	20 04.1	+17 04	5.9 + 9.1	276	190.7	
			6.8	320	203.7	
α¹ Cap	20 17.6	-12 30	4.2 + 8.6	221	45.4	*
α² Cap	20 18.1	-12 33	3.6 + 10.4	172	6.6	Algedi *
α¹,α² Cap	20 18.1	-12 33	3.6 + 4.2	291	377.7	*
σ Cap	20 19.4	-19 07	5.5 + 9.0	179	55.9	
π Cap	20 27.3	-18 13	5.1 + 8.3	148	3.2	*
ρ Cap	20 28.9	-17 49	5.0 + 10.0	194	1.3	*
1 Del	20 30.3	+10 54	6.1 + 8.1	346	0.9	
γ Del	20 46.7	+16 07	4.5 + 5.5	268	9.6	
13 Del	20 47.8	+06 00	5.6 + 9.2	194	1.6	
1 Equ	20 59.1	+04 18	6.0 + 6.3	284	0.8	ε Equ: P = 101.4 yr
γ Equ	21 10.3	+10 08	4.7 + 11.5	268	1.9	
			12.5	5	47.7	
ζ Aqr	22 28.8	-00 01	5.9	153	352.5	
			4.3 + 4.5	192	2.1	P = 856 yr*
37 Peg	22 30.0	+04 26	5.8 + 7.1	118	0.7	P = 140 yr
107 Aqr	23 46.0	-18 41	5.7 + 6.7	136	6.6	

OPEN CLUSTER

NGC/IC	Other desig.	Constellation	RA h m	Declination ° '	Magnitude	Diameter '	No.	Notes
6994	M73	Aqr	20 59.0	-12 38	8.9	2.8	4	Not a true cluster *

GLOBULAR CLUSTERS

NGC/IC	Other desig.	Constellation	RA h m	Declination ° '	Magnitude	Diameter '	Notes
6934		Del	20 34.2	+07 24	8.9	5.9	
6981	M72	Aqr	20 53.5	-12 32	9.4	5.9	*
7006		Del	21 01.5	+16 11	10.6	2.8	
7078	M15	Peg	21 30.0	+12 10	6.4	12.3	*
7089	M2	Aqr	21 33.5	-00 49	6.5	12.9	*
7492		Aqr	23 08.4	-15 37	11.5	6.2	

PLANETARY NEBULAE

NGC/IC	Other desig.	Constellation	RA h m	Declination ° '	Magnitude	Diameter '	Magnitude star	Notes
6879		Sge	20 10.5	+16 55	13.0	5	15:	
6886		Sge	20 12.7	+19 59	12.2	4	15.7	
6891		Del	20 15.2	+12 42	11.7	12 (74)	12.4	
IC 4997		Sge	20 20.2	+16 45	11.6	2	13:	
7009		Aqr	21 04.2	-11 22	8.3	25 (100)	11.5	Saturn Nebula *

GALAXIES

NGC/IC	Other desig.	Constellation	RA h m	Declination ° '	Magnitude	Size	Type	Notes
7448		Peg	23 00.1	+15 59	11.7	2.7 × 1.3	Sc	
7479		Peg	23 04.9	+12 19	11.0	4.1 × 3.2	SBb	
7606		Aqr	23 19.1	-08 29	10.8	5.8 × 2.6	Sb	*
7723		Aqr	23 38.9	-12 58	11.1	3.6 × 2.6	Sb	
7727		Aqr	23 39.9	-12 18	10.7	4.2 × 3.4	SBa	

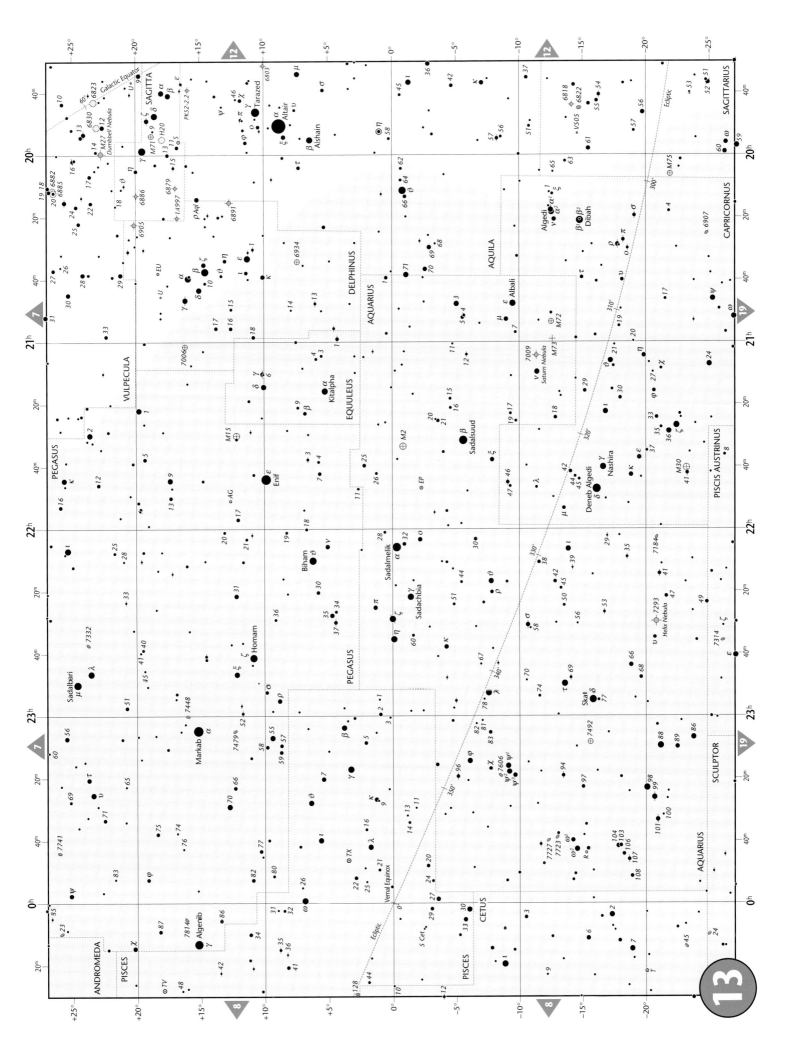

14 | Right Ascension 0h to 4h, Declination -20° to -65°

VARIABLE STARS

Star	RA h m	Declination ° '	Range	Type	Period (days)	Spectrum	Notes
S Scl	00 15.4	-32 03	5.5-13.6	M	365.3	M	
T Cet	00 21.8	-20 03	5.0-6.9	SR	158.9	M	
ζ Phe	01 08.4	-55 15	3.9-4.4	EA	1.67	B	*
R Scl	01 27.0	-32 33	9.1-12.8 p	SR	370	M	
AA Cet	01 59.0	-22 55	6.0-6.5	EW	0.54	F	
R Hor	02 53.9	-49 53	4.7-14.3	M	404.0	M	*
γ Hor	03 03.5	-58 56	8.7-9.8 p	SR	–	M	
W Hor	03 12.6	-57 19	5.3-6.0	SR	158:	K	

DOUBLE AND MULTIPLE STARS

Star	RA h m	Declination ° '	Magnitude	Position Angle °	Separation "	Notes
κ¹ Scl	00 09.3	-27 59	6.1+6.2	265	1.4	*
β Tuc	00 31.5	-62 58	4.4+4.8	169	27.1	
ξ Phe	00 41.8	-56 30	5.8+10.2	253	13.2	
λ¹ Scl	00 42.7	-38 28	6.7+7.0	3	0.5	
β Phe	01 06.1	-46 43	4.0+4.2	346	1.4	
π Eri	01 39.8	-56 12	5.8+5.8	191	11.5	P=483.7 yr
ε Scl	01 45.6	-25 03	5.4+8.6	23	4.7	P=1192 yr *
ω For	02 33.8	-28 14	5.0+7.7	244	10.8	
η² For	02 50.2	-35 51	5.9+10.1	14	5.0	
θ Eri	02 58.3	-40 18	3.4+4.5	88	8.2	
τ⁴ Eri	03 12.1	-28 59	4.0+7.0 v	299	5.1	P=314 yr
τ⁵ Eri	03 19.5	-21 45	3.7+9.2	288	5.7	
			9.7	236	160.2	
χ¹ For	03 28.2	-35 51	6.5+10.5	248	6.3	

GLOBULAR CLUSTERS

NGC/IC	Other desig.	Constellation	RA h m	Declination ° '	Magnitude	Diameter '	Notes
288		Scl	00 52.8	-26 35	8.1	13.8	
1261		Hor	03 12.3	-55 13	8.4	6.9	

PLANETARY NEBULAE

NGC/IC	Other desig.	Constellation	RA h m	Declination ° '	Magnitude	Diameter "	Magnitude star	Notes
1360		For	03 33.3	-25 51	9.4	390	11.4	

GALAXIES

NGC/IC	Other desig.	Constellation	RA h m	Declination ° '	Magnitude	Size '	Type	Notes
24		Scl	00 09.9	-24 58	11.5	5.5×1.6	Sb	
45		Cet	00 14.1	-23 11	10.4	8.1×5.8	S	
55		Scl	00 14.9	-39 11	8.2	32.4×6.5	SB	*
134		Scl	00 30.4	-33 15	10.1	8.1×2.6	SBb	
150		Scl	00 34.3	-27 48	11.1	4.2×2.3	S	
247		Cet	00 47.1	-20 46	8.9	20.0×7.4	Sc	*
253		Scl	00 47.6	-25 17	7.1	25.1×7.4	Sc	
289		Scl	00 52.7	-31 12	11.6	3.7×2.7	Sc	
300		Scl	00 54.9	-37 41	8.7	20.0×14.8	Sd	
–	E 351-30	Scl	00 59.9	-33 42	10.5	35'×29'	dE3	Sculptor Dwarf
578		Cet	01 30.5	-22 40	10.9	4.8×3.2	Sc	
613		Scl	01 34.3	-29 25	10.0	5.8×4.6	SBb	
685		Eri	01 47.8	-52 47	11.8	4.1×4.0	SBb	
908		Cet	02 23.1	-21 14	10.2	5.5×2.8	SBb	
986		For	02 33.6	-39 02	11.0	3.7×2.8	Sc	
–	E 356-4	For	02 39.9	-34 32	9.0	63'×48'	dE3	Fornax Dwarf
1097		For	02 46.3	-30 17	9.3	9.3×6.6	SBb	
1187		Eri	03 02.6	-22 52	10.9	5.0×4.0	SBc	
1201		For	03 04.1	-26 04	10.6	4.4×2.8	Sa	
1232		Eri	03 09.8	-20 35	9.9	7.8×6.9	Sc	
1249		Hor	03 10.1	-53 21	11.7	5.2×2.7	SBc	
1255		For	03 13.5	-25 44	11.1	4.1×2.8	Sc	
1291		Eri	03 17.3	-41 08	8.5	10.5×9.1	SBa	
1302		For	03 19.9	-26 04	11.5	4.4×4.2	SBa	
1316		For	03 22.7	-37 12	8.9	7.1×5.5	SB0	
1326		For	03 23.9	-36 28	10.5	4.0×3.0	SB0	
1332		Eri	03 26.3	-21 20	10.3	4.6×1.7	E7	
1344		For	03 28.3	-31 04	10.3	3.9×2.3	E3	
1350		For	03 31.1	-33 38	10.5	4.3×2.4	SBb	
1365		For	03 33.6	-36 08	9.5	9.8×5.5	SBb	
1371		For	03 35.0	-24 56	11.5	5.4×4.0	SBa	
1380		For	03 36.5	-34 59	11.1	4.9×1.9	S0	
1385		For	03 37.5	-24 30	11.2	3.0×2.0	Sc	
1395		Eri	03 38.5	-23 02	11.3	3.2×2.5	E3	
1398		For	03 38.9	-26 20	9.7	6.6×5.2	SBb	
1399		For	03 38.5	-35 27	9.9	3.2×3.1	E1p	
1411		Hor	03 38.8	-44 05	11.9	2.8×2.3	S0	
1404		For	03 38.9	-35 35	10.3	2.5×2.3	E1	
1433		Hor	03 42.0	-47 13	10.0	6.8×6.0	SBb	
1425		For	03 42.2	-29 54	11.7	5.4×2.7	Sb	
1448		Hor	03 44.5	-44 39	11.3	8.1×1.8	Sc	
1493		Hor	03 57.5	-46 12	11.8	2.6×2.3	SBc	

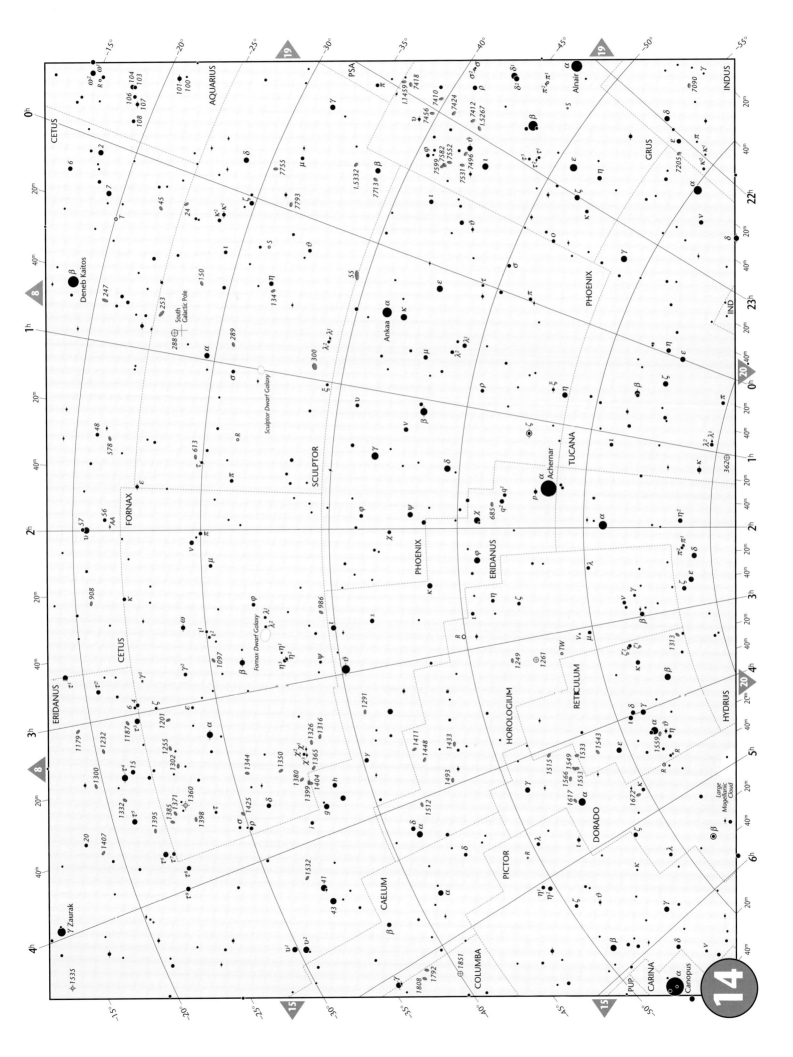

15 | Right Ascension 4ʰ to 8ʰ, Declination -20° to -65°

VARIABLE STARS

Star	RA h m	Declination ° '	Range	Type	Period (days)	Notes
R Ret	04 33.5	-63 02	6.5-14.0	M	278.3	
R Dor	04 36.8	-62 05	4.8-6.6	M	338:	
R Pic	04 46.2	-49 15	6.7-10.0	SR	164.2	
β Dor	05 33.6	-62 29	3.5-4.1	Cep	9.84	
S Lep	06 05.8	-24 12	6.0-7.6	SR	90	
L² Pup	07 13.5	-44 39	2.6-6.2	SR	140.4	*
ω CMa	07 14.8	-26 46	3.6-4.2	Irr	–	
V Pup	07 58.2	-49 15	4.4-4.9	EB	1.45	*

DOUBLE AND MULTIPLE STARS

Star	RA h m	Declination ° '	Magnitude	Position Angle°	Separation "	Notes
γ Cae	05 40.4	-25 29	4.6 + 8.1	308	2.9	*
θ Pic	05 24.8	-52 19	6.3 + 6.8	287	38.2	
β Lep	05 28.2	-20 46	2.8 + 7.3	330	2.5	Nihal
γ Lep	05 44.5	-22 27	3.7 + 6.3	350	96.3	
μ Pic	06 32.0	-58 45	5.8 + 9.0	231	2.4	
17 CMa	06 55.0	-20 24	5.8 + 9.3	147	44.4	
π CMa	06 55.6	-20 08	4.7 + 9.7	18	11.6	
ε CMa	06 58.6	-28 58	1.5 + 7.4	161	7.5	Adhara *
σ Pup	07 29.2	-43 18	3.3 + 9.4	74	22.3	

OPEN CLUSTERS

NGC/IC	Other desig.	Constellation	RA h m	Declination ° '	Magnitude	Diameter '	No.	Notes
2287	M41	CMa	06 47.0	-20 44	4.5	38	80	*
2354		CMa	07 14.3	-25 44	6.5	20	100	
2367		CMa	07 20.1	-21 56	7.9	3.5	30	
2362		CMa	07 18.8	-24 57	4.1	8	60	
–	Cr 135	Pup	07 17.0	-36 50	2.1	50	–	Contains π Pup
2383		CMa	07 24.8	-20 56	8.4	6	40	
2384		CMa	07 25.1	-21 02	7.4	2.5	15	
2421		Pup	07 36.3	-20 37	8.3	10	70	
2439		Pup	07 40.8	-31 39	6.9	10	80	
2447	M93	Pup	07 44.6	-23 52	6.2	22	80	*
2451		Pup	07 45.4	-37 58	2.8	45	40	Contains c Pup *
2453		Pup	07 47.8	-27 14	8.3	5	30	
2477		Pup	07 52.3	-38 33	5.8	27	160	*
2467		Pup	07 52.6	-26 23	7.1	16	50	Contains nebula
2482		Pup	07 54.9	-24 18	7.3	12	411	
2489		Pup	07 56.2	-30 04	7.9	8	45	
2515		Car	07 58.3	-60 53	3.8	30	80	*

GLOBULAR CLUSTERS

NGC/IC	Other desig.	Constellation	RA h m	Declination ° '	Magnitude	Diameter '	Notes
1851		Col	05 14.1	-40 03	7.3	11.0	
1904	M79	Lep	05 24.5	-24 33	8.0	8.7	*
2298		Pup	06 49.0	-36 00	9.4	6.8	

BRIGHT DIFFUSE NEBULA

NGC/IC	Other desig.	Constellation	RA h m	Declination ° '	Type	Diameter '	Magnitude star	Notes
2467		Pup	07 52.6	-26 24	E	8 × 7	9.2	In cluster

GALAXIES

NGC/IC	Other desig.	Constellation	RA h m	Declination ° '	Magnitude	Size	Type	Notes
1512		Hor	04 03.9	-43 21	10.6	4.0 × 3.2	SBa	
1515		Dor	04 04.1	-54 06	11.0	5.4 × 1.3	SBb	
1532		Eri	04 12.1	-32 52	11.1	5.6 × 1.8	Sb	
1533		Dor	04 16.2	-55 47	9.5	4.1 × 2.8	S0	
1543		Ret	04 12.8	-57 44	10.6	3.9 × 2.1	SB0	
1549		Dor	04 15.7	-55 36	9.9	3.7 × 3.2	E0	
1553		Dor	04 16.2	-55 47	9.5	4.1 × 2.3	S0	
1559		Ret	04 17.6	-62 47	10.5	3.3 × 2.1	SBc	
1566		Dor	04 20.0	-54 56	9.4	7.6 × 6.2	SBb	
1617		Dor	04 31.7	-54 36	10.4	4.7 × 2.4	SBc	
1672		Dor	04 45.7	-59 15	11.0	4.8 × 3.9	SBb	
1744		Lep	05 00.0	-26 01	11.2	6.8 × 4.1	SBc	
1792		Col	05 05.2	-37 59	10.2	4.0 × 2.1	Sb	*
1808		Col	05 07.7	-37 31	9.9	7.2 × 4.1	SBa	*
1964		Lep	05 33.4	-21 57	10.8	6.2 × 2.5	Sb	
2090		Col	05 47.0	-34 14	11.8	4.5 × 2.3	Sc	
2207		CMa	06 16.4	-21 22	10.7	4.3 × 2.9	Sc	
2217		CMa	06 21.7	-27 14	10.4	4.8 × 4.4	SBa	*
2223		CMa	06 24.6	-22 50	11.4	3.3 × 3.0	SBb	
2280		CMa	06 44.8	-27 38	11.8	5.6 × 3.2	Sb	

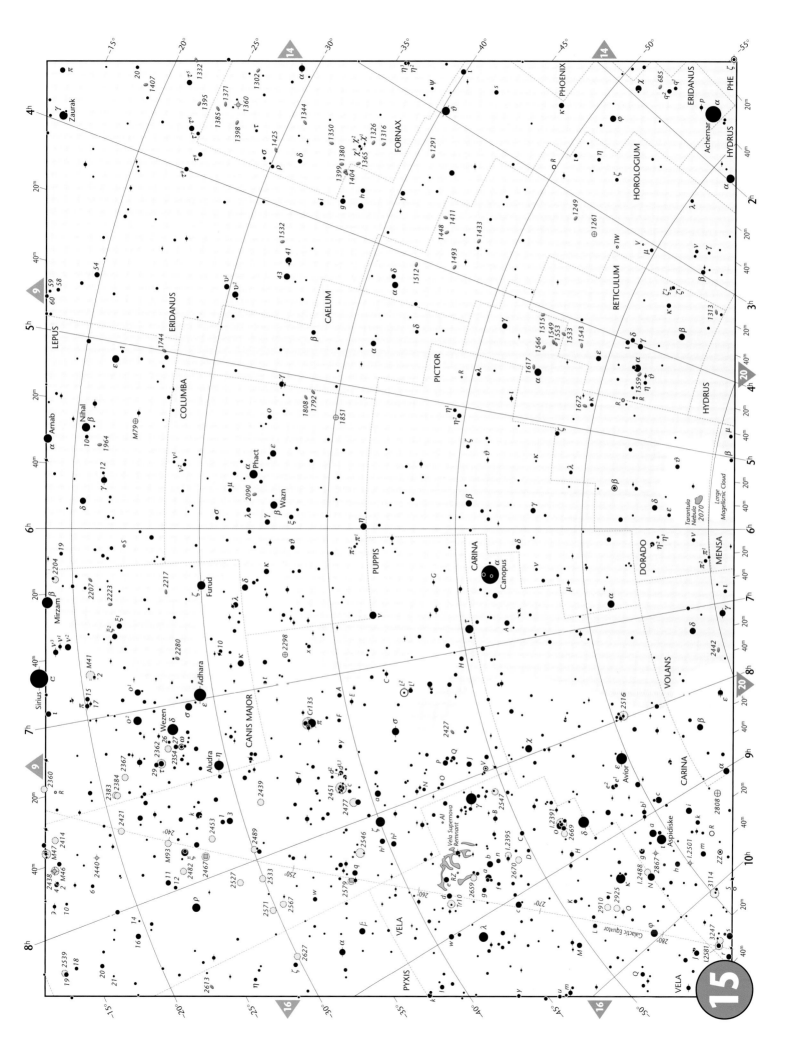

16 | Right Ascension 8ʰ to 12ʰ, Declination -20° to -65°

VARIABLE STARS

Star	RA h m	Declination ° '	Range	Type	Period (days)	Spectrum	Notes
AI Vel	08 14.1	-44 34	6.4-7.1	δ Sct	0.11	A-F	
RZ Vel	08 37.0	-44 07	6.4-7.6	Cep	20.39	G	
R Car	09 32.2	-62 47	3.9-10.5	M	308.7	M	
ZZ Car	09 45.2	-62 30	3.3-4.2	Cep	35.53	F-K	
γ Hya	09 51.1	-23 01	8.3-12.0 p	SR	302.8	K	
S Car	10 09.4	-61 33	4.5-9.9	M	149.5	K-M	
U Ant	10 35.2	-39 34	8.1-9.7 p	Irr	-	K	
η Car	10 45.1	-59 41	-0.8-7.9	SD	-	Pec	*
U Car	10 57.8	-59 44	5.7-7.0	Cep	38.76	F-C	
ER Car	11 09.7	-58 50	6.6-7.1	Cep	7.72	F-C	
cl¹ Cen	11 31.8	-59 27	4.7-5.5	SR	200:	C	

DOUBLE AND MULTIPLE STARS

Star	RA h m	Declination ° '	Magnitude	Position Angle °	Separation "	Notes
γ Vel	08 09.5	-47 20	1.9+4.2	220	41.2	AB *
			8.3	151	62.3	AC
			9.1	141	93.5	AD
			12.5	146	1.8	DE
δ Vel	08 44.7	-54 43	2.1+5.1	153	2.6	
H Vel	08 56.3	-52 43	4.8+7.4	339	2.7	
K Pyx	09 06.0	-25 52	4.6+9.8	263	2.1	
ζ Ant	09 30.8	-31 53	6.2+7.1	212	8.0	*
δ Ant	10 29.6	-30 36	5.6+9.6	226	11.0	*
μ Vel	10 46.8	-49 25	2.7+6.4	58	2.5	P=116.2yr *
β Hya	11 52.9	-33 54	4.7+5.5	8	0.9	

OPEN CLUSTERS

NGC/IC	Other desig.	RA h m	Constellation	Declination ° '	Magnitude	Diameter '	No.	Notes
2527		08 05.3	Pup	-28 10	6.5	22	40	
2533		08 07.0	Pup	-29 54	7.6	3.5	60	
2547		08 10.7	Vel	-49 16	4.7	20	80	*
2546		08 12.4	Pup	-37 38	6.3	41	40	
2567		08 18.6	Pup	-30 38	7.4	10	40	
2571		08 18.9	Pup	-29 44	7.0	13	30	
2579		08 21.1	Pyx	-36 11	7.5	10	20	
2627		08 37.3	Vel	-29 57	8.4	11	60	
IC 2391		08 40.2	Vel	-53 04	2.5	50	30	o Velorum cluster *
IC 2395		08 41.1	Vel	-48 12	4.6	8	40	*
2669		08 44.9	Vel	-52 58	6.1	12	40	
2670		08 45.5	Vel	-48 47	7.8	9	30	
-	Tr 10	08 47.8	Vel	-42 29	4.6	15	40	
2818		09 16.0	Pyx	-36 37	8.2	9	40	
1.2488		09 27.6	Vel	-56 59	7.4	15	70	
2910		09 30.4	Vel	-52 54	7.2	5	30	
2925		09 33.7	Vel	-53 26	8.3	12	40	
3114		10 02.7	Car	-60 07	4.2	35	100	*
3247		10 25.9	Car	-57 56	7.6	7	20	
IC 2581		10 27.4	Car	-57 38	4.3	8	25	
3293		10 35.8	Car	-58 14	4.7	6	30	
3324		10 37.3	Car	-58 38	6.7	6	10	
IC 2602		10 43.2	Car	-64 24	1.9	50	60	Southern Pleiades *
3532		11 06.4	Car	-58 40	3.0	55	150	
3572		11 10.4	Car	-60 14	6.6	7	35	
3590		11 12.9	Car	-60 47	8.2	4	25	
IC 2714		11 17.9	Car	-62 42	8.2	12	100	*
-	Mn 105	11 19.5	Car	-63 30	7.0	4	70	
3680		11 25.7	Cen	-43 15	7.6	12	30	*
3766		11 36.1	Cen	-61 37	5.3	12	100	
IC 2944		11 36.6	Cen	-63 02	4.5	15	30	λ Centauri cluster *
3960		11 50.9	Cen	-55 42	8.3	7	45	

GLOBULAR CLUSTERS

NGC/IC	Other desig.	Constellation	RA h m	Declination ° '	Magnitude	Diameter '	Notes
2808		Car	09 12.0	-64 52	6.3	13.8	*
3201		Vel	10 17.6	-46 25	6.8	18.2	*

BRIGHT DIFFUSE NEBULAE

NGC/IC	Other desig.	Constellation	RA h m	Declination ° '	Type	Diameter '	Magnitude star	Notes
2579		Pup	08 20.9	-36 13	E	2	1.2	
-	Gum 12	Vel	08 30:	-45:	E	1200×720		Vela SNR *
3372		Car	10 43.8	-59 52	E	120×120	6.2	Eta Carinae Nebula *

PLANETARY NEBULAE

NGC/IC	Other desig.	Constellation	RA h m	Declination ° '	Magnitude	Diameter "	Magnitude Star	Notes
2818		Pyx	09 16.0	-36 38	13.0	38	-	In open cluster
2867		Car	09 21.4	-58 19	9.7	11	13.6	
IC 2501		Car	09 38.8	-60 05	11.3	25		
3132		Vel	10 07.7	-40 26	8.2	47	10.1	*
3211		Car	10 17.8	-62 40	11.8	12		
3918		Cen	11 50.3	-57 11	8.4	12	10.8	

GALAXIES

NGC/IC	Other desig.	Constellation	RA h m	Declination ° '	Magnitude	Size '	Type	Notes
2613		Pyx	08 33.4	-22 58	10.4	7.2×2.1	Sb	
2784		Hya	09 12.3	-24 10	10.1	5.1×2.3	S0	
2835		Hya	09 17.9	-22 21	11.1	6.3×4.4	S	
2935		Hya	09 36.7	-21 08	11.9	3.5×3.0	SBb	
2997		Ant	09 45.6	-31 11	10.6	8.1×6.5	Sc	*
3109		Hya	10 03.1	-26 09	10.4	14.5×3.5	Irr	
3223		Ant	10 21.6	-34 16	11.8	4.1×2.6	Sb	*
3256		Vel	10 27.8	-43 54	11.3	3.5×2.0	Pec	
3309		Hya	10 36.6	-27 31	11.9	1.9×1.7	E0	
3511		Crt	11 03.4	-23 05	11.6	5.4×2.2	Sc	
3513		Crt	11 03.8	-23 15	12.0	2.8×2.3	SBc	
3557		Cen	11 10.0	-37 32	10.4	4.0×2.7	E3	
3585		Hya	11 13.3	-26 45	10.0	2.9×1.6	E5	
3621		Hya	11 18.3	-32 49	9.9	10.0×6.5	Sc	
3904		Hya	11 49.2	-29 17	11.0	2.2×1.7	E2	
3923		Hya	11 51.0	-28 48	10.1	2.9×1.9	E3	

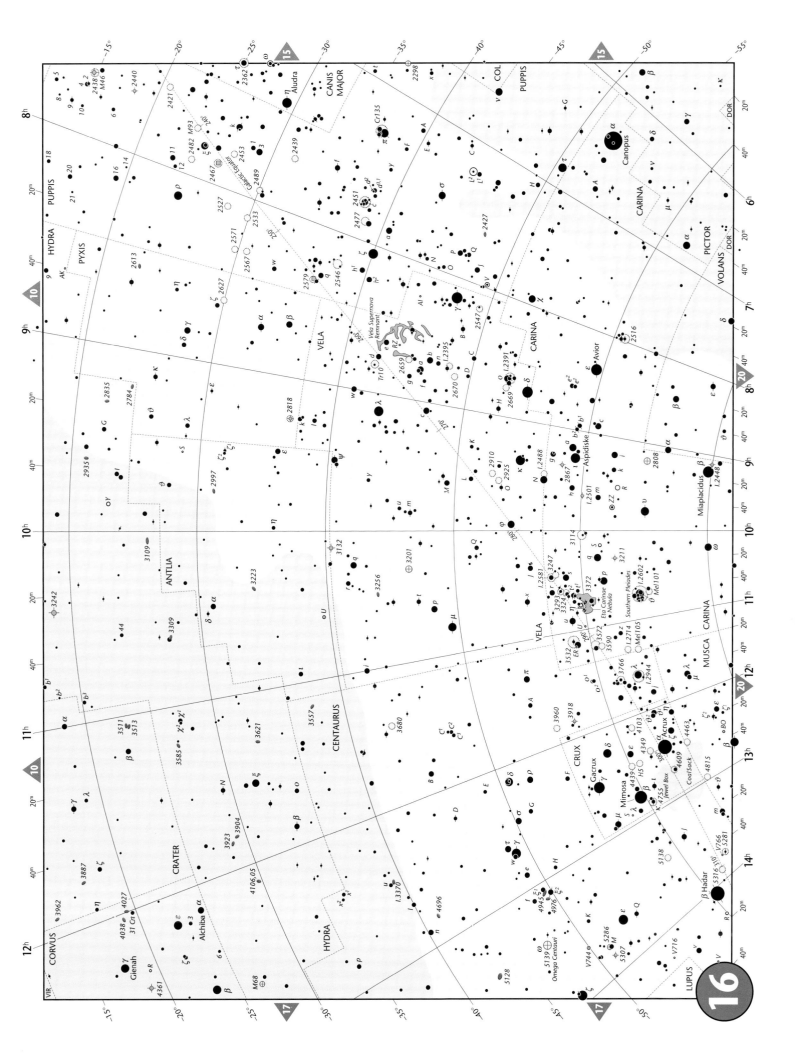

17 | Right Ascension 12ʰ to 16ʰ, Declination -20° to -65°

VARIABLE STARS

Star	RA h m	Declination ° '	Range	Type	Period (days)	Spectrum	Notes
S Cru	12 54.4	-58 26	6.2-6.9	Cep	4.69	F-G	
R Hya	13 29.7	-23 17	3.5-10.9	M	389.6	M	
V744 Cen	13 40.0	-49 57	5.1-6.6	SR	90:	M	
T Cen	13 41.8	-33 36	5.5-9.0	SR	90.44	K-M	
V766 Cen	13 47.2	-62 35	6.2-7.5	SD?	–	G	
μ Cen	13 49.6	-42 28	2.9-3.5	Irr	–	B	
V716 Cen	14 13.7	-54 38	6.0-6.5	EB	1.49	B	
R Cen	14 16.6	-59 55	5.3-11.8	M	546.2	M	
GG Lup	15 32.2	-23 53	5.5-6.0	SR	–	M	*
R Nor	15 36.0	-49 30	6.5-13.9	M	492.7	M	
T Nor	15 44.1	-54 59	6.2-13.6	M	242.6	M	

DOUBLE AND MULTIPLE STARS

Star	RA h m	Declination ° '	Magnitude	Position Angle °	Separation "	Notes
α Cru	12 26.6	-63 06	1.4 + 1.9	111	4.1	Acrux *
			4.9	202	90.1	
γ Cru	12 31.2	-57 07	1.6 + 6.7	31	110.6	Gacrux *
			9.5	82	155.2	
γ Cen	12 41.5	-48 58	2.9 + 2.9	347	1.0	P = 84.5 yr
ι Cru	12 45.6	-60 59	4.7 + 9.5	22	26.9	
μ Cru	12 54.6	-57 11	4.3 + 5.3	17	34.9	
3 Cen	13 51.8	-33 00	4.5 + 6.0	108	7.9	
4 Cen	13 53.2	-31 56	4.7 + 8.4	185	14.9	
β Cen	14 03.8	-60 22	0.7 + 3.9	251	1.3	Hadar *
α Cen	14 39.6	-60 50	0.0 + 1.2	222	14.1	Rigil Kent; P = 79.9 yrs *
			11.0	211:	7866 (131')	Proxima Centauri *
α Cir	14 42.5	-64 59	3.2 + 8.6	232	15.7	*
54 Hya	14 46.0	-25 27	5.1 + 7.1	126	8.6	*
59 Hya	14 58.7	-27 39	6.3 + 6.6	80	0.3	P = 339.3 yr
π Lup	15 05.1	-47 03	4.6 + 4.7	73	1.4	*
κ Lup	15 11.9	-48 44	3.9 + 5.8	144	26.8	*
μ Lup	15 18.5	-47 53	5.1 + 5.2	142	1.2	*
γ Cir	15 23.4	-59 19	7.2	130	23.7	P = 180 yr *
			5.1 + 5.5	20	0.7	
2 Sco	15 53.6	-25 20	4.7 + 7.4	274	2.5	
ξ Lup	15 56.9	-33 58	5.3 + 5.8	49	10.4	

OPEN CLUSTERS

NGC/IC	Other desig.	Constellation	RA h m	Declination ° '	Magnitude	Diameter '	No.	Notes
4103		Cru	12 06.7	-61 15	7.4	7	45	
4349		Cru	12 24.5	-61 54	7.4	16	30	
4439		Cru	12 28.4	-60 06	8.4	4	–	
–	H5	Cur	12 29.0	-60 46	7.1	6	–	
4463		Mus	12 30.0	-64 48	7.2	5	30	
4609		Cru	12 42.3	-62 58	6.9	5	40	
4755		Cru	12 53.6	-60 20	4.2	10	50	Jewel Box, κ Crucis *
4815		Mus	12 58.0	-64 57	8.6	3	100	
5138		Cen	13 27.3	-59 01	7.6	8	40	
5281		Cen	13 46.6	-62 54	5.9	5	40	
5316		Cen	13 53.9	-61 52	6.0	14	80	
5460		Cen	14 07.6	-48 19	5.6	25	40	
5606		Cen	14 27.8	-59 38	7.7	3	15	
5617		Cen	14 29.8	-60 43	6.3	10	80	
5662		Cen	14 35.2	-56 33	5.5	12	70	
5749		Lup	14 48.9	-54 31	8.8	8	30	
5822		Lup	15 05.2	-54 21	6.5	40	150	
5823		Cir	15 05.7	-55 36	7.9	10	100	
5925		Nor	15 27.7	-54 31	8.4	15	120	

GLOBULAR CLUSTERS

NGC/IC	Other desig.	Constellation	RA h m	Declination ° '	Magnitude	Diameter '	Notes
4590	M68	Hya	12 39.5	-26 45	8.2	12.0	
5139	ω Cen	Cen	13 26.8	-47 29	3.7	36.3	Omega Centauri *
5286		Cen	13 46.4	-51 22	7.6	9.1	
5824		Lup	15 04.0	-33 04	9.0	6.2	
5897		Lib	15 17.4	-21 01	8.6	12.6	
5927		Lup	15 28.0	-50 40	8.3	12.0	
5946		Nor	15 35.5	-50 40	9.6	7.1	
5986		Lup	15 46.1	-37 47	7.1	9.8	

BRIGHT OR DARK NEBULAE

NGC/IC	Other desig.	Constellation	RA h m	Declination ° '	Type	Diameter '	Notes
–	Coalsack	Cru	12 53:	-63:	–	400 × 300	Dark nebula
5367		Cen	13 57.7	-39 59	R	4 × 3	

PLANETARY NEBULAE

NGC/IC	Other desig.	Constellation	RA h m	Declination ° '	Magnitude	Diameter "	Magnitude star	Notes
	PK303+40.1	Hya	12 53.6	-22 52	12.0	709	9.6	
5307		Cen	13 51.1	-51 12	12.1	13	–	
IC 4406		Lup	14 22.4	-44 09	10.6	28	14.7	
5873		Lup	15 12.8	-38 08	13.3	3	13.6	
5882		Lup	15 16.8	-45 39	10.5	7	12.0	

GALAXIES

NGC/IC	Other desig.	Constellation	RA h m	Declination ° '	Magnitude	Size '	Type	Notes
4105		Hya	12 06.7	-29 46	12.0	2.4 × 1.9	E2	
4106		Hya	12 06.8	-29 46	11.4	1.9 × 1.5	E8	
IC 3370		Cen	12 27.6	-39 20	11.1	2.8 × 2.4	E2	
4696		Cen	12 48.8	-41 19	10.7	3.5 × 3.2	E1	
4945		Cen	13 05.4	-49 28	9.5	20.0 × 4.4	SBn	
4976		Cen	13 08.6	-49 30	10.2	4.3 × 2.6	E4	
5061		Hya	13 18.1	-26 50	11.7	2.6 × 2.3	E2	
5068		Vir	13 18.9	-21 02	10.8	6.9 × 6.3	SBc	
5078		Hya	13 19.8	-27 24	12:	3.2 × 1.7	Sc	
5085		Hya	13 20.3	-24 26	11.9	3.4 × 3.0	Sb	
5101		Hya	13 21.8	-27 26	10.2	5.5 × 4.9	SBa	
5102		Cen	13 22.0	-36 38	9.7	9.3 × 3.5	S0	
5128		Cen	13 25.5	-43 01	7.0	18.2 × 14.5	S0	
IC 4296		Hya	13 36.6	-33 58	11.6	2.7 × 2.7	E0	
5236	M83	Hya	13 37.0	-29 52	8.2	11.2 × 10.2	Sc	*
5253		Cen	13 39.9	-31 39	10.6	4.0 × 1.7	E5	
5483		Cen	14 10.4	-43 19	12.0	3.1 × 2.8	Sc	
5530		Lup	14 18.5	-43 24	11.9	4.1 × 2.2	Sb	
5643		Lup	14 32.7	-44 10	10.7	4.6 × 4.1	Sbc	

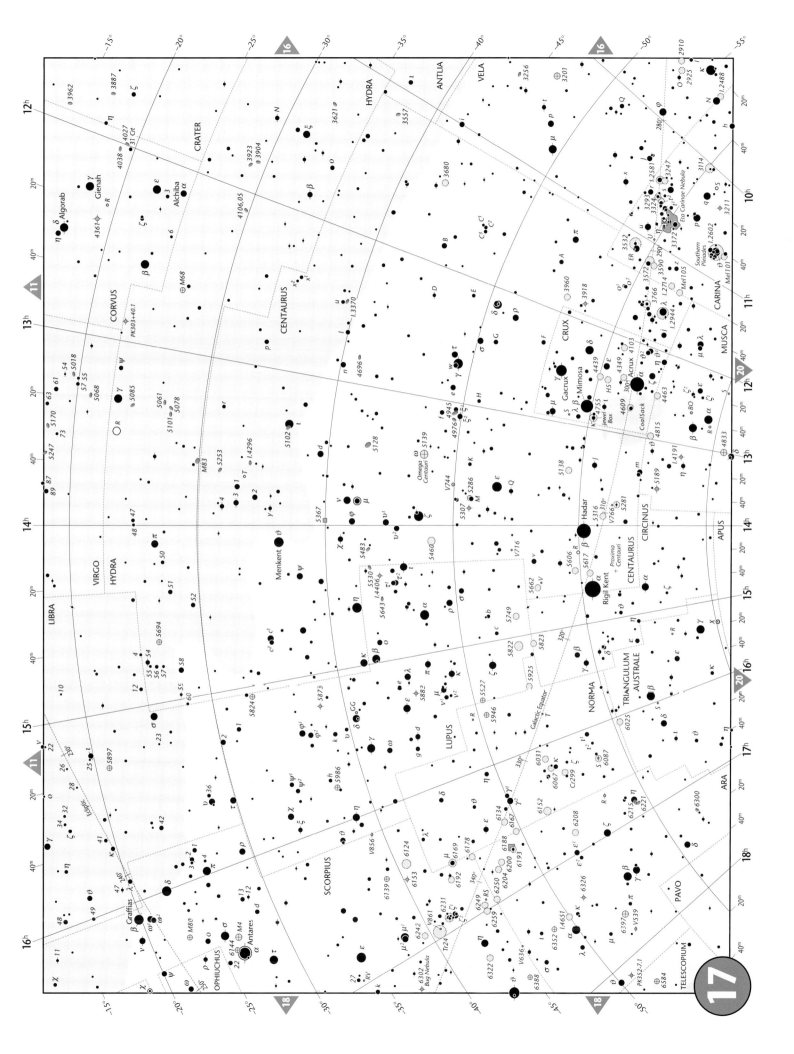

18 | Right Ascension 16ʰ to 20ʰ, Declination -20° to -65°

VARIABLE STARS

Star	RA h m	Declination ° '	Range	Type	Period (days)	Spectrum	Notes
S TrA	16 01.2	-63 47	6.1-6.8	Cep	6.32	F	
S Nor	16 18.9	-57 54	6.1-6.8	Cep	9.75	F-G	
α Sco	16 29.4	-26 26	0.9-1.8	SR	1733	M+B	Antares *
R Ara	16 39.7	-57 00	6.0-6.9	EA	4.43	B	
RS Sco	16 55.6	-45 06	6.2-13.0	M	320.1	M	
RR Sco	16 56.6	-30 35	5.0-12.4	M	279.40	M	
RV Sco	16 58.3	-33 37	6.6-7.5	Cep	6.06	F-G	
V636 Sco	17 22.8	-45 37	6.0-6.9	Cep	6.80	G	
BM Sco	17 41.0	-32 13	5.0-6.9	SR	850:	K	
W Sgr	18 05.0	-29 35	4.3-5.1	Cep	7.59	F-G	
RS Sgr	18 17.6	-34 06	6.0-6.9	EA	2.42	B	
V1017 Sgr	18 32.1	-29 24	6.2-14.7	ZAND?	–	G	
RY Ser	19 16.5	-33 31	6.0-15.0	RCB	–	G	
S Pav	19 55.2	-59 12	6.6-10.4	SR	386.3	M	
RR Sgr	19 55.9	-29 11	5.6-14.0	M	334.6	M	
RU Sgr	19 58.7	-41 51	6.0-13.8	M	240.3	M	

DOUBLE AND MULTIPLE STARS

Star	RA h m	Declination ° '	Magnitude	Position Angle °	Separation "	Notes
12 Sco	16 12.3	-28 25	5.9+7.9	73	3.8	*
σ Sco	16 21.2	-25 36	2.9+8.5	273	20.0	
ε Nor	16 27.2	-47 33	4.8+7.5	335	22.8	
α Sco	16 29.4	-26 26	1.2v+5.4	275	2.9	Antares: var.; P = 878 yrs *
36 Oph	17 15.3	-26 36	5.1+5.1	146	4.9	P = 548.7 yrs *
γ Ara	17 25.4	-56 23	3.3+10.3	328	17.9	*
τ Sgr	18 17.6	-36 46	3.2+7.8	105	3.6	
ξ Pav	18 23.2	-61 30	4.4+8.6	154	3.3	*
21 Sgr	18 25.3	-20 32	4.9+7.4	289	1.8	
λ CrA	18 43.8	-38 19	5.1+9.7	214	29.2	P = 120.4 yrs
γ CrA	19 06.4	-37 04	4.8+5.1	55	1.3	*
π Sgr	19 09.8	-21 01	5.9	122	0.4	AB
β² Sgr	19 22.6	-44 28	4.0+7.1	77	28.3	AB
52 Sgr	19 36.7	-24 53	4.7+9.2	170	2.5	AC

OPEN CLUSTERS

NGC/IC	Other desig.	Constellation	RA h m	Declination ° '	Magnitude	Diameter '	No.	Notes
6025		TrA	16 03.7	-60 30	5.1	12	60	
6067		Nor	16 13.2	-54 13	5.6	13	100	
6087	Cr 299	Nor	16 18.4	-55 07	5.4	20	–	
6124		Nor	16 18.9	-57 54	5.8	29	40	
6167		Sco	16 25.6	-40 40	6.6	7	100	
6169		Lup	16 34.1	-44 03	6.6	8	40	
6178		Nor	16 34.4	-49 36	6.7	4	12	
6193		Sco	16 35.7	-45 38	5.2	15	–	Around μ Normae
6231		Ara	16 41.3	-48 46	2.6	15	–	*
6242		Sco	16 54.0	-41 48	6.4	9	60	
6250		Sco	16 55.6	-39 30	5.9	8	80	
6322		Ara	16 58.0	-45 48	6.0	10	30	
IC 4651		Sco	17 18.5	-42 57	6.9	12	80	
6383		Ara	17 24.7	-49 57	5.5	5	40	
6405	M6	Sco	17 34.8	-32 34	4.2	15	80	*
6416		Sco	17 40.1	-32 13	4.7	18	15	
6475	M7	Sco	17 44.4	-32 21	3.3	80	40	*
6520		Sgr	18 03.4	-34 49	7.6	6	60	*
6531	M21	Sgr	18 04.6	-22 30	5.9	13	17	*
6530		Sgr	18 04.8	-24 20	4.6	15	–	In M8

GLOBULAR CLUSTERS

NGC/IC	Other desig.	RA h m	Declination ° '	Magnitude	Diameter '	Notes
6093	M80	16 17.0	-22 59	7.2	8.9	*
6121	M4	16 23.6	-26 32	5.9	26.3	*
6266	M62	17 01.2	-30 07	6.6	14.1	*
6273	M19	17 02.6	-26 16	7.2	13.5	*
6293		17 10.2	-26 35	8.2	7.9	
6304		17 14.5	-29 28	8.4	6.8	
6352		17 25.5	-48 25	7.8	7.1	*
6388		17 36.3	-44 44	6.9	8.7	*
6397		17 40.7	-53 40	5.7	15.7	*
6441		17 50.2	-37 03	7.4	7.8	*
6544		18 07.3	-25 00	8.3	8.9	*
6541		18 08.0	-43 42	6.7	13.1	*
6553		18 09.3	-25 54	8.3	8.1	
6584		18 18.6	-52 13	9.2	7.9	*
6624		18 23.7	-30 22	8.3	5.9	*
6626	M28	18 24.5	-24 52	6.9	11.2	*
6637	M69	18 31.4	-32 21	7.7	7.1	*
6642		18 31.9	-23 29	8.8	4.5	*
6652		18 35.8	-32 59	8.9	3.5	
6656	M22	18 36.4	-23 54	5.1	24.0	*
6681	M70	18 43.2	-32 18	8.1	7.8	*
6715	M54	18 55.1	-30 29	7.7	9.1	*
6723		18 59.6	-36 38	7.3	11.0	*
6752		19 10.9	-59 59	5.4	20.4	*
6809	M55	19 40.0	-30 58	7.0	19.0	*

BRIGHT DIFFUSE NEBULAE

NGC/IC	Other desig.	Constellation	RA h m	Declination ° '	Type	Magnitude star	Diameter '	Notes
6188, 6193		Ara	16 40.5	-48 47	E+A	–	20×12	*
6514	M20	Sgr	18 02.6	-23 02	E+A	7.6	29×27	Trifid Nebula *
6523	M8	Sgr	18 03.8	-24 23	E	0.0	90×40	Lagoon Nebula *

PLANETARY NEBULAE

NGC/IC	Other desig.	Constellation	RA h m	Declination ° '	Magnitude	Diameter "	Magnitude star	Notes
6153		Sco	16 31.5	-40 15	11.5	25	–	*
IC 4634		Oph	17 01.6	-21 50	10.7	9	15 p	
6302		Sco	17 13.7	-37 06	12.8	50	–	Bug Nebula *
–	PK 352.7,1	Ara	18 00.2	-38 50	11.4	25	–	
IC 4699		Tel	18 18.5	-45 59	11.9	10	–	*
6629		Sgr	18 25.7	-23 12	11.6	15	12.8	
IC 1297		CrA	19 17.4	-39 37	10.7	7	12.9	

GALAXIES

NGC/IC	Other desig.	Constellation	RA h m	Declination ° '	Magnitude	Size '	Type	Notes
6215		Ara	16 51.1	-58 59	11.8	2.0×1.6	Sc	*
6221		Ara	16 52.8	-59 13	11.5	3.2×2.3	SBc	*
6300		Ara	17 17.0	-62 49	11.1	5.4×3.5	SBc	
6744		Pav	19 09.8	-63 51	9.0	15.5×10.2	SBb	*
6753		Pav	19 11.4	-57 03	11.9	2.5×2.2	Sb	*

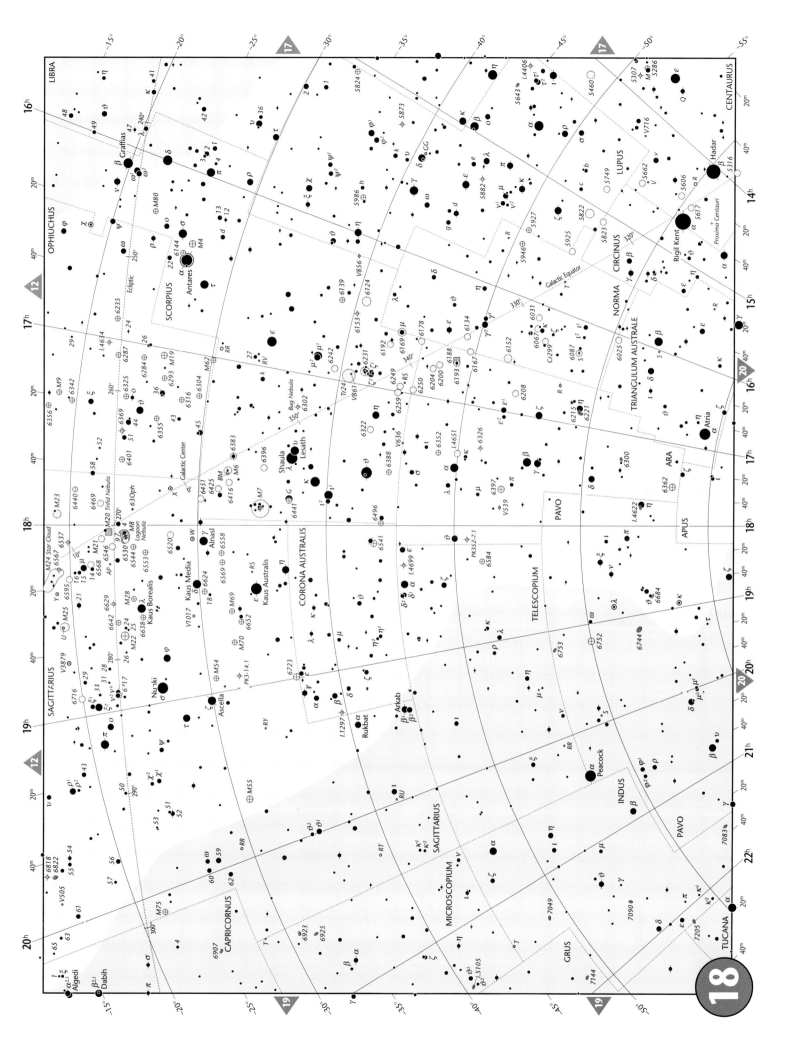

19 | Right Ascension 20ʰ to 0ʰ, Declination -20° to -65°

VARIABLE STARS

Star	RA h m	Declination ° '	Range	Type	Period (days)	Spectrum	Notes
RR Tel	20 04.2	-55 43	6.5–16.5 p	ZAND	–	F	
RT Sgr	20 17.7	-39 07	6.0–14.1	M	305.3	M	
T Mic	20 27.9	-28 16	7.7–9.6 p	SR	344	M	
T Ind	21 20.2	-45 01	5.5–6.5	SR	320:	M	
T Gru	22 25.7	-37 34	7.8–12.3 p	M	136.5	M	
S Gru	22 26.1	-48 26	6.0–15.0	M	401.4	M	

DOUBLE AND MULTIPLE STARS

Star	RA h m	Declination ° '	Magnitude	Position Angle °	Separation "	Notes
α Mic	20 50.0	-33 47	5.0 + 10.0	166	20.5	
θ Ind	21 19.9	-53 27	4.5 + 7.0	275	6.0	
η PsA	22 00.8	-28 27	5.8 + 6.8	115	1.7	
41 Aqr	22 14.3	-21 04	5.6 + 7.1	114	5.0	
δ Tuc	22 27.3	-64 58	4.5 + 9.0	282	6.9	
β PsA	22 31.5	-32 21	4.9 + 7.9	172	30.3	
γ PsA	22 52.5	-32 53	4.5 + 8.0	262	4.2	
δ PsA	22 55.9	-32 32	4.2 + 9.2	244	5.0	
υ Gru	23 06.9	-38 54	5.7 + 8.0	211	1.1	
θ Gru	23 06.9	-43 31	4.5 + 7.0	75	1.1	

GLOBULAR CLUSTERS

NGC/IC	Other desig.	Constellation	RA h m	Declination ° '	Magnitude	Diameter '	Notes
6864	M75	Sgr	20 06.1	-21 55	8.6	6.0	*
7099	M30	Cap	21 40.4	-23 11	7.5	11.0	*

GALAXIES

NGC/IC	Other desig.	Constellation	RA h m	Declination ° '	Magnitude	Size '	Type	Notes
6907		Cap	20 25.1	-24 49	11.3	3.4 × 3.0	SBb	
6923		Mic	20 31.7	-30 50	12.1	2.5 × 1.4	Sb	
6925		Mic	20 34.3	-31 59	11.3	4.1 × 1.6	Sb	
7049		Ind	21 19.0	-48 34	10.7	2.8 × 2.2	S0	
IC5105		Mic	21 24.4	-40 37	11.5	2.5 × 1.5	E4	
7083		Ind	21 35.7	-63 54	11.8	4.5 × 2.9	Sb	
7090		Ind	21 36.5	-54 33	10.7	7.1 × 1.4	SBc	
7144		Gru	21 52.7	-48 15	10.7	3.5 × 3.5	E0	
7172		PsA	22 02.0	-31 52	11.9	2.2 × 1.3	S	
7174		PsA	22 02.1	-31 59	12.6	1.3 × 0.7	S	
7176		PsA	22 02.1	-31 59	11.9	1.3 × 1.3	E0	
7184		Aqr	22 02.7	-20 49	12.0	5.8 × 1.8	Sb	
7205		Ind	22 08.5	-57 25	11.1	4.3 × 2.2	–	
7221		PsA	22 11.3	-30 37	12:	2.2 × 1.9	Sc	
7314		PsA	22 35.8	-26 03	10.9	4.6 × 2.3	SBa	
7410		Gru	22 55.0	-39 40	10.4	5.5 × 2.0	SBb	
7412		Gru	22 55.8	-42 39	11.4	4.0 × 3.1	SBc	
7418		Gru	22 56.6	-37 02	11.4	3.3 × 2.8	E3	
IC1459		Gru	22 57.2	-36 28	10.0	3.4 × 2.5	S0	
IC5267		Gru	22 57.2	-43 24	10.5	5.0 × 4.1	SBc	
7424		Gru	22 57.3	-41 04	10.5	7.6 × 6.8	Sc	
7456		Gru	23 02.1	-39 35	11.9	5.9 × 1.8	SBb	
7496		Gru	23 09.8	-43 26	11.1	3.5 × 2.8	Sb	
7531		Gru	23 14.8	-43 36	11.3	3.5 × 1.5	SEb	
7552		Gru	23 16.2	-42 35	10.7	3.5 × 2.5	SBb	
7582		Gru	23 18.4	-42 22	10.6	4.6 × 2.2	SBb	
7599		Gru	23 19.3	-42 15	11.4	4.4 × 1.5	Sc	
IC5332		Scl	23 34.5	-36 06	10.6	6.8 × 5.1	Sd	
7713		Scl	23 36.5	-37 56	11.6	4.3 × 2.0	SBd	
7755		Scl	23 47.9	-30 31	11.8	3.7 × 3.0	SBb	
7793		Scl	23 57.8	-32 35	9.1	9.1 × 6.6	Sd	

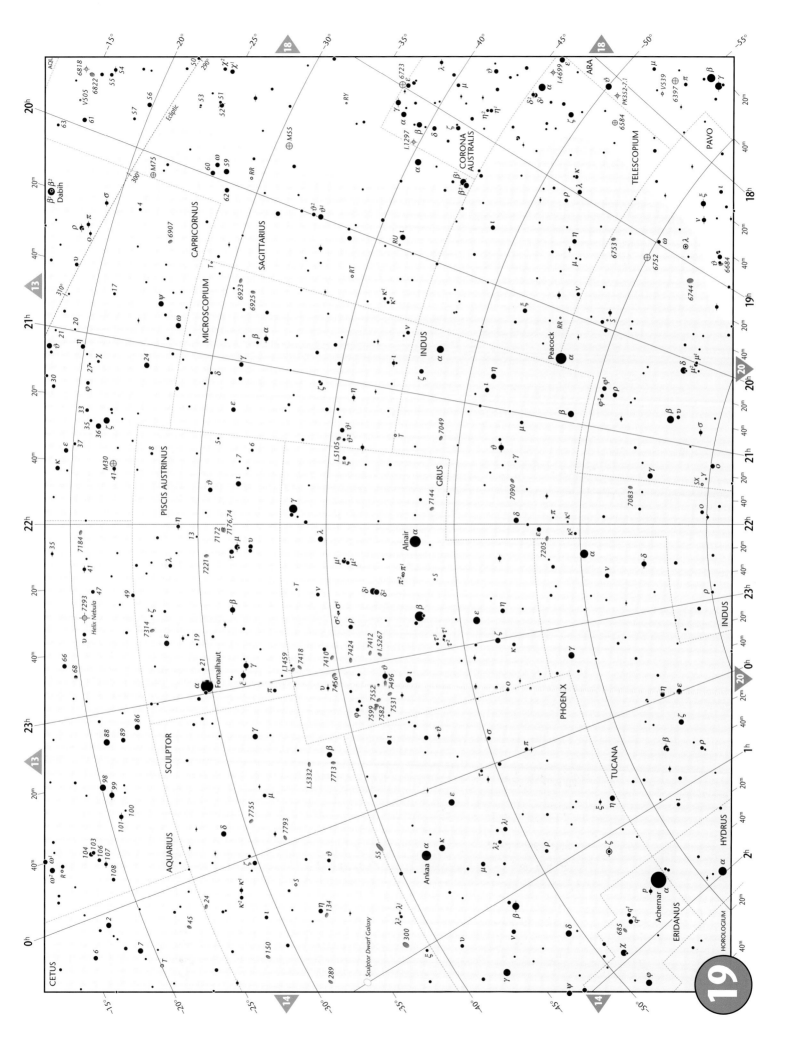

20 | South of Declination -65°

VARIABLE STARS

Star	RA h m	Declination ° '	Range	Type	Period (days)	Spectrum	Notes
U Men	04 09.6	-81 51	8.0-10.9 p	M	407	M	
R Oct	05 26.1	-86 23	6.4-13.2	M	405.6	M	*
TZ Men	05 30.2	-84 47	6.2-6.9	EA	8.57	B	
RS Cha	08 43.2	-79 04	6.0-6.7	EA+δ Sct	1.67	A+A	
S Mus	12 12.8	-70 09	5.9-6.4	Cep	9.66	F	
BO Mus	12 34.9	-67 45	6.0-6.7	Irr	-	M	
R Mus	12 42.1	-69 24	5.9-6.7	Cep	7.48	B	
θ Aps	13 08.1	-65 18	6.4-8.6	SR	199	B	
X TrA	15 14.3	-70 05	5.0-6.4	Irr	-	K	
R TrA	15 19.8	-66 30	6.4-6.9	Cep	3.39	G	
κ Pav	18 16.9	-67 14	3.9-4.6	Cep	9.09	F	
Y Pav	21 24.3	-69 44	5.6-7.3	SR	233.3	M	
SX Pav	21 28.7	-69 30	5.4-6.0	SR	50:	M	

DOUBLE AND MULTIPLE STARS

Star	RA h m	Declination ° '	Magnitude	Position Angle °	Separation "	Notes
κ Tuc	01 15.8	-68 53	5.1 + 7.3	336	5.4	*
γ Vol	07 08.8	-70 30	4.0 + 5.9	300	13.6	
ζ Vol	07 41.8	-72 36	4.0 + 9.8	116	16.7	
κ Vol	08 19.8	-71 31	5.4 + 5.7	57	65.0	
ε Cha	11 59.6	-78 13	5.4 + 6.0	188	0.9	
β Mus	12 46.3	-68 06	3.7 + 4.0	43	1.3	P = 383.1 years
ι Oct	12 55.0	-85 07	6.0 + 6.5	230	0.6	
θ Mus	13 08.1	-65 18	5.7 + 7.3	187	5.3	*
δ¹·² Aps	16 20.3	-78 42	4.7 + 5.1	12	102.9	*
μ² Oct	20 41.7	-75 21	7.1 + 7.6	17	17.4	*
λ Oct	21 50.9	-82 43	5.4 + 7.7	70	3.1	*

OPEN CLUSTER

NGC/IC	Other desig.	Constellation	RA h m	Declination ° '	Magnitude	Diameter '	No.	Notes
-	Mel 101	Car	10 42.1	-65 06	8.0:	14	50	Close to IC2605

GLOBULAR CLUSTERS

NGC/IC	Other desig.	Constellation	RA h m	Declination ° '	Magnitude	Diameter '	Notes
104		Tuc	00 24.1	-72 05	4.0	30.9	47 Tucanae *
362		Tuc	01 03.2	-70 51	6.6	12.9	*
4372		Mus	12 25.8	-72 40	7.8	16.8	
4833		Mus	12 59.6	-70 53	7.4	13.5	
6101		Aps	16 25.8	-72 12	9.3	10.7	*
6362		Ara	17 31.9	-67 03	8.3	8.0	*

BRIGHT DIFFUSE NEBULA

NGC/IC	Other desig.	Constellation	RA h m	Declination ° '	Type	Diameter '	Notes
2070	30 Dor	Dor	05 38.7	-69 06	E	40 × 25	Tarantula Nebula *

PLANETARY NEBULAE

NGC/IC	Other desig.	Constellation	RA h m	Declination ° '	Magnitude	Diameter '	Magnitude star
IC2448		Car	09 07.1	-69 57	11.5	8	12.9
IC4191		Mus	13 08.8	-67 39	12.0	5	
5189		Mus	13 33.5	-65 59	10.3	153	14.0

GALAXIES

NGC/IC	Other desig.	Constellation	RA h m	Declination ° '	Magnitude	Size '	Type	Notes
1313		Ret	03 18.3	-66 30	9.4	8.5 × 6.6	SB	
2442		Vol	07 36.4	-69 32	11.2	6.0 × 5.5	SB	
3059		Car	09 50.2	-73 55	12.0	3.2 × 3.0	SB	*
6684		Pav	18 49.0	-65 11	11.4	3.7 × 2.7	SB	*

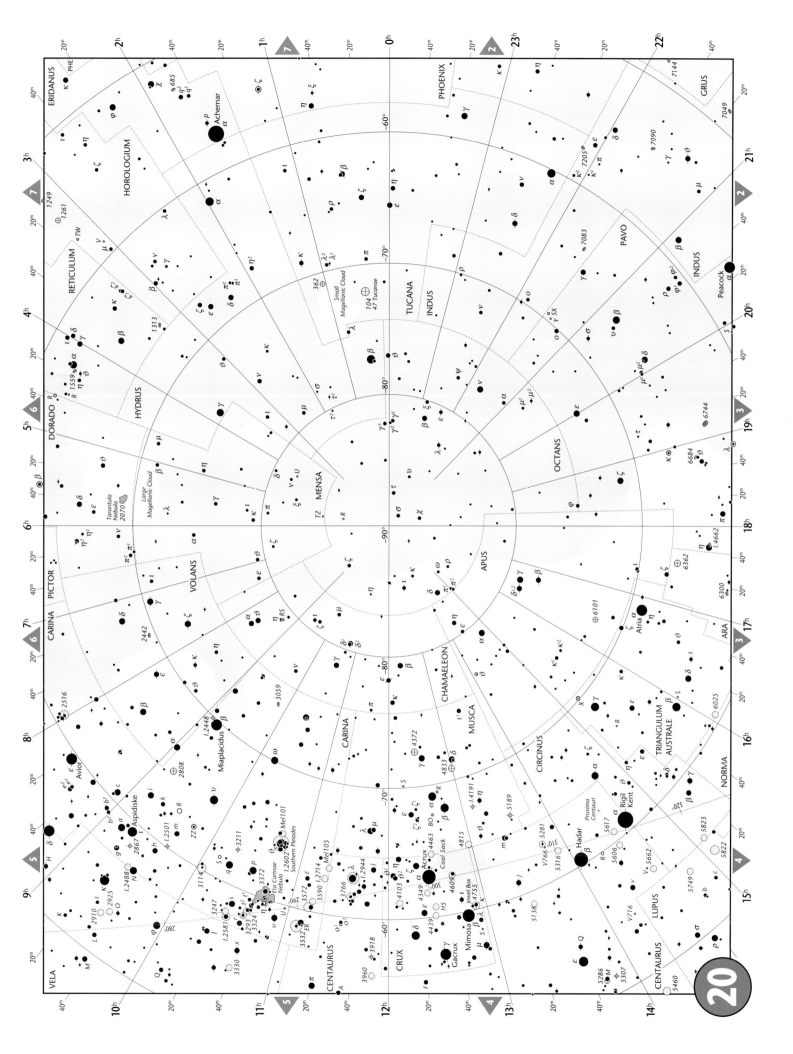

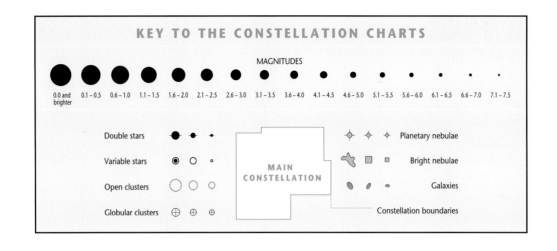

KEY TO THE CONSTELLATION CHARTS

MAGNITUDES

0.0 and brighter · 0.1 – 0.5 · 0.6 – 1.0 · 1.1 – 1.5 · 1.6 – 2.0 · 2.1 – 2.5 · 2.6 – 3.0 · 3.1 – 3.5 · 3.6 – 4.0 · 4.1 – 4.5 · 4.6 – 5.0 · 5.1 – 5.5 · 5.6 – 6.0 · 6.1 – 6.5 · 6.6 – 7.0 · 7.1 – 7.5

Double stars

Variable stars

Open clusters

Globular clusters

MAIN CONSTELLATION

Planetary nebulae

Bright nebulae

Galaxies

Constellation boundaries

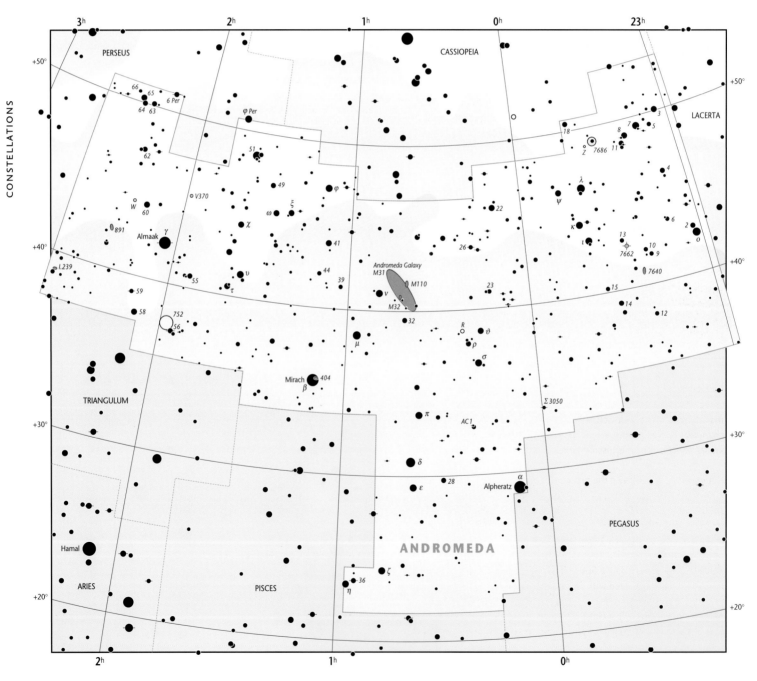

Andromeda

ANDROMEDAE • And • (ANDROMEDA)

Main chart(s): 2 (1, 3, 7)
Area: 722 sq. deg. (19th)
Culminates 00:00 local time: late September

Andromeda lies just outside the main portion of the Milky Way and therefore is occasionally the site of novae, although none has been particularly notable. One striking event, however, was the eruption of S Andromedae that was observed in M31 in 1885. At that time the true nature of galaxies was not understood, and the star was thought to be an ordinary nova. Indeed, it was considered to be a factor indicating that the Andromeda 'Nebula' was a nearby object. The determination of the true distance and nature of M31 brought with it the realization that S And was a completely new type of eruptive star and far more energetic than previously thought. It is now classified as a Type 1 supernova.

γ And (02ʰ04ᵐ.1, +42°21'), Almaak: a triple system (d = 355 l.y.). The bright components (mags. 2.3 and 5.0) form a striking orange and blue pair (PA 63°, Sep. 9".6; K0 and B9 spectra). The B9 star (designated Ba) has a blue companion, Bb (mag. 6.3), which will reach periastron in 2013 and is currently becoming difficult to resolve.

υ And (01ʰ37ᵐ.0, +41°25'): a star (mag. 4.1) that is slightly more massive and brighter than the Sun, d = 44 l.y. It has an extrasolar planetary system, with evidence of three large planets, one of which orbits the star at about 0.056 AU in just 4.61 days. The planet has a minimum mass of 0.65 Jupiter masses. Such planets are known as 'hot Jupiters' and the system resembles that discovered around 51 Peg.

56 And (01ʰ56ᵐ.4, +37°16'), southwest of NGC 752: an optical double of two unrelated stars: one an orange (G8) giant, mag. 5.7, d = 360 l.y., and the other a red (K5) giant, mag. 5.9, d = 990 l.y. Easily resolved in binoculars. Both stars appear to be binary systems with additional components of mag. 11.0 and 9.2, respectively.

R And (00ʰ24ᵐ.0, +38°35'): a long-period (Mira) variable, with an overall range of mag. 5.6–14.9, so it is clearly visible to the naked eye at maximum. It has a well-defined period of 409.33 days, and its spectrum changes with magnitude from S3.5 to S8.8. It may also be classified as an M7 spectrum with emission lines.

Z And (23ʰ33ᵐ.7, +48°49'): the prototype of the Z Andromedae stars (also known as symbiotic stars), all of which are close binary systems. It lies southeast of **NGC 7686**. Its overall range is mag. 6.9–11.3, and is thus clearly visible in binoculars at maximum. The primary is an M2 giant, and the secondary has a B1 spectrum.

Σ 3050 (23ʰ59ᵐ.5, +33°43'): a fine pair of yellow stars (mags. 6.5 and 6.7, P ≈ 355 yrs). Just resolved with 75 mm telescopes.

AC 1 (00ʰ20ᵐ.9, +32°59'): a close binary system (mags 7.5, 8.0; PA 289°, Sep. 1".8). A yellow (F5) pair of dwarf stars, originally discovered by the famous telescope-maker, Alvan Clark, in 1857. There is a striking orange-red star about 4'.5 to the southwest.

M31 (NGC 224: 00ʰ42ᵐ.7, +41°16'), the Great Andromeda Galaxy: visible to the naked eye as a hazy spot of about mag. 3.4. First recorded in the 10th century by the Persian astronomer Al Sufi. A giant spiral (Sb), it is the largest object in the Local Group, about twice as massive as our own galaxy. It lies at a distance of about 3 million light-years. Under good conditions, even small-aperture binoculars will show its elliptical shape, and telescopes reveal some of its spiral structure, most notably its yellowish, starlike nucleus, and a dark lane at the northwestern edge. It has several satellite galaxies, the most prominent of which are M32 and M110.

M32 (NGC 221: 00ʰ42ᵐ.7, +40°52'): a dwarf elliptical (E2) galaxy, visible in binoculars, but easy to mistake for a star of mag. 8.2. With a low-power telescopic view it initially appears circular, but closer examination reveals a fainter, elliptical outer region.

M110 (NGC 205: 00ʰ40ᵐ.4, +41°41'): like M32, a dwarf elliptical (E6) galaxy of mag. 8.5. Although larger than M32, it is more difficult to detect.

NGC 404 (01ʰ09ᵐ.4, +35°43'): a small, S0 spiral galaxy, mag. 10.1. It is about 6.5' northwest of β And, and is visible in small telescopes only if the star is hidden.

NGC 752 (01ʰ57ᵐ.8, +37°41'): a large open cluster, mag. 5.7, northeast of 56 And, d ≈ 1200 l.y. Visible with the naked eye under very good conditions, and readily detected in binoculars. A telescope reveals that it consists of about 60 stars, the brightest of which are mag. 9.

NGC 7662 (23ʰ25ᵐ.9, +42°33'), the Blue Snowball: a planetary nebula. Detectable in binoculars as a starlike object (mag. 8.6, d ≈ 2610 l.y.) southeast of Fl 13, but a telescope shows a pale blue or greenish disk with a distinct core.

NGC 7686 (23ʰ30ᵐ.2, +49°08'): a moderate-sized open cluster (diameter 15'), overall mag. 5.6, with about 20 members. A binocular and telescopic object.

CONSTELLATIONS

Antlia

ANTLIAE • Ant • THE AIR PUMP

Main chart(s): 16 (15, 17)
Area: 239 sq. deg. (62nd)
Culminates 00:00 local time: late February

Antlia is one of the small, faint, southern constellations introduced by Abbé Nicolas-Louis de La Caille, and was originally known as Antlia Pneumatica. Although it lies on the border of the Milky Way, no novae have been observed. There is a concentration of faint galaxies, the Antlia Cluster, the brighter members of which are detectable with amateur equipment. The planetary nebula NGC 3132 (the 'Eight-Burst Nebula') lies just over its southern border, in Vela.

δ Ant (10h29m.6, -30°36'): thought to be a very long-period binary (mags. 5.6, 9.6; PA 226°, Sep. 11".0; B9 and F5 spectra), d = 481 l.y. A 75 mm telescope shows the fainter component. First observed by Jacob in 1856, but there has been no change in separation or position angle. The stars probably form a binary because they show the same proper motion.

ζ¹ Ant (09h30m.8, -31°53'): a pair of yellow stars (mags 6.2, 7.1; PA 212°, Sep. 8".0; A0 and A2 spectra). As with δ Ant, this appears to be a true binary despite little change since first observed in 1836 by John Herschel. The stars have a common proper motion, and lie at a distance of 372 l.y.

S Ant (09h32m.3, -28°32'): a bright eclipsing binary of the EW type, showing continuous variations. Its amplitude is mag. 6.4–6.9, with a period of 0.648 days (15 hrs 33 min), which means that it is possible to follow its complete range over a single night.

U Ant (10h35m.2, -39°34'): an irregular variable, range mag. 6.0–7.6, and readily visible in binoculars. It is a giant, with a carbon spectrum (C5.3).

NGC 2997 (09h45m.6, -31°11'): a face-on spiral galaxy (Sc, mag. 10.6:). A moderate-sized amateur telescope is required to detect its extended nature and spiral structure. Its distance is about 10 Mpc (≈ 32 million l.y.).

NGC 3223 (IC 2571, 10h21m.6, -34°16'): a faint (approx. mag. 12) barred spiral galaxy. Its maximum dimension is about 4'.1, so a moderately large amateur telescope is required to detect its extended nature.

NGC 3271 (10h30m.5, -35°22'): the brightest (at about mag. 11.7) of several spiral galaxies in this area that are members of the Antlia Cluster.

NGC 3267 (10h29m.9, -34°55'): a lenticular (S0) galaxy, mag. 12.9p. There is a suspicion that a bar may be present.

NGC 3268 (10h30m.0, -35°20'): an elliptical (E2) galaxy, mag. 12.4:, appearing almost circular with a brighter core.

NGC 3269 (10h30m.0, -35°13'): another lenticular (S0) galaxy, mag. 12.6p.

NGC 3258 (10h28m.9, -35°36'): an elliptical (E1) galaxy, mag. 12.8, appearing perfectly round in amateur telescopes.

NGC 3260 (10h29m.1, -35°36'): a probable elliptical (E2) galaxy, mag. 12.6:. There is some doubt about its classification, but it is probably an elliptical galaxy.

NGC 3281 (10h31m.9, -34°51'): a large spiral (Sb) galaxy, mag. 12.6.

These seven members of the Antlia Cluster are all detectable with large apertures. The cluster lies at a distance of approximately 30 Mpc (≈ 98 million l.y.).

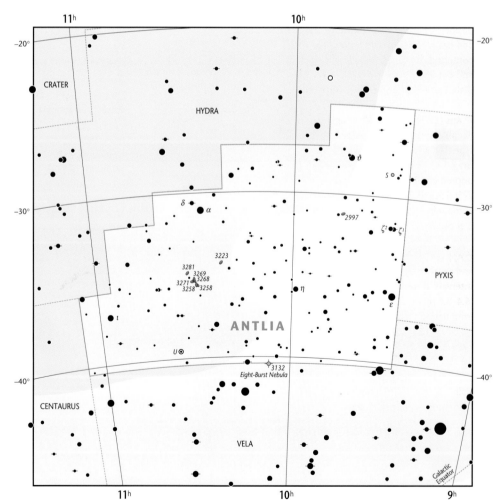

Apus

APODIS • Aps • BIRD OF PARADISE

Main chart(s): 20 (17, 18)
Area: 206 sq. deg. (67th)
Culminates 00:00 local time: late May

Apus is one of the small constellations introduced by Keyser and de Houtman in the late 16th century. It lies on the borders of the Milky Way, close to the South Celestial Pole and contains only four moderately bright stars, which, by coincidence, are all orange or orange-red giants or subgiants. There are no recorded novae or bright extragalactic objects, but the constellation does contain S Apodis, one of the rare R Coronae Borealis stars, which exhibit sudden, unpredictable declines from normal magnitude. Unfortunately this star is rather faint at maximum (about mag. 9.6), but has a minimum (mag. 15.2) only slightly less than R CrB itself.

Although it is not detectable visually, the constellation contains an unusual, very large reflection nebula to the east of β and γ Aps that stretches towards the South Celestial Pole. Rather than being illuminated by a nearby star, this 'galactic cirrus' is actually reflecting generalized light from the disk of the Milky Way.

δ¹, δ² **Aps** (16ʰ20ᵐ.3, -78°42'): an optical double, generally visible with the naked eye, and easily resolved with binoculars. The components are red (M5 giant, mag. 4.7) and orange (K3 giant, mag. 5.1), lying at distances of 765 and 663 l.y., respectively.

κ¹ **Aps** (15ʰ31ᵐ.9, -73°24'): a rapidly rotating variable of the γ-Cassiopeiae type (spectral type B1), d ≈ 1020 l.y. Normally about mag. 5.4, it may eject material at unpredictable intervals, becoming brighter as it does so. There is an 12th-magnitude companion (PA 254°, Sep. 27".0), and κ¹ itself is probably a spectroscopic binary.

ϑ **Aps** (14ʰ05ᵐ.3, -76°48'): a red (M7) giant and semiregular variable. It exhibits intervals of moderately regular variation (6.4–8.6 p), P ≈ 119 days, interspersed with irregular non-periodic fluctuations.

I 236 (14ʰ53ᵐ.2, -73°11'): a true binary (mags. 5.8, 8.0; PA 115°, Sep. 2".0) with two yellow components (G7 giant and F9 subgiant), visible with 75 mm. It lies in the middle of a field of numerous faint stars.

CapO 15 (15ʰ06ᵐ.3, -72°11'): probably a true binary (mags. 6.9, 8.7; PA 43°, Sep. 1".6). Pale yellow (A0) primary and white secondary, visible with difficulty with 75 mm, but clear in 100 mm. Has shown little change since measures at the Cape Observatory in 1880.

NGC 6101 (16ʰ25ᵐ.8, -72°12'): a rich 9th-magnitude globular cluster with an angular diameter of 10.7'. Not readily resolved into individual stars when observed with apertures of less than 200 mm.

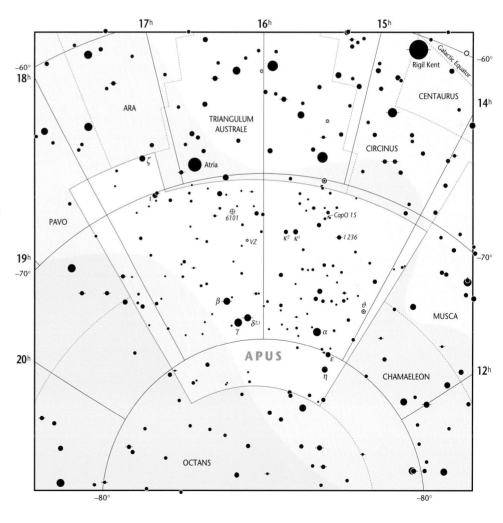

Aquarius

AQUARII · Aqr · THE WATER CARRIER

Main chart(s): 13 (19)
Area: 980 sq. deg. (10th)
Culminates 00:00 local time: late August

This large, Zodiacal constellation has relatively few bright extragalactic objects, being fairly close to the galactic plane. It does, however contain some remarkable objects, such as R Aqr, a symbiotic system (described below); VY Aqr, a recurrent nova with outbursts in 1907 and 1962, reaching approximate mags. 8 and 9, respectively; and AE Aqr (close to Fl 71 Aqr), an extraordinary object with complex variations, now classed as an X-ray pulsar. It shows similarities to both flare stars and dwarf novae, and is regularly monitored by amateurs, but has a range of about mag. 10.4 to 12.6, and therefore requires a moderate-sized telescope.

α **Aqr** ($22^h06^m.0$, -00°19'), Sadalmelik: an extremely bright yellow (G2) supergiant of apparent mag. 2.95. Its surface temperature and spectrum are similar to the Sun's, but the stars have completely different luminosity classes (Ib and V, respectively). At its distance (≈ 760 l.y.), its absolute magnitude (M) is -3.9, about 30,000 times as luminous as the Sun.

β **Aqr** ($21^h31^m.8$, -05°34'), Sadalsud: remarkably similar to α Aqr, in that it is also a bright yellow (G0) supergiant, mag. 2.9. It is slightly closer (612 l.y.), so its absolute magnitude is less (3.5). Both stars are about 120 times the diameter of the Sun.

ζ **Aqr** ($22^h28^m.8$, -0°01'): a yellow binary (mags. 3.7 and 3.9; PA 179°, Sep. 2".0; d = 107 l.y.), easily observed with a 75 mm aperture. It has an extremely long period, believed to be about 700–800 years. The separation is currently decreasing very slowly.

4 Aqr ($20^h51^m.4$, -05°38'): a yellow binary (mags. 6.0 and 7.0; PA 22°.5, Sep. 0".8; d = 192 l.y). The period is about 187 years, and the separation is slowly decreasing.

29 Aqr ($20^h02^m.7$, -16°57'; mags. 6.4–6.8, 7.2; PA 66°.2, Sep. 3".9; d = 470 l.y.): the brighter component is a β Lyrae eclipsing binary (DX Aqr), P ≈ 0.945 day.

41 Aqr ($22^h14^m.5$, -21°03'): a long-period binary (mags 5.6, 7.1; PA 113°, Sep. 5".1). Little change since discovered in the 19th century.

53 Aqr ($22^h26^m.6$, -16°45'): a binary system (mags 6.4, 6.6; PA 350°, Sep. 2".2), resolved with 75 mm aperture.

107 Aqr ($23^h46^m.2$, -18°41'): a binary with an extremely long period (mags 5.7, 6.7; PA 136°, Sep. 6".8), also visible with a small telescope.

R Aqr ($23^h43^m.8$, -15°17'): an extraordinary star. First thought to be a long-period variable (type M) with a period of about 387 days, it is now known to be at the centre of expanding nebulosity with a complex structure. It exhibits spectral characteristics indicating the simultaneous existence of extremely cool and hot components. Such systems are known as symbiotic stars, where a hot component, here probably a white dwarf, is accreting material from the cooler, red companion.

M2 (NGC 7089, $21^h33^m.7$, -00°49'): a large, bright globular cluster, mag. 6.5, d ≈ 35,880 l.y., that lies almost due north of β Aqr. Easily detectable in binoculars, it is distinctly elongated. It starts to be resolved with 150 mm. In still larger telescopes it presents a granular structure.

M72 (NGC 6981, $20^h53^m.7$, -12°31'): a fainter globular cluster than M2 (mag. 9.5:, d ≈ 18 kpc or 58,710 l.y.), at the limit even for good binoculars. It appears nebulous with an aperture of about 100 mm, and fairly well resolved with 200 mm. **NGC 7492** ($23^h08^m.4$, -15°37') is a more distant globular (d ≈ 25 kpc or 81,500 l.y.), with a slightly larger apparent diameter. It is a telescopic object (mag. 11.5:).

M73 (20^h59^m, -12°38'): a 'Y'-shaped asterism of four 10th-magnitude stars, which are not thought to be associated, and therefore do not warrant being called a sparse open cluster. It is uncertain why Messier included this group in his catalogue, but it is easily resolved with a telescope of about 75 mm aperture.

NGC 7009 ($21^h04^m.2$, -11°22'), the Saturn Nebula: a bright blue planetary nebula, mag. 8.0, d ≈ 2395 l.y. Large apertures (over 300 mm) show two faint extensions on either side of the main disk, hence its name.

NGC 7293 (22^h30^m, -20°48'), the Helix Nebula: the closest planetary nebula (d ≈ 450 l.y.). It also has the largest apparent size, with a diameter of approximately 0.25° (half the apparent size of the Moon). Just visible in binoculars, west of υ Aqr, but is rather faint (about mag. 8.0) and difficult to locate, requiring extremely good conditions.

NGC 7606 ($23^h19^m.1$, -08°29'): an edgewise spiral (Sb) galaxy, mag. 10.8, and a relatively difficult object. Elongation visible with 150 mm, general form with 200 mm, and signs of structure with 300 mm aperture.

δ-**Aquarids** (double radiant: 22^h36^m, -17°, and 23^h04^m, +02°): a fine southern meteor shower, visible July 15 to Aug. 20. Maxima are on Jly. 29 and Aug. 06, respectively, for the two radiants, with zenithal hourly rates of 20 and 10. The meteors are relatively faint, but the southern component is richer in numbers.

η-**Aquarids** (radiant at approximately 22^h20^m, -01°): a fine meteor shower, although difficult to observe from most northern latitudes. There is a multiple radiant and a broad maximum, being visible Apr. 24 to May 20, with maximum on May 04, when the zenithal hourly rate is about 40.

ι-**Aquarids** (double radiant: 22^h20^m, -15°, and 22^h04^m, -06°): a shower, rich in faint meteors. Telescopic observations by experienced amateurs. Active July to August, maximum Aug. 06, zenithal hourly rate approx. 8.

CONSTELLATIONS

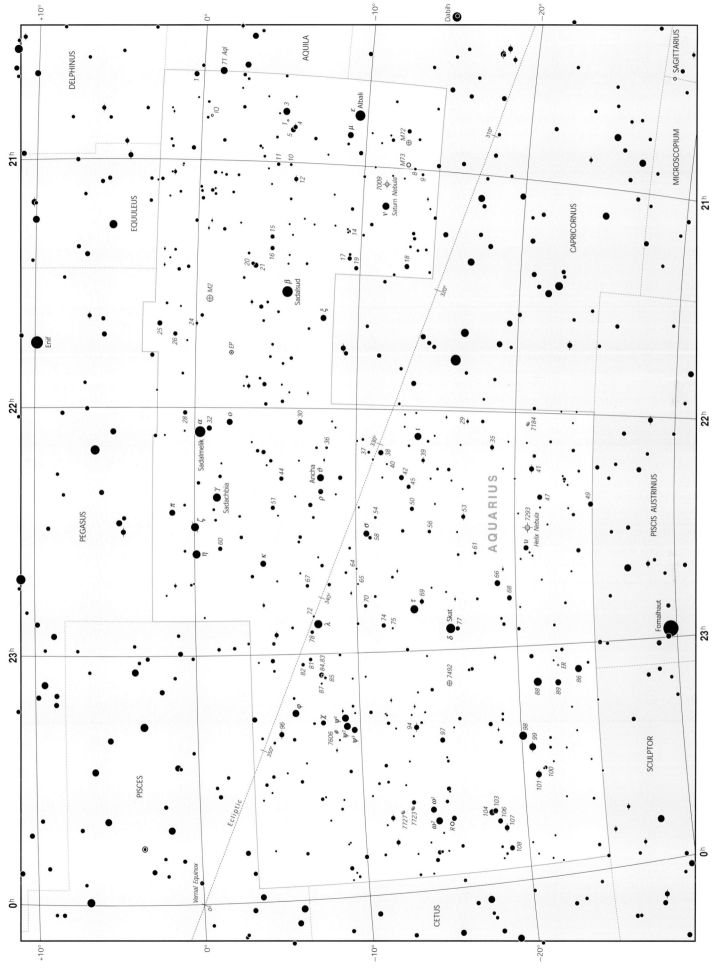

Aquila

AQUILAE • Aql • THE EAGLE

Main chart(s): 12 (13)
Area: 652 sq. deg. (22nd)
Culminates 00:00 local time: mid-July

This constellation lies across the Milky Way, bordered on its northwestern side by the Great Rift. α Aql, Altair, is one of the three prominent stars that form the (northern) Summer Triangle. It is also one of the closest stars to us, lying just 17 light-years away.

Aquila contains few clusters, and all its planetary nebulae are faint (mag. 11 or below). Because of its position near the galactic plane, it has been the site of many novae, particularly Nova Aquilae 1918 (V603 Aql)

which reached mag. -1.4 (equal to Sirius) on June 9. It showed striking oscillations in brightness following an initial sharp fall. The material ejected as an expanding nebulosity lies in two cone-shaped regions and two polar 'blobs', symmetrical about the binary's orbital axis. There are many double stars, only a few of which are described here. One extraordinary binary, SS 433, has complex variations with periods of 6.4 and 164 days. It consists of a hot (O- or B-type) star and an invisible neutron-star

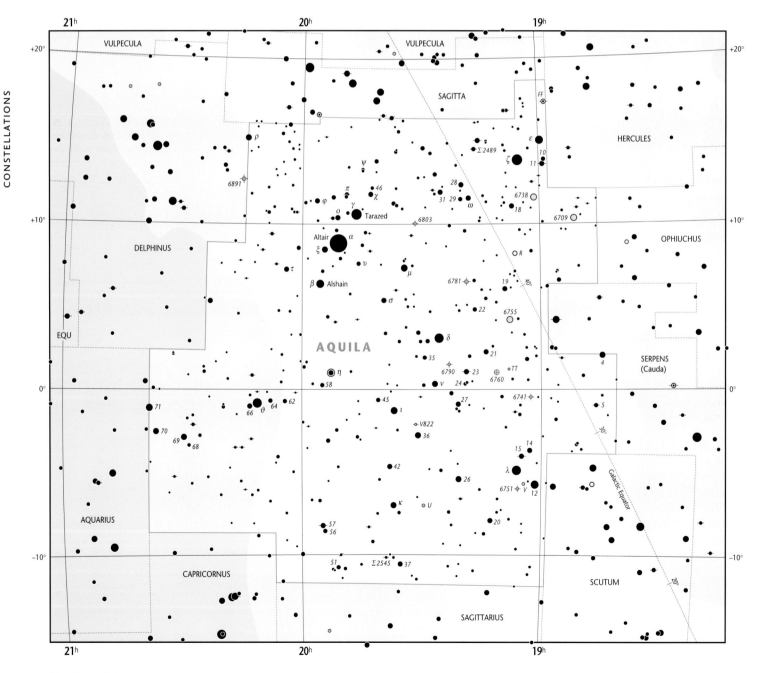

companion. Powerful jets simultaneously produce red- and blue-shifted emission lines. It is visible at maximum with a 150 mm telescope.

η Aql (19ʰ52ᵐ.7, +01°01'): one of the very first variables to be discovered (by Pigott in September 1784). It is a Cepheid variable (a pulsating F1 supergiant) at a distance of about 1173 l.y. By coincidence, it has exactly the same range, mag. 3.5–4.4, as δ Cep, after which the class is named, but with a longer period of 7.2 days.

R Aql (19ʰ06ᵐ.4, +08°09'): a long-period Mira variable, easily visible with binoculars (and even with the naked eye) at maximum (about mag. 5.5), but which fades to mag. 12.0 at minimum, requiring a moderately sized telescope to be detected. The variations have a period of 284 days.

15 Aql (19ʰ05ᵐ.2, -04°02'): close to λ Aql, a wide double (mags. 5.4, 7.1; PA 209°, Sep. 38".2), which is detectable under good conditions with binoculars, and easily resolved with a telescope.

57 Aql (19ʰ54ᵐ.6, -08°14'): another wide double, generally regarded as even easier than 15 Aql (mags. 5.7, 6.5; PA 170°, Sep. 35".7).

Σ 2489 (19ʰ16ᵐ.4, +14°33'): appears to be a true long-period binary (mags. 5.6, 9.3; PA 346°, Sep. 8".2; spectra B9.5 and G2). The brighter star is a close binary with a 9-year period.

Σ 2545 (19ʰ38ᵐ.7, -10°09'): a yellow binary (mags. 2.9, 8.7; PA 324°, Sep. 3".8) that may be a triple system, with an 11th-mag. star (PA 166°, Sep. 27") visible in a 75 mm aperture.

NGC 6709 (18ʰ51ᵐ.5, +10°21'): a loose open cluster with a combined magnitude of about 7.5. The individual stars are too faint (mag. 9.5 to 11) to be resolved in binoculars, requiring a larger aperture.

NGC 6760 (19ʰ11ᵐ.4, +01°02'): a globular cluster (mag. 9.0, d ≈ 6 kpc or 19,570 l.y.) that appears as a hazy spot in small apertures (150 mm), and begins to be resolved with 300 mm.

NGC 6790 (19h23m.2, +01°31'): a blue planetary nebula, mag. 10.5. Relatively small and bright, being detectable with 75 mm and much easier with 100 mm.

Ara

ARAE • Ara • ALTAR

Because of its position near the galactic plane, Ara contains both dark and emission nebulae, various open clusters, and several globular clusters. The planetary nebulae are all faint, the brightest being PK352-7.1 (18ʰ00ᵐ.2, -38°50'), with a visual magnitude of about 11.4. A small cluster of external galaxies is visible through a 'window' near η Arae that has low interstellar absorption.

γ Arae (17ʰ25ᵐ.4, -56°36'): a triple system (d = 1136 l.y.), of a bright star and two fainter ones. The main pair (AB: mags. 3.3, 10.3; PA 328°, Sep. 17".9) has a more distant companion (mag. 12.0, PA (AC) 65°, Sep. 41".7).

R Arae (16ʰ39ᵐ.7, -57°00'): an eclipsing binary (mag. 6.8–7.9, P = 4.43 days; d = 262 l.y.), which probably forms a triple system with a red star (mag. 8.3), about 3".6 north.

Brs 13 (17ʰ19ᵐ.1, -46°38'): a fine yellow and orange binary (mags. 5.5, 8.5; PA 248°, Sep. 8".3; spectra G9 and M0) in a sparse field south preceding γ Arae. It is relatively close to us: d ≈ 26 l.y.

NGC 6193 (16ʰ41ᵐ.3, -48°46'): a loose, bright (5th mag.) open cluster (d = 4565 l.y.). Its brightest member is a binary system (mags. 5.6, 8.9; PA 14°, Sep. 1".6). The cluster is associated with the nebula **NGC 6188** (16ʰ40ᵐ.5, -48°47'). The latter is primarily a dark absorption nebula but there is a small area of reflection nebulosity adjacent to the open cluster.

NGC 6215 (16ʰ51ᵐ.1, -58°59'): a spiral galaxy, mag. 11.8, 10' west and slightly north of η Arae (mag. 3.8, K5 spectrum). A marginally brighter barred spiral galaxy **NGC 6221** (16ʰ52ᵐ.8, -59°13'), mag. 11.5, lies in the

Main chart(s): 18 (17, 19, 20)
Area: 237 sq. deg. (63rd)
Culminates 00:00 local time: mid-June

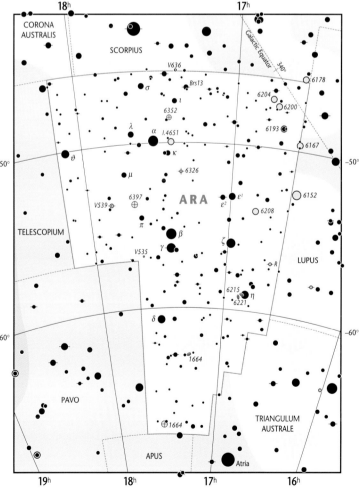

same field, 25' southwest of η Arae. Both are visible with 150 mm, and NGC 6221 shows spiral structure with 300 mm aperture.

NGC 6352 (17ʰ25ᵐ.5, -48°25'): a large, relatively loose, globular cluster (mag. 7.8, d ≈ 6 kpc or 19,570 l.y.), which is resolved into faint stars with apertures of 150 mm and above. A slightly brighter globular, **NGC 6362** (17ʰ31ᵐ.9, -67°03', mag. 7.6) is well resolved with 150 mm aperture.

NGC 6362 (17ʰ31ᵐ.9, -67°03'): a globular cluster (mag. 8.3, d ≈ 7 kpc or 22,830 l.y.), with very irregular edges; resolved with 150 mm aperture.

NGC 6397 (17ʰ40ᵐ.7, -53°40'): a large, bright globular cluster (mag. 5.8), about 16' across. It is resolved with apertures of just 75 mm and the brightest stars, some orange in colour, are about mag. 10. It is one of the closest globular clusters to the Sun at about 2 kpc or 6500 l.y. – about the same distance as M4 in Scorpius.

Aries

ARIETIS • Ari • THE RAM

Main chart(s): 2, 8 (9)
Area: 441 sq. deg. (39th)
Culminates 00:00 local time: late October

About 3000 years ago, this constellation contained the point at which the Sun, moving along the ecliptic, crossed the celestial equator from south to north at the spring (vernal) equinox. This point is still known as the First Point of Aries, even though precession has now carried it into the neighbouring constellation of Pisces. The Sun does not cross into Aries until April 19. Aries is regarded as the first constellation in the zodiac.

Although this constellation contains several double and multiple systems, there are no easy open or globular clusters, nor any planetary nebulae. Only one galaxy, NGC 722, is bright enough to be seen using amateur-sized telescopes.

γ **Ari** (01ʰ53ᵐ.5, +19°18'), Mesartim: a beautiful blue-white double, discovered by Robert Hooke in 1664 (mags. 4.6, 4.7; PA 1°, Sep. 7".6; d = 204 l.y.). The common proper motion suggests that this is a binary with an extremely long period. The slightly brighter component is a low-amplitude, magnetic variable of the α-CVn type.

ε **Ari** (02ʰ59ᵐ.2, +21°20'): a long-period binary (mags. 5.2, 5.5; PA 203°, Sep. 1".5; d = 290 l.y.), which should be resolved with a 75 mm aperture. The components are yellow (A spectra).

λ **Ari** (01ʰ58ᵐ.1, +23°37'): a pair of stars (mags. 4.8, 7.3; PA 48°, Sep. 36".8; d = 41 l.y.), just visible in binoculars under good conditions.

π **Ari** (02ʰ49ᵐ.3, +17°28'): a multiple system, including a telescopic binary (mags. 5.2, 8.7; PA 118°, Sep. 3".3). The bright star is a spectroscopic binary with a period of 3.85 days. Lunar-occultation observations have established that there is a fourth companion, details of which are still uncertain.

NGC 772 (01ʰ59ᵐ.3, +19°01'): a spiral galaxy (Sb, mag. 10.3), detectable as a hazy spot with 150 mm aperture, but revealing no more than a slight central condensation through a 300 mm telescope.

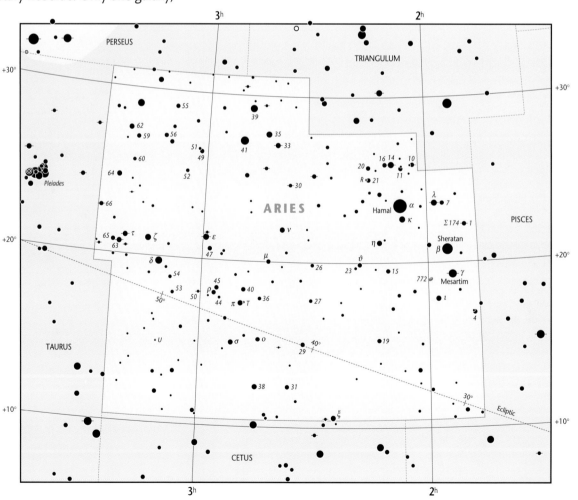

Auriga
AURIGAE • Aur • THE CHARIOTEER

Main chart(s): 3 (2, 4)
Area: 657 sq. deg. (21st)
Culminates 00:00 local time: late December

Auriga lies across the galactic plane and therefore contains a number of open clusters and a small number of emission nebulae. There are, however, no bright globular clusters, and just one planetary nebula. The few galaxies are all faint.

ε **Aur** (05ʰ02ᵐ.0, +43°49'): a remarkable eclipsing binary, with the extremely long period of 27 years (9892 days). The visible star is a white supergiant (mag. 3.0, F0 spectrum), but the eclipsing body is unknown. It may be a disk of dust surrounding an invisible pair of white dwarfs. It takes years for the star to fade and recover, with the minimum (mag. 3.8) lasting about one year. The last eclipse was 1983–84, and the next will begin in about 2006–2007.

ζ **Aur** (05ʰ02ᵐ.5, +41°05'): another extraordinary eclipsing binary, consisting of a pair of supergiant stars, 5 and 200 times the diameter of the Sun. Placed at the centre of the Solar System, the larger star would nearly fill the orbit of the Earth. The orbital period is 972.16 days, and during an eclipse the stars' combined magnitude drops from 3.7 to 4.0.

θ **Aur** (05ʰ59ᵐ.7, +37°13'): a quadruple system at 176 l.y. The AB pair (mags. 2.6, 7.1; PA 313°, Sep. 3".6) requires an aperture of at least 100 mm. The other components are still fainter, but more distant. C (mag. 10.6; PA AC 297°, Sep. 50".0); D (mag. 9.2; PA AD 349°, Sep. 137".5).

ψ¹ **Aur** (06ʰ24ᵐ.9, +49°17'): a highly luminous, orange (K1) supergiant. It is an irregular variable, range 4.7–5.7. Its radius is uncertain, but is probably about 3.0 AU. If it occupied the Sun's place in the Solar System,

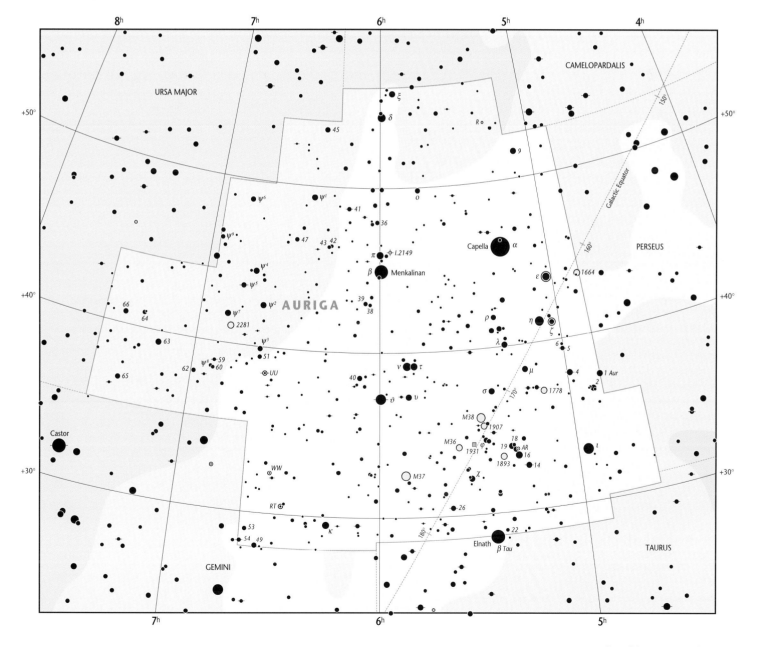

CONSTELLATIONS

it would engulf the Earth and Mars, and reach more than halfway to Jupiter. Its distance is uncertain, but is about 1180 pc (≈ 3850 l.y.), so its luminosity is approximately 11,000 times that of the Sun.

RT Aur (06ʰ28ᵐ.6, +30°29'): a bright Cepheid variable, range mag. 5.3–6.6, P = 3.728261 days.

UU Aur (06ʰ36ᵐ.5, +38°27'): a deep red (C spectrum) semi-regular variable, range mag. 7.8–10.0, occasionally showing a periodicity of about 234 days.

M36 (NGC 1960, 05ʰ36ᵐ.5, +34°08') is a small, bright (mag. 6.5) open cluster, d = 1.3 kpc (≈ 4240 l.y.), readily visible in binoculars, but very striking in a larger telescope.

M37 (NGC 2099, 05ʰ52ᵐ.4, +32°33'): a large, striking 6th-magnitude open cluster, almost the diameter of the Moon and with about 150 members (d ≈ 1.4 kpc or 4570 l.y.). It appears as a hazy spot in binoculars, but with even the smallest telescope is resolved into a large number of stars, including several red giants, with an orange star near the centre.

M38 (NGC 1912, 05ʰ28ᵐ.7, +35°50'): slightly fainter than M36 (mag. 7.0), but larger, and may sometimes be resolved with binoculars. It is, however, rather scattered, and is best observed at low power with apertures of 100–150 mm. The brightest star is a G0 giant (mag. 7.9).

NGC 2281 (06ʰ49ᵐ.3, +41°03'): another open cluster visible in binoculars, appearing approximately the same brightness as M36 (mag. 6.5).

IC 2149 (05ʰ56ᵐ.3, +46°07'): a planetary nebula (mag. 10.6), detectable as such with apertures of around 100 mm, although larger telescopes will be required to reveal its bluish colour.

Boötes

BOÖTES • Boo • THE HERDSMAN

Main chart(s): 5 (11)
Area: 907 sq. deg. (13th)
Culminates 00:00 local time: late April

Although a fairly large constellation, Boötes has remarkably few deep-sky objects, with just one globular cluster and one galaxy visible with moderate-sized telescopes. It does, however, contain many interesting double stars. It also includes the radiant for the Quadrantid meteor shower, named after a former constellation, Quadrans Muralis (the Mural Quadrant).

α Boo (14ʰ15ᵐ.8, +19°11'), Arcturus: the fourth brightest star, and the brightest in the northern hemisphere (mag. -0.05, d = 37 l.y.). It is an orange giant (spectrum K1.5) and its colour causes it to appear fainter to the naked eye than α Lyrae (Vega), which actually has the slightly lower magnitude of 0.03. Unlike the Sun, and most nearby stars, the orbit of Arcturus around the galactic centre is not in the galactic plane, but highly inclined to it, carrying it far out into the galactic halo.

ε Boo (14ʰ45ᵐ.0, +27°04'), Izar or Pulcherima ('most beautiful'): a famous double (mags. 2.5, 4.9; PA 341°, Sep. 2".9), with an orange, K0 giant primary and blue-white, A2 companion. Requires a moderate degree of magnification to ensure that the bright primary does not mask the secondary.

ι Boo (14ʰ16ᵐ.3, +51°22'), sometimes called Asellus Secundus: a wide double visible in binoculars (mags. 4.8, 7.7; PA 32°, Sep. 38".6). There is also a much fainter third component (mag. 12.6; PA 196°, Sep. 85".8).

μ Boo (15ʰ24ᵐ.6, +37°22'), Alkalurops: a multiple star. Binoculars show a wide double (mags. 4.3, 6.5; PA 171°, Sep. 108".3). The stars are sometimes plotted separately on charts as μ¹ and μ² Boo. The fainter star (μ²) is a binary system (mags. 7.0, 7.6; PA 9°, Sep. 2".3), which can be resolved with 50 mm, but normally requires a larger aperture.

ν Boo (15ʰ31ᵐ.1, +40°50'): an optical double (ν¹, ν²) consisting of two mag. 5.0 stars of contrasting colours, one (ν²), a white, A5 dwarf (d = 430 l.y.), and (ν¹), a more distant orange, K5 giant (d = 872 l.y.).

τ Boo (13ʰ47ᵐ.5, +17°27'): the central star of an extrasolar planetary system at a distance of 51 l.y. The star itself (mag. 4.5) is slightly more massive and brighter than the Sun – very similar to υ And, also an extrasolar system. The planet is at least 3.7 times the mass of Jupiter and orbits just 0.045 AU from the star, with the exceptionally short period of 3.31 days. It is an extreme case of a so-called 'hot Jupiter' planetary system.

44 Boo (15ʰ03ᵐ.8, +47°39'): a double, one component of which is variable. The binary (mags. 5.3, 6.2; PA 49°, Sep. 1".7) has a period of 225 years. The separation is decreasing and the stars will not be resolved by amateur equipment near periastron in 2028. The fainter component is an eclipsing binary of the W Ursae Majoris type (EW), showing continuous variations with a period of 6.4 hours and an amplitude of 0.6 mag.

Other notable binaries (excluding those in lists for Charts 5 & 11):

ξ **Boo** (14ʰ51ᵐ.4, +19°06'; mags. 4.7, 6.9; PA 121°, Sep. 7".2; G8, K6)
1 **Boo** (13ʰ40ᵐ.7, +19°57'; mags. 5.8, 8.7, PA 134°, Sep. 4".8; A1, F8)
Σ 1785 (13ʰ49ᵐ.1, +26°59'; mags. 7.6, 8.0; PA 167°, Sep. 3".5; K6, K6)
Σ 1835 (14ʰ23ᵐ.4, +08°27'; mags. 5.1, 6.9; PA 192°, Sep. 6".3; A0, F0; third F2 component not readily resolved)
Σ 1884 (14ʰ48ᵐ.4, +24°22'; mags. 6.3, 8.0; PA 56°, Sep. 2".0; F6)
Σ 1910 (15ʰ07ᵐ.5, +09°14'; mags. 7.3, 7.4; PA 211°, Sep. 4".3; G2, G3)

NGC 5248 (13ʰ37ᵐ.5, +08°53'): an Sc spiral galaxy (mag. 10.2). A difficult object. Although a hazy spot is visible with an aperture as small as 120 mm, even with 300 mm it still remains without distinct features.

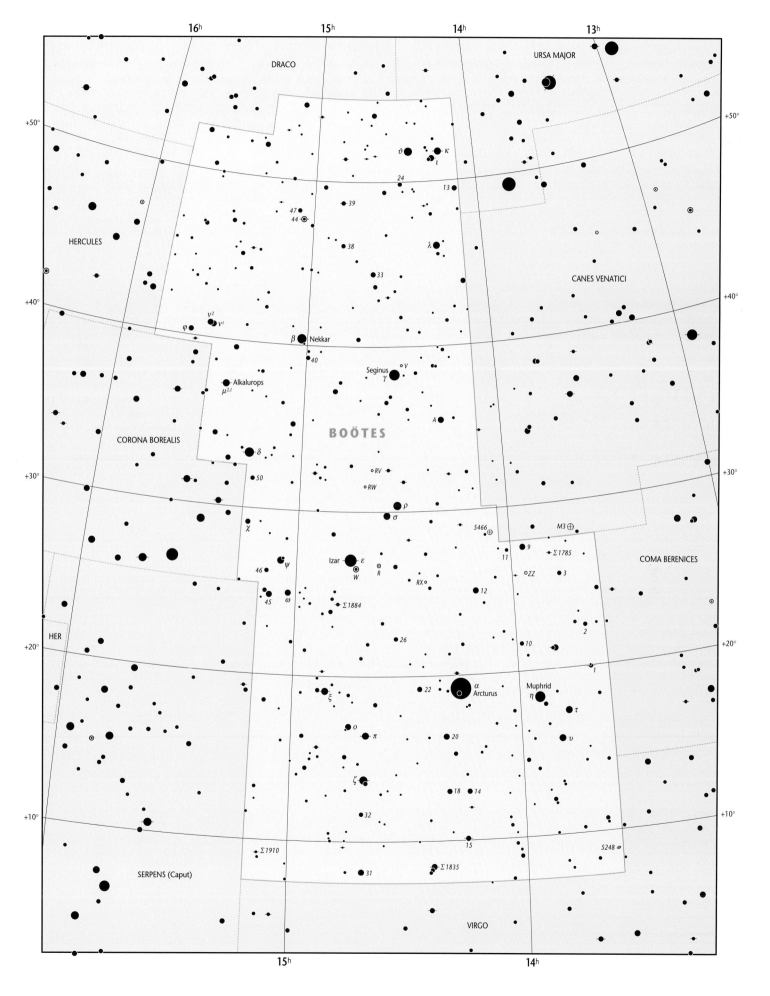

NGC 5466 (14^h^05^m^.5, +28°32'): a poorly condensed globular cluster (mag. 9.1), requiring at least 150 mm to be detected, but which starts to be resolved with an aperture of 250 mm. Its distance is about 16 kpc (≈ 52,200 l.y.).

Quadrantids (radiant at 15h28m, +50°): a short-lived, but reliable meteor shower, visible Jan. 01–06, with maximum on Jan. 03. The meteors are generally bright, bluish-white or yellowish-green in colour. The shower is associated with a small, recently discovered body, 2003 EH1, which is about 2 km across. It is believed to be a defunct, short-period comet, possibly a fragment of Comet C/1490 Y1, observed from China, Japan, and Korea in 1490 and 1491.

Caelum
CAELI • Cae • THE BURIN

Main chart(s): 15 (14)
Area: 125 sq. deg. (81st)
Culminates 00:00 local time: late November

This is another of the small constellations created by de La Caille in 1756. (A burin is a specialized tool, similar to a chisel, used by engravers.) It lies between Columba and Eridanus and consists of approximately 20 stars, none of which is brighter than mag. 4.5. Because it lies some distance from the galactic plane, there are no open or globular clusters within its boundaries. Unlike Sculptor and Fornax, farther east, it is still subject to some interstellar absorption, however, so galaxies are largely absent. There is just one moderately bright barred spiral, NGC 1679.

α **Cae** (04^h^40^m^.7, -41°51'): a very difficult binary because of the great difference in the magnitudes (4.5, 12.5; PA 121°, Sep.6".6).

γ **Cae** (05^h^04^m^.4, -35°29'): orange/yellow long-period binary (mags. 4.6, 8.5; PA 309°, Sep. 3".2).

h 3650 (04^h^26^m^.6, -40°32'): a relatively easy binary for small telescopes (75 mm or more). It has shown little change since discovered in 1836 (mags. 7.1, 8.3; PA 183°, Sep. 3".0).

NGC 1679 (04^h^50^m^.0, -31°59'): a faint (mag. 11.5) peculiar, barred spiral galaxy (SBp), requiring an aperture greater than 150 mm.

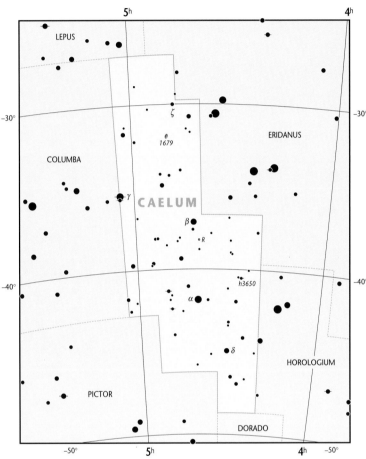

Camelopardalis
CAMELOPARDALIS • Cam • THE GIRAFFE

Main chart(s): 1, 3
Area: 757 sq. deg. (18th)
Culminates 00:00 local time: late December

This constellation was first proposed by the Dutch astronomer Petrus Plancius in 1613, mainly to fill a large, sparsely populated area in the northern circumpolar region. The first representation in an atlas was published by Jakob Bartschius in 1624. Although the constellation contains a number of galaxies, most of these require large apertures to be visible as anything other than faint hazy spots of light.

β **Cam** (05^h^03^m^.8, +60°27'): a yellow (G0) supergiant, the brightest star in the constellation (mag. 4.0), and a triple system, with a distant companion of mag. 7.4 (PA 209°, Sep. 83".4). The third component (mag. 11.4) lies near the secondary (PA 166, Sep. BC 13".9).

11 Cam (05^h^06^m^.5, +58°58'): at magnitude 5.1, forms an extremely wide double with **12 Cam** (PA 10°, Sep. 178".5), which is about the limit of normal naked-eye visibility at mag. 6.3, but easily seen with any optical aid. There are two fainter stars in the system, components C (mag. 10.8) and D (mag. 13.3). For BC, PA 19°, Sep. 173".4'.

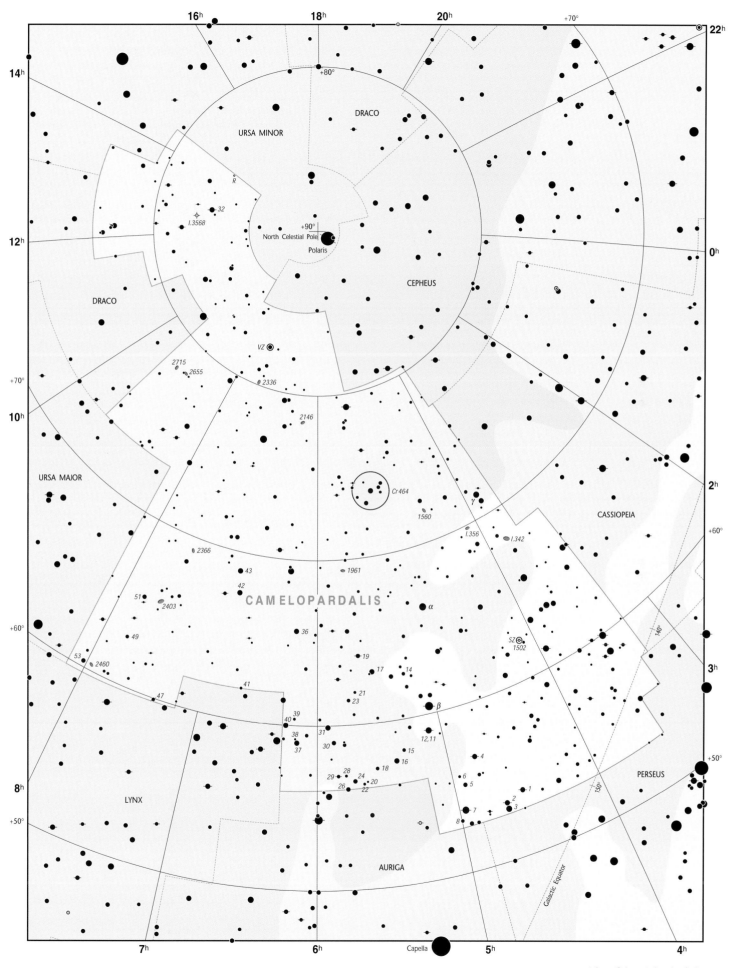

16ʰ 18ʰ 20ʰ +70° 22ʰ

14ʰ

+80°

DRACO

URSA MINOR

R

32

I.3568

+90°
North Celestial Pole
Polaris

12ʰ 0ʰ

CEPHEUS

DRACO

VZ

2715 2655

2336

+70°

10ʰ

2146

+70°

URSA MAJOR

Cr 464

1560

γ

2366

I.356 I.342

+60°

2ʰ

CASSIOPEIA

1961

43

42

51

2403

CAMELOPARDALIS

α

36

SZ
1502

49

19

53 2460

17 14

41

21

23

47

39

40

31

β

38 30

12,11

37

15

16 4

29 28 18

6

24 20

5

26 22

8ʰ

+60°

3ʰ

+60°

140°

PERSEUS

+50°

150°

1

2

7 3

8

+50°

LYNX

AURIGA

Galactic Equator

7ʰ 6ʰ Capella 5ʰ 4ʰ

32 Cam or **Σ 1694** (12ʰ49ᵐ.2, +83°24'): a pair of blue-white stars (mags. 5.3, 5.7; PA 326°, Sep. 21".5). Both stars have A0 spectra, and the double is an easy object for small telescopes. This star is also sometimes known as 78 Cam.

VZ Cam (07ʰ31ᵐ.9, +82°25'): a semiregular variable, with a range of mag. 4.8–5.2. This small range and the star's M4 spectral type makes it difficult to study accurately using visual estimates.

NGC 1502 (04ʰ08ᵐ.0, +62°20'): a small, but reasonably bright (6th-magnitude) open cluster, visible in binoculars. Its distance is 950 pc (≈ 3100 l.y.).

NGC 2403 (07ʰ37ᵐ.3, +65°35'): an Sc spiral galaxy, reasonably easy to detect in binoculars under good conditions, despite its quoted magnitude of 8.4. It appears elliptical with apertures of 100 mm or more.

IC 342 (03ʰ46ᵐ.8, +68°06'): a spiral (Sc) galaxy, mag. 9.1. It is fairly large (about 20' across) so has a low surface brightness. It requires at least 100 mm aperture, and preferably more, to be detected.

Cr 464 (5ʰ22ᵐ.9, +73°17'): Collinder 464, a little-known, large open cluster, about 2° in diameter, overall mag. 4.2. Although this cluster has about 50 members, they are spread over a large area, so it is not particularly conspicuous.

Cancer
CANCRI • Cnc • THE CRAB

Main chart(s): 10 (3, 4, 9)
Area: 506 sq. deg. (31st)
Culminates 00:00 local time: late January

This faint zodiacal constellation was once particularly important because the Sun was in it at the northern summer solstice. The Tropic of Cancer is so named because, along it, the Sun reaches the zenith at the solstice. Because of precession, the Sun now reaches its highest declination on the border of Gemini and Taurus. Lying outside the main plane of the Milky Way, Cancer has no emission nebulae, nor does it have any globular clusters or bright planetary nebulae. There are two open clusters, but only one reasonably bright galaxy.

ζ Cnc (08ʰ12ᵐ.2, +17°39'): a known triple system, may be quadruple. The close pair (AB, mags. 5.6, 6.0; PA 161°, Sep. 0".6); P = 59.7 yrs) requires an aperture of approx. 200 mm. The third component (C, mag. 6.2; AC, PA 80°, Sep. 6".0; P = 1150 yrs) appears to be affected by an invisible companion, perhaps a white dwarf (P = 17.5 yrs).

ι Cnc (08ʰ46ᵐ.7, +28°45'): a moderately difficult binocular double; a yellow (G8) giant and white (A3) dwarf (mags. 4.0, 6.6; PA 307°, Sep. 0".5).

R Cnc (08ʰ16ᵐ.6, +11°44'): a long-period variable, readily visible in binoculars for a long time around maximum. Its range is mag. 6.1–11.8, with a period of 361.6 days.

RS Cnc (09ʰ10ᵐ.6, +30°58'): a semiregular, red (M6) supergiant variable, with occasional periodicity of approx. 120 days.

M44 (NGC 2632, 08ʰ40ᵐ.1, +19°59'), Praesepe: a loose open cluster at a distance of about 160 pc (≈ 590 l.y.). It has about 200 members, including an orange star with a fainter red companion. There are a number of faint galaxies in the area, but these are difficult to detect because of bright foreground stars.

M67 (NGC 2682, 08ʰ50ᵐ.4, +11°49'): a relatively large open cluster (mag. 7) with about the same apparent size as the Moon (0°.5),

readily visible in binoculars. It begins to be resolved with apertures of 75 mm; larger instruments will show colour in the brighter members. The distance is 800 pc (≈ 2350 l.y.).

NGC 2775 (09ʰ10ᵐ.3, +07°02'): a spiral (Sa) galaxy, which is detectable with 100 mm aperture, but even 300 mm fails to show any structure.

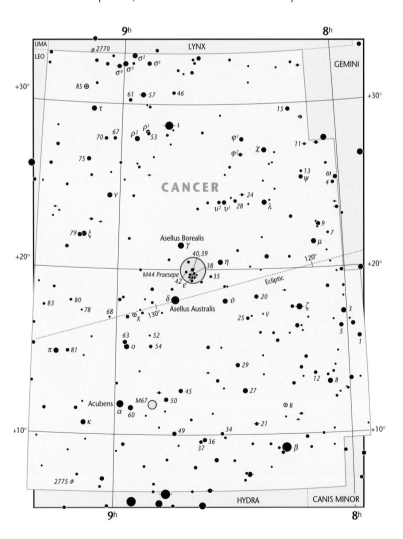

Canes Venatici

CANUM VENATICORUM • Cvn • THE HUNTING DOGS

Main chart(s): 5 (4)
Area: 465 sq. deg. (38th)
Culminates 00:00 local time: early April

This small constellation (introduced by Hevelius in 1687), does not contain any open clusters, gaseous nebulae or planetary nebulae. There is one fine globular cluster, M3, and there are numerous galaxies, particularly in the eastern and southern parts which border on Ursa Major and Coma Berenices, both constellations that contain major clusters of galaxies.

α **CVn** (12ʰ56ᵐ.0, +38°19'), Cor Caroli: a wide double (mags. 2.9, 5.6; PA 229°, Sep. 19".4). The brighter (α² CVn) is the prototype for a class of magnetic variable stars with very small amplitudes (about 0.1 mag.).

25 CVn (13ʰ37ᵐ.6, +36°16'): (mags. 5.0, 6.9; PA 100°, Sep. 1".9), resolved with 75 mm aperture.

Y CVn (12ʰ45ᵐ.1, +45°26'), La Superba: a semiregular, red giant variable, mag. 4.9–6.0, with occasional periodicity of 157 days.

M3 (NGC 5272, 13ʰ42ᵐ.2, +28°23'): a bright globular cluster, on the limit of naked-eye visibility (mag. 6.3), but readily seen in binoculars. Resolved with 100 mm aperture. Rivals M13 in Hercules as the finest globular in the northern hemisphere. Distance 10.4 kpc (≈ 34,000 l.y.).

M51 (NGC 5194, 13ʰ29ᵐ.9, +47°12'), the Whirlpool Galaxy: an open (Sc) spiral, with a nearby peculiar (Pec.) companion, NGC 5195. Although the nuclei of both may be seen with small apertures, **M51** alone begins to show structure with apertures of 200 mm or more. Its distance is about 8 Mpc (≈ 26 million l.y.).

M63 (NGC 5055, 13ʰ15ᵐ.8, +42°02'), the Sunflower Galaxy: an (Sb) spiral, mag. 8.6, clearly visible with apertures of 100 mm and above. Its distance is about 7 Mpc (≈ 22.8 million l.y.).

M94 (NGC 4736, 12ʰ50ᵐ.9, +41°07'): a spiral (Sb) galaxy, mag. 8.2, resembles a globular cluster or comet in small apertures. The distance is thought to be about 4 Mpc (≈ 13 million l.y.).

M106 (NGC 4258, 12ʰ19ᵐ.0, +47°18'): an elongated spiral (Sb) galaxy, mag. 8.3, its elongation visible with apertures of 100 mm and above. Its distance is 6 Mpc (≈ 20 million l.y.).

NGC 4449 (12ʰ28ᵐ.2, +44°06'), the Box Galaxy: an irregular galaxy, mag. 9.4, visible with 75 mm.

2 CVn (12ʰ16ᵐ.1, +40°40'): with common proper motion but no orbital change, this is a very long-period binary (mags 5.8, 8.1; PA 260°, Sep. 11".4). The primary displays an M0.5 giant spectrum, but is also a spectroscopic binary. The secondary is an F7 dwarf.

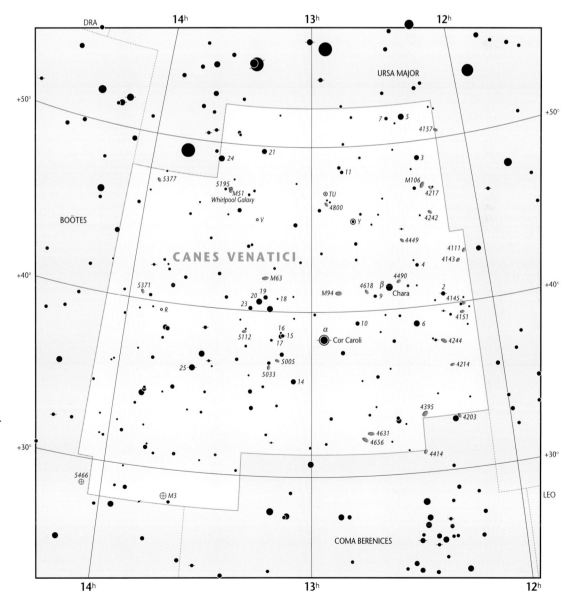

Canis Major

CANIS MAJORIS • Cma • THE GREAT DOG

Main chart(s): 9, 15 (10, 16)
Area: 380 sq. deg. (43rd)
Culminates 00:00 local time: early January

Lying just south of the galactic equator, Canis Major has several open clusters and interesting double stars. There are no globular clusters but there are a number of galaxies, although none are particularly bright.

α **CMa** (06ʰ45ᵐ.1, -16°43'), Sirius: the brightest star in the sky (mag. -1.44, A1 spectrum, d = 8.6 l.y.), and the sixth closest star to the Sun. A binary system with the first white dwarf to be discovered (mag. 8.5). The period is 50 years, and the separation is currently increasing. The companion is visible with apertures of at least 200 mm, under good conditions, generally only if the brightness of the primary is reduced (for example with a neutral density filter).

ε **CMa** (06ʰ58.6ᵐ, -28°58'), Adhara: a fairly difficult double (mags. 1.5, 7.4; PA 161°, Sep. 7".5), because of the brilliance of the B2 primary. The secondary is yellow, visible with 75 mm aperture or greater, especially if glare from primary is eliminated.

ν **CMa** (06ʰ36ᵐ.4, -18°40'): a long-period binary (mags. 5.8, 8.5; PA 262°, 17".5), contrasting colours: yellow-orange (G8) and white (A8).

M41 (NGC 2287: 06ʰ47ᵐ.2, -20°43'): an open cluster, about the size of the Moon (0.5°) and consisting of about 50 stars including B- and K-type giants. Visible with the naked eye under good conditions and a fine telescopic object. Its distance is about 700 pc (≈ 2300 l.y.).

NGC 2207 (06ʰ16ᵐ.4, -21°22'): a spiral (Sc) galaxy, mag. 10.7, with a condensed, elongated nucleus, visible in 150 mm aperture. A companion galaxy (**IC 2163**) may be detected nearby on the eastern side.

NGC 2217 (06ʰ21ᵐ.7, -27°14'): a barred spiral (SBa) galaxy, mag. 10.2. The bright nucleus is visible with 150 mm, but the outer regions require an aperture of about 300 mm.

NGC 2360 (07ʰ17ᵐ.7, -15°38'): a rich open cluster, mag. 7.2, clearly visible with binoculars. It has a diameter of about 13', contains some 80 members, and lies at a distance of about 1.1 kpc (≈ 3700 l.y.). It was discovered by Caroline Herschel in 1785.

NGC 2362 (07ʰ19ᵐ.0, -20°42'): a beautiful open cluster, d ≈ 5200 l.y. It appears to surround τ CMa, which is a blue-white (O9) supergiant (mag. 4.4). This is actually a foreground star at a distance of 3200 l.y. and interferes with the visibility of the cluster. The larger the aperture, the better the view.

NGC 2383 (07ʰ24ᵐ.8, -20°56'): an open cluster, mag. 8.4, with a diameter of about 8', and having some 40 members.

NGC 2384 (07ʰ25ᵐ.1, -21°02'): another, smaller open cluster, lying about 7' southeast of **NGC 2383**. It is mag. 7.4, and has about 15 members.

The field around **NGC 2383** and **2384** is thickly populated with stars, including the orange binary β **198** (mags 8.0, 9.5; PA 215°, Sep. 5".7), northeast of **NGC 2384**.

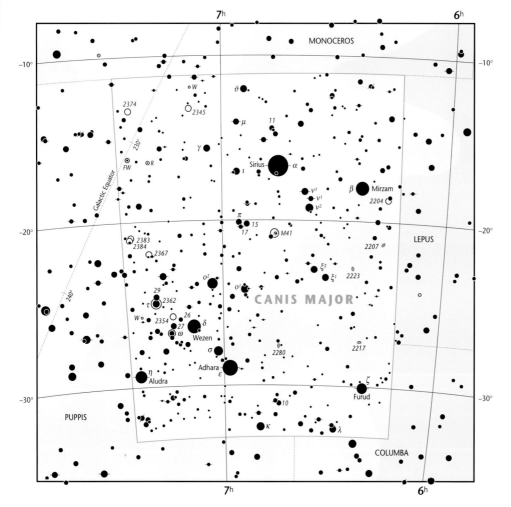

Canis Minor

CANIS MINORIS • Cmi • THE LITTLE DOG

Main chart(s): 9 (10)
Area: 183 sq. deg. (71st)
Culminates 00:00 local time: mid-January

Although this small constellation includes part of the Milky Way, it contains no clusters or nebulae of interest. There are a few unremarkable variable stars and just one or two doubles.

α **CMi** (07ʰ39ᵐ.5, +05°13'), Procyon: by coincidence, this star (mag. 0.4) is part of a binary, like Sirius, that contains a white-dwarf companion (mag. 11.3, P = 40.65 yrs). This is not detectable with standard amateur instruments. The system lies at 11.4 l.y., making it 15th in order of distance from the Sun.

η **CMi** (07ʰ28ᵐ.2, +06°56'): a binary system with a yellow (F0) primary and much fainter secondary (mags. 5.3, 11.1; PA 25°, Sep. 4".0). Little orbital change, but the common proper motion indicates that it is a binary.

Σ **1126** (07ʰ40ᵐ.1, +05°14'): a long-period binary (mags. 6.6, 6.9; PA 168°, Sep. 1".0). It requires an aperture of 150 mm or more to be resolved.

White dwarfs

White dwarf stars are condensed stellar remnants (the final stage in the evolution of low-mass stars) and are generally comparable in size to the Earth, with diameters of approximately 10,000 km. They have varying compositions but masses are below 1.44 solar masses. (Higher mass remnants undergo a further collapse into neutron stars, with diameters of 10–20 km.)

Because of their low luminosity, white dwarfs are most easily found in binary systems, and they play an active part in many eruptive variables, including novae and certain supernovae. Some notable systems in which white dwarfs occur are: ε **Aur**; α **CMa** (d = 8.6 l.y.); α **CMi** (d = 11.4 l.y.); and o² **Eri** (d = 16.5 l.y.). **Van Maanen's Star** in Pisces (d = 13.4 l.y.) is an isolated star, but the easiest white dwarf to detect with amateur-sized instruments is probably the mag. 9.4 central star in the planetary nebula, **NGC 1514**, in Taurus.

CONSTELLATIONS

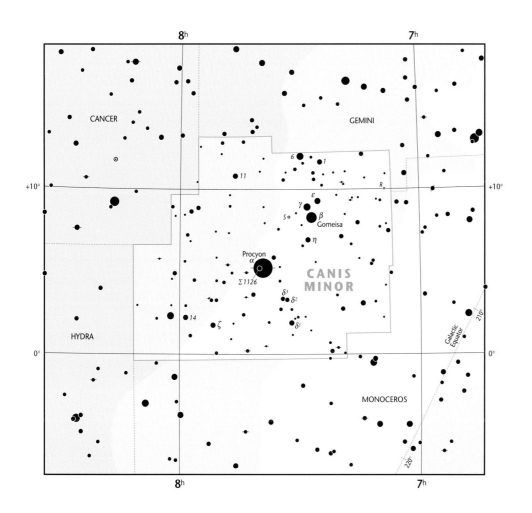

Capricornus
CAPRICORNI • Cap • THE SEA GOAT

Main chart(s): 13, 19 (12, 18)
Area: 414 sq. deg. (40th)
Culminates 00:00 local time: early August

Some two thousand years ago, the Sun reached its southernmost declination in Capricornus at the (northern) winter solstice. Although precession has caused the Sun's position at the solstice to move into Sagittarius, the connection is preserved in the name of the Tropic of Capricorn, the line of latitude at which the Sun reaches the zenith on December 21 or 22. The constellation has one fine globular cluster, but no open clusters, or diffuse or planetary nebulae. The brightest galaxy (NGC 6907) is mag. 11.3 and all others are much fainter.

α^1 Cap ($20^h17^m.9$, -12°30'), Prima Giedi, and α^2 Cap ($20^h18^m.3$, -12°32'), Secunda Giedi: a very wide visual double, readily visible to the naked eye (mags. 4.2, 3.6; PA 111°, Sep. 378"). The fainter star (α^1) is a yellow (G3) supergiant, d = 690 l.y., and has a companion (E) (mag. 8.6; PA (AE) 355°, Sep. 0".7), detectable with 75 mm aperture. The brighter star (α^2) is a yellow (G9) dwarf, d = 110 l.y., which 150 mm aperture will show to have a companion (PA 172°, Sep. 6".6). An aperture of 200 mm reveals that this secondary is a close pair (mags. 11.0, 11.3; PA (BC) 240°, Sep. 1".2).

β^1 & β^2 Cap ($20^h21^m.2$, -14°47'), Dabih: another complex system, consisting of a wide pair of yellow and white stars (mags. 3.1, 6.2; PA 267°, Sep. 205"). The bright star (β^1) is a spectroscopic triple system, with contrasting spectral types (A = K0 giant, B = B8 dwarf, and C = G dwarf).

The periods are 1374.1 days for A–BC, and 8.68 days for BC. The fainter star (β^2) has a B9 dwarf spectrum. There is a very close companion (mag. 10.2; PA 106°, Sep. 0".85), requiring at least 300 mm aperture.

o Cap ($20^h29^m.9$, -18°35'): a wide binary, consisting to two white stars (mags. 5.9, 6.7; PA 239°, Sep. 18".9; spectra A3 and A7 dwarf spectra).

π Cap ($20^h27^m.3$, -18°13'): a probable binary (mags. 5.2, 8.3; PA 148°, Sep. 3".4), requiring an aperture of at least 75 mm.

ρ Cap ($20^h28^m.9$, -17°49'): a wide optical double (Sep. 4.5'), with pale yellow (F3) and orange stars 5.0 and 6.6, easily separated in binoculars. The brighter star has a faint companion in a very eccentric orbit (mag. 10.0; PA 194°, Sep. 1".3; P ≈ 278 yrs), requiring at least 200 mm aperture.

M30 (NGC 7009: $21^h40^m.6$, -23°10'): fine globular cluster (mag. 7.4), detectable in binoculars. Resolved with 100 mm aperture. Its distance is 8 kpc (≈ 26,100 l.y.).

Capricornids (radiants at 20^h44^m, -15° and 21^h00^m, -15°): shower with bright yellow-blue meteors. Active July–August, but may have multiple radiants, because it appears to show three maxima: July 08, July 15, and July 26. Zenithal hourly rate at maxima about 5.

α Capricornids (radiant 20^h36^m, -10°): meteor shower active July 15 to Aug. 20, maximum Aug. 02, with zenithal hourly rate of 5. Many long, slow fireballs.

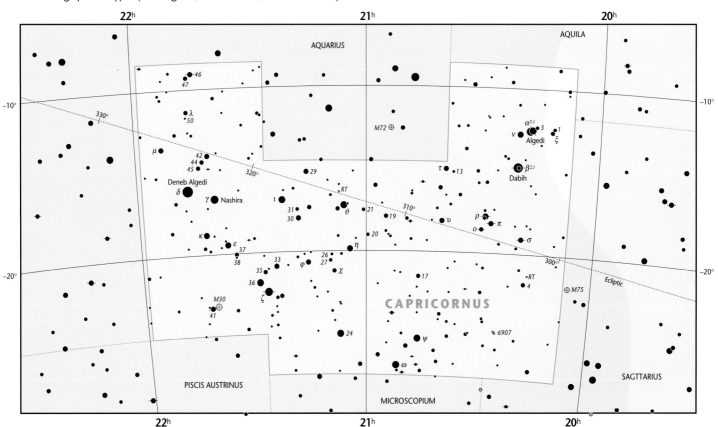

Carina

CARINAE • Car • KEEL

Main chart(s) 16 (15, 17, 20)
Area: 494 sq. deg. (40th)
Culminates 00:00 local time: late January

This constellation includes large portions of the Milky Way, and is exceptionally rich in interesting and striking objects, only a few of which can be described here. There are at least 50 open clusters, but because of the obscuration in the galactic plane only one galaxy is detectable with amateur instruments. The stars ε and ι Carinae, together with δ and κ Velorum, form the 'False Cross', which is sometimes confused with the real Southern Cross (Crux).

α **Car** (06ʰ24ᵐ.0, +52°42'), Canopus: the second brightest star in the sky (mag. -0.62). It is a pale yellow (F0) supergiant, d = 313 l.y.

η **Car** (10ʰ45ᵐ.1, -59°41'): an extremely luminous, hot, blue variable, with irregular fluctuations (type SDOR). Reached mag. -0.8 in 1843, second only to Sirius; subsequently declined to mag. 6, with occasional variations. Currently about mag. 5, η Car is thought to be about 100 times the mass of the Sun, and about 4 million times as luminous. Surrounded by nebulosity (NGC 3372), including expanding shells of material immediately around the star.

υ **Car** (09ʰ47ᵐ.2, -65°04'): a wide binary (mags. 3.0, 6.2; PA 127°, Sep. 5".0; spectra A6, B7), an easy object for small apertures.

l **Car** (09ʰ45ᵐ.4, -62°32'): the brightest Cepheid variable, range mag. 3.3–4.2, and therefore visible to the naked eye. Its period is 35.5 days.

t² **Car** (10ʰ38ᵐ.7, -59°11'): a fine double (mags. 4.7, 8.1; PA 21°, Sep. 2".2), visible even with small apertures. The bright star is orange-red (M1), and the fainter is white.

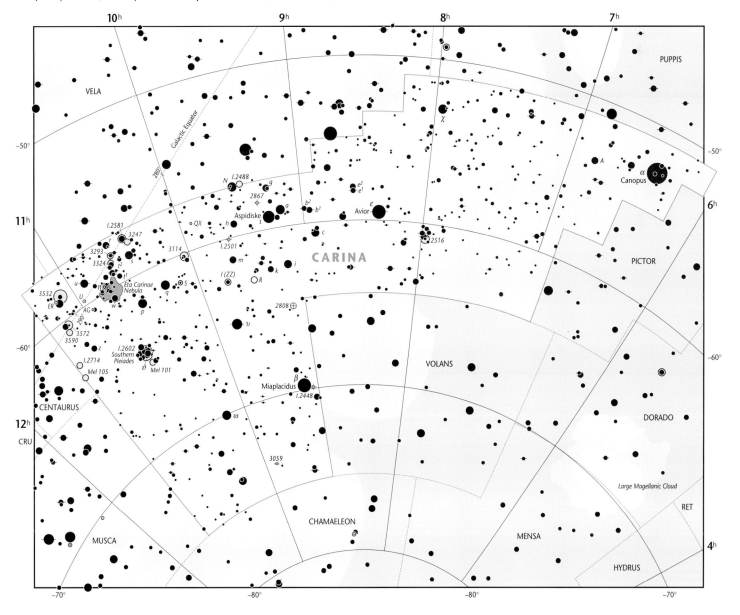

CONSTELLATIONS

R Car (09ʰ32ᵐ.2, -62°47') and S Car (10ʰ09ᵐ.4, -61°33') are both long-period variables (type M), with ranges of mag. 3.9–10.5 and mag. 4.5–9.9, respectively. At maximum, their orange-red colour distinguishes them from surrounding field stars.

NGC 2516 (07ʰ58ᵐ.3, -60°52'): a beautiful, large open cluster about 50' across, containing three bright orange stars that contrast with surrounding stars. The distance is about 400 pc (≈ 13,000 l.y.).

NGC 2808 (09ʰ12ᵐ.0, -64°52'): bright (mag. 6.2) globular cluster, resolved with 150 mm aperture. The distance is about 7.5 kpc (≈ 24,500 l.y.).

NGC 3059 (09ʰ50ᵐ.2, -73°55'): the only galaxy readily detectable with amateur instruments, a barred spiral (SB) galaxy, mag. 12.0.

NGC 3114 (10ʰ02ᵐ.7, -60°07'): a very large, loose open cluster, best observed with binoculars or small apertures and wide field. Its distance is about 900 pc (≈ 28,400 l.y.).

NGC 3372 (10ʰ45ᵐ.1, -59°52') η Carinae Nebula: bright diffuse nebula surrounding η Carinae, easily visible to the naked eye. It is a star-forming region and its complex structure of bright areas of gaseous emission and dark absorption lanes bears examination with a range of apertures. It contains various star clusters, and several double stars. The distance to this region of nebulosity is 3.2 kpc (≈ 10,400 l.y.).

NGC 3532 (11ʰ06ᵐ.4, -58°40'): large, bright open cluster, easily visible with the naked eye, and containing over 150 stars, including some

orange giants, d ≈ 400 pc or 13,000 l.y. It is very large, being about 60' × 30', and is probably best observed with binoculars.

IC 2602 (10ʰ43ᵐ, -64°24'), the Southern Pleiades: a very large, bright open cluster, over 1° across, easily visible to the naked eye. Surrounds the hot (B0.5) dwarf star ϑ Car, mag. 2.7, d = 440 l.y.

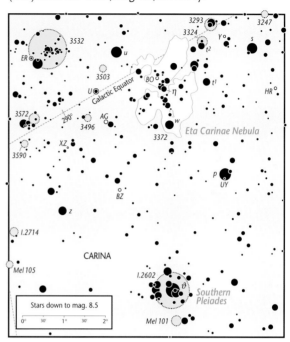

Cassiopeia
CASSIOPEIAE • Cas • (QUEEN CASSIOPEIA)

Main chart(s): 2 (1, 7)
Area: 598 sq. deg. (25th)
Culminates 00:00 local time: early October

The Milky Way crosses this constellation, which has many open clusters, some of which are difficult to distinguish from the background star clouds. Three galaxies are visible near the border with Andromeda. There has been one recorded nova in the constellation, but far more significant was the eruption in 1572 of the star now known to have been a supernova. This star, known as B Cas, 'Tycho's Star', or 'Tycho's Supernova' reached mag. -4.0 at maximum. It was closely observed over many months by Tycho Brahe, the famous Danish astronomer. His observations of this supernova and of the comet of 1577 helped to dispel the ancient and medieval notion that the heavens were unchanging.

γ Cas (00ʰ56ᵐ.7, +60°43'): a variable star and binary system (mags. 1.6–3.0, 11.2; PA 238°, Sep. 2".1). The bright component is normally about mag. 2.5, but occasionally fainter, as low as mag. 3.0. At unpredictable intervals it sheds a shell of gas, and may then become as bright as mag. 1.6. It is accompanied by both emission and reflection nebulosity.

η Cas (0ʰ49ᵐ.1, +57°49'): a complex multiple system with eight components. The two main components, visible in small telescopes (mags 3.5, 7.5; PA 317°, Sep. 12".9) and have yellow and red (GoV and dMo spectra). The other six components have wide separations. Three are moderately bright: component E (mag. 9.0; PA AE 124°, Sep. 99".5); component G (mag. 8.9; PA AG 255°, Sep. 407".7); and component H (mag. 8.6; PA BH 355°, Sep. 679".3). The remaining three stars are mag. 11.4 or fainter.

ρ Cas (23ʰ54ᵐ.4, +57°30'): an unusual semiregular variable, range mag.4.4–5.2, P ≈ 320 days. Between 1945 and 1947 it faded, reaching mag. 6.2 at minimum. The reasons for this fade and subsequent recovery remain a mystery.

RZ Cas (02ʰ48ᵐ.9, +69°38'): an unusual eclipsing system, with variable eclipse period, currently about 1.195247 days. Range mag. 6.2–7.7.

M52 (NGC 7654: 23ʰ24ᵐ.8, +61°36'): very rich open cluster, diameter 13', mag. 7.5:, with orange 8th-mag. star at one side. Approximately 100 members, which begin to be resolved with binoculars.

M103 (NGC 581: 01ʰ33ᵐ.4, +60°40'): compact open cluster, mag. 7.5:, partially resolved in binoculars, with about 50 members.

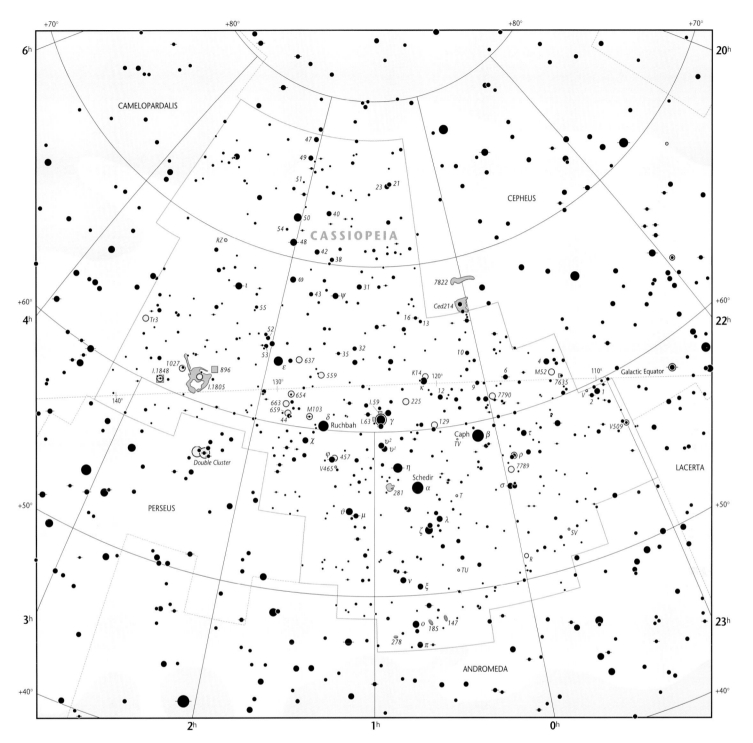

NGC 147 (00ʰ33ᵐ.2, +48°30'): and **NGC 185** (00ʰ39ᵐ.0, +48°20'): two elliptical galaxies (E4 and E0; mags. 9.3 and 9.4, respectively).

NGC 457 (01ʰ19ᵐ.1, +58°20'): an open cluster, slightly brighter than the two Messier objects (mag. 6.4:). The brightest stars are easily resolved in binoculars. These include a blue and yellow pair, the principal components (mags. 5.2, 7.9; PA 231°, Sep. 135") of the multiple star φ Cas (01ʰ20ᵐ.3, +58°15'); as well as a striking red star. This cluster is actually in the Perseus Arm of our galaxy, at a distance of 8000 l.y.

NGC 559 (01ʰ19ᵐ.5, +63°18'): a bright open cluster, which although nominally mag. 9.5, is distinct even in binoculars. Its diameter is

variously given as 4'.4 and 7', and is probably closer to the latter value. It has a total of about 120 members, but the brightest is only mag. 9. It distance is about 1.1 kpc (≈ 3700 l.y.).

St 2 (02ʰ15ᵐ.0, +59°0'), Stock 2: a little-known open cluster. Just 2° north of the famous, and much more conspicuous, Double Cluster in Perseus, is often missed, despite being about 1° in diameter. Its overall magnitude is 4.4, and it consists of about 50 stars, the brightest of which are approximately mag. 8. Many members are readily visible even in low-power binoculars.

Centaurus

CENTAURI • Cen • THE CENTAUR

Main chart(s): 17 (16, 18, 20)
Area: 1060 sq. deg. (9th)
Culminates 00:00 local time: early April

A large, Milky Way constellation, with many interesting objects (only a few mentioned here), including the finest globular cluster (ω Centauri), the closest star to the Sun (Proxima Centauri) and a remarkable radio source (NGC 5128). It also contains more naked-eye stars than any other constellation.

Roughly half-way between the famous Coalsack dark nebula (in Crux) and b Cen (Hadar), lies an unnamed, but conspicuous, dark nebula in a fine field at approximately $13^h29^m.5$, -63°32'. It is clearly visible with an aperture of 75 mm or more.

α Cen ($14^h39^m.6$, -60°50'), Rigil Kent: a binary star, mag. -0.3 to the naked eye, which any optical aid reveals as two stars (mags. -0.01, 1.3; PA 222°, Sep. 14".1; P = 80 yrs, d = 4.4 l.y.). **Proxima Centauri** ($14^h29^m.8$, -62°41') is a third, extremely wide component (PA 210°:, Sep. 2°31'). The closest star to the Sun (d = 4.22 l.y.), it is a red (M5) dwarf, normally mag. 11.0. It is also a variable star, V645 Cen, of the UV Ceti type, exhibiting flares of up to two magnitudes. It was once thought to be a permanent member of the α Centauri system, but is now known to be on a hyperbolic (open) orbit, which will eventually carry it back into interstellar space.

γ Cen ($12^h45^m.5$, -48°58'): a bright binary (mags. 2.9, 3.0; PA 347°, Sep. 1".0), but currently closing. Blue-white giant components (B9.5, A0), P = 85 yrs.

ω Cen (NGC 5139: $13^h26^m.8$, -47°29'): the largest and brightest globular cluster in the sky, mag. 3.7, approximately the same size as the Full Moon, but slightly elliptical in shape. It is relatively close (17,000 l.y.) compared with the distances of other globular clusters.

R Cen ($14^h16^m.6$, -59°55'): a bright giant, long-period variable (M) with a particularly long period (546.2 days), mag. 5.3–11.8, spectrum M4–M8.

3 Cen ($13^h51^m.8$, -33°00'): a very slow binary with white stars (mags. 4.5, 6.0; PA 108°, Sep. 7".9; spectra: giant B5, subgiant B9).

4 Cen ($13^h53^m.2$, -31°56'): a probable binary (mags. 4.7, 8.4; PA 185°, Sep. 14".9). Both stars are spectroscopic binaries.

NGC 3699 ($11^h28^m.0$, -59°57'): a planetary nebula, mag. 11.3, in a fine field. The nebula is detectable with 100 mm, and a dark rift running across it becomes visible with 200 mm and larger apertures.

NGC 3766 ($11^h36^m.1$, -61°37'): a scattered open cluster, mag. 5.3, with numerous bright, coloured stars. It lies at a distance of 1.7 kpc (≈ 5500 l.y.) and has an estimated age of 20 million years.

NGC 3918 ($11^h50^m.3$, -57°11'), the Blue Planetary Nebula: mag. 8.4, visible even with binoculars, estimated distance 3250 l.y.

NGC 4696 ($12^h48^m.8$, -49°19'): the brightest elliptical (E1) galaxy in the Centaurus Cluster (mag. 10.7), clearly visible in 150 mm aperture. Slightly south and approximately 15' west is NGC 4709, an elliptical just visible with 150 mm aperture. Larger apertures show more galaxies west of NGC 4709. The distance of the Centaurus Cluster is about 30 Mpc (≈ 98 million l.y.).

NGC 4945 ($13^h05^m.1$, -49°28'): a bright (mag. 8.4:) barred spiral (SBc) galaxy, lying in a beautiful field and detectable with 75 mm aperture.

NGC 4976 ($13^h08^m.6$, -49°30'): a fairly bright (mag. 10.2), conspicuous, elliptical (E4) galaxy, with a bright nucleus. It is detectable with 100 mm aperture, 5' west of a bright yellow star. It lies at a distance of about 15 Mpc (≈ 49 million l.y.).

NGC 5102 ($13^h22^m.0$, -36°38'): a lenticular (S0) galaxy, mag. 9.7, close to ι Cen, and just visible with 75 mm aperture. A member of a small group that includes NGC 4695 and NGC 5128 in Centaurus, and M83 in Hydra, all at distances of approximately 4 Mpc (≈ 13 million l.y.).

NGC 5128 ($13^h25^m.5$, -43°01'): an unusual galaxy, appearing elliptical with a dark lane across the short axis. Sometimes classified S0, but probably a merger between elliptical and spiral galaxies. Mag. 7.0, and visible with binoculars, but 100 mm aperture or larger required to see the dark band. A powerful radio source (Cen A). Distance 3.5 Mpc (≈ 11.4 million l.y.).

IC 2944 ($11^h36^m.6$, -63°02'), λ Centauri cluster: a sparse open cluster (30 members), approximately 1° across. **IC 2948**, an emission nebula, surrounds λ Cen, and is just detectable with 150 mm aperture, but really requires larger equipment and a nebular filter.

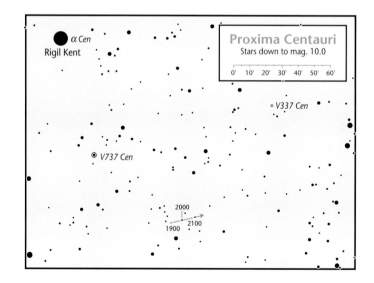

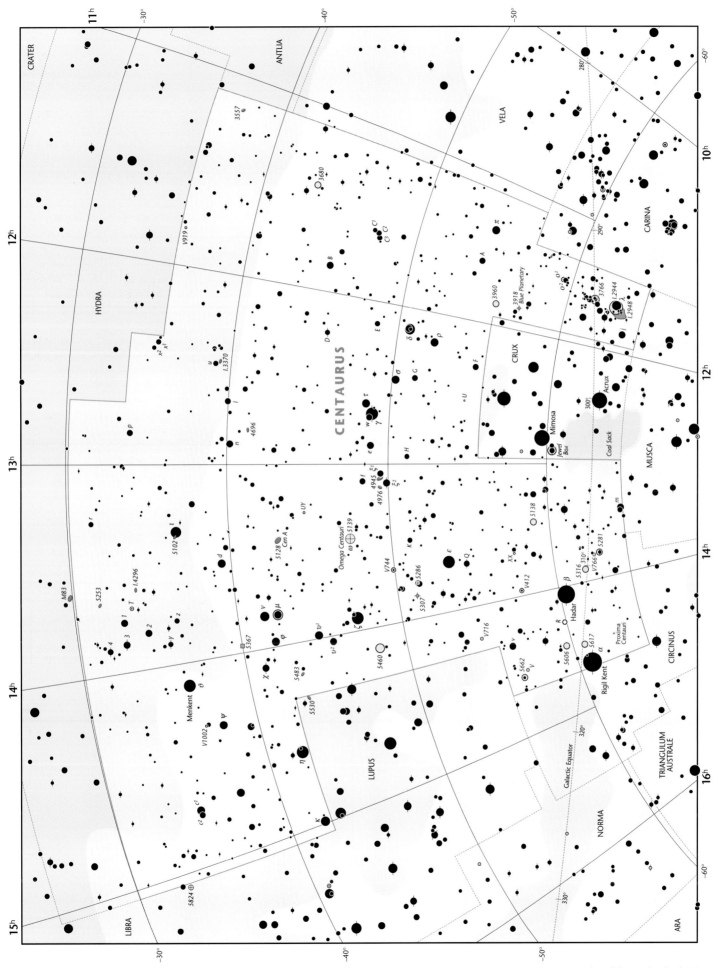

CONSTELLATIONS

Cepheus

CEPHEI • Cep • (KING CEPHEUS)

Main chart(s): 1, 7 (2, 6)
Area: 588 sq. deg. (27th)
Culminates 00:00 local time: late September

The brightest star (α Cep) in this inconspicuous, circumpolar constellation is mag. 2.5. The southern portion of the constellation lies close to the galactic equator, and contains three stars of exceptional interest and importance: δ, μ, and VV Cephei.

Harrington 11 is an area of diffuse nebulosity, which extends northeastwards from the main band of the Milky Way. Although appearing as a hazy band to the naked eye, Harrington 11 is resolved into innumerable stars in binoculars or telescopes. Many of these stars form part of the **Cepheus OB2** association of young, hot stars. There are so many stars in this area that it is sometimes difficult to pick out some of the fainter stars and clusters in the region.

δ Cep (22ʰ29ᵐ.2, +58°25'): the type star for the important class of Cepheid variables. It varies between magnitude 3.5 and 4.4, with a period of 5.366341 days, and is a bright yellow (F5–G1) supergiant at a distance of 982 l.y. It is also a double star, with a second component of mag. 7.5 (PA 191°, Sep. 41".0), readily visible in small telescopes.

Cepheids exhibit extremely regular periods and light-curves. There is a direct relationship between their period and their luminosity: the longer the period, the greater the luminosity. By determining a star's period, it is possible to determine the exact absolute magnitude, and hence the distance. Because Cepheids are highly luminous supergiants, they are detectable in external galaxies. They form an essential link in the chain of methods used to determine the scale of the universe.

Comparisons for δ Cep:

A = ζ Cep	3.35	D = α Lac	3.77	F = ν Cep	4.29
B = η Cep	3.43	E = ε Cep	4.19	G = β Lac	4.44
C = ι Cep	3.53				

μ Cep (21ʰ43ᵐ.5, +58°47'), the Garnet Star: a deep orange (M2 spectrum) star, clearly visible in binoculars. It is a red supergiant, the largest star known, being about 2400 times the diameter of the Sun – about 22 astronomical units (AU). In our own Solar System it would extend far beyond the orbit of Saturn (which orbits at about 9.55 AU). It is a semiregular variable, varying between magnitude 3.4 and 5.1, exhibiting periods of approximately 740 and 4400 days, as well as intervals with little change. Use the same comparisons as for δ Cep, with the following additions:

H =	4.52	L = π¹ Cyg	4.67
J = 4 Lac	4.58	M = 9 Cep	4.75

VV Cep (21ʰ56ᵐ.7, +63°38'): an eclipsing binary with an exceptionally long period, 7430 days (20.36 yrs), range mag. 4.8–5.4. Consists of a B dwarf, and an M2 supergiant, possibly second only to μ Cep in size, with a radius of 7.4 AU. In the Solar System it would thus extend to roughly halfway between Jupiter (5.2 AU) and Saturn (9.55 AU). The supergiant is a semiregular variable, amplitude 0.3 mag., P = 118: days.

NGC 188 (00ʰ44ᵐ.4, +85°20'): an extremely old open cluster, thought to be about 5000 million years old – which may be compared with 48 million years for M45, the Pleiades, in Taurus. Very close to α UMi (Polaris), mag. 8.1, and about 15' across. Requires at least 100 mm aperture.

NGC 6939 (20ʰ31ᵐ.4, +60°38'): a very rich open cluster, mag. 8.0, only 8' in diameter. Requires at least 200 mm to begin to be resolved.

NGC 6946 (20ʰ34ᵐ.8, +60°09'): face-on spiral (Sc) galaxy, mag. 8.9. Requires a minimum aperture of at least 150 mm.

NGC 7023 (21ʰ01ᵐ.8, +68°12'): a reflection nebula illuminated by a small cluster. The surrounding dark nebulosity is probably part of the same complex.

NGC 7160 (21ʰ53ᵐ.7, +62°36'): a bright open cluster (mag. 6.1), about 7' across, and with about 12 members.

NGC 7380 (22ʰ47ᵐ.0, +58°06'): a fairly bright open cluster (mag. 7.2), lying east of δ Cep. It has about 40 members.

NGC 7510 (23ʰ11ᵐ.5, +60°34'): an open cluster (mag. 7.9), close to the border with Cassiopeia and the open cluster M52, with around 60 members.

IC 1396 (21ʰ39ᵐ.1, +57°30'): an emission nebula and a sparsely populated open cluster, south of μ Cep. The emission nebulosity is actually visible with the naked eye under perfect conditions. The cluster itself is best seen with very low magnification.

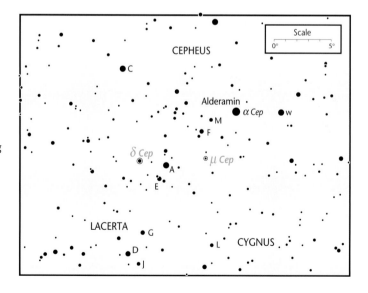

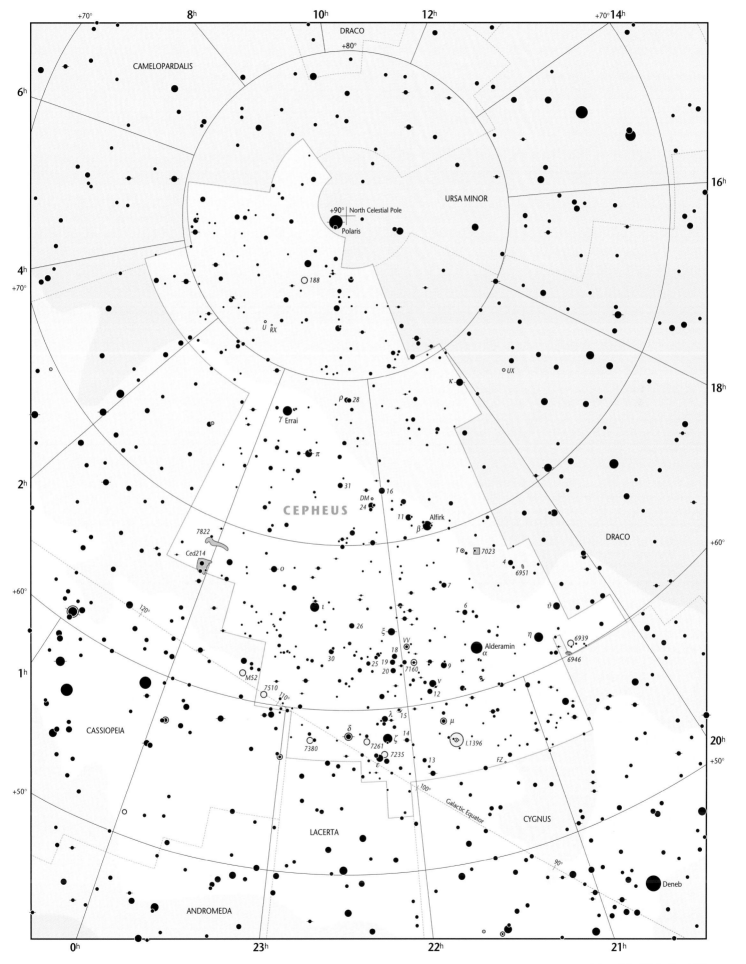

CONSTELLATIONS

Cetus

CETI • Cet • THE WHALE

Main chart(s): 8 (13, 14)
Area: 1231 sq. deg. (4th)
Culminates 00:00 local time: mid-October

While a very large constellation (the fourth largest), Cetus has surprisingly few objects of interest. Although commonly called 'The Whale', it would be better known as 'The Sea Monster', because mythologically it represents the monster sent by Poseidon to ravage the coast of Aethiopia (Joppa in Palestine).

α **Cet** ($03^h02^m.5$, +04°06'), Menkar: a red (M2) giant, mag. 2.5, d = 220 l.y., which forms a wide optical double with a bluish star (mag. 5.6), almost exactly twice as far away (446 l.y.).

γ **Cet** ($02^h43^m.3$, +03°14'): a suspected long-period binary (mags. 3.5, 6.2; PA 294°, Sep. 2".8) white (A3) and yellow (F3) components. Requires an aperture of at least 60 mm.

ο **Cet** ($02^h19^m.3$, -02°59') Mira: the most famous variable star, and the first to be discovered. The prototype for a class of variables, the Mira stars (M), otherwise known as long-period variables (LPVs), the most numerous class of variable star. All are red pulsating giants or supergiants, in a late stage in stellar evolution. Mira reaches mag. 3.5 (or more) at maximum, and drops to mag. 9.5 or less at minimum, with a mean period of 331.96 days. At minimum it is deep red, with a temperature of about 1900 K.

Comparisons for ο Cet (Mira):

A = α Ari	2.2	J = ξ² Cet	4.4	S		6.4
B = β Cet	2.4	K = μ Cet	4.6	T		6.7
C = α Cet	2.7	L = λ Cet	4.9	U		7.3
D = β Ari	3.0	M = υ Cet	5.1	W		8.0
E = γ Cet	3.6	N = 75 Cet	5.4	X		8.6
F = α Psc	3.8	P = 70 Cet	5.5	Y		8.8
G = δ Cet	4.1	Q	5.7	Z		9.2
H = ξ¹ Cet	4.3	R	6.1	AA		10.0

h 2036 ($01^h20^m.0$, -15°49'): a binary system: (mags 6.8, 7.3; PA 344°, Sep. 2".0). Resolved with 75 mm aperture. The system has an unknown, but fairly long period, with separation increasing only slowly since discovery by John Herschel in 1836. Both stars have G0 spectra, and the primary is a subgiant and the secondary a dwarf.

M77 (NGC 1068: $02^h42^m.7$, +00°01'): a spiral (Sb) galaxy, with a very bright nucleus, which is moderately easy to detect with binoculars, but at least 200 mm is required to see more detail. It is a Seyfert galaxy, a class that is noted for bright nuclei and considerable activity at their centres, with strong radio emission. Its distance is about 12 Mpc ≈ 39 million l.y.).

NGC 246 ($00^h47^m.0$, -11°53'): a very large (225") and fairly bright (mag. 8.5) planetary nebula, (d = 1470 l.y.). Requires an aperture of about 150 mm. Has an extremely hot central star, with a temperature of 135,000 K or more.

NGC 247 ($00^h47^m.1$, -20°46'): a nearly edge-on spiral galaxy, mag. 8.9. Its elongated shape is detectable with 150 mm aperture or greater. A member of the Sculptor group of galaxies.

NGC 908 ($02^h23^m.1$, -21°14'): an edgewise, barred spiral (SBb) galaxy, mag. 10.2. Visible as an elongated object with 100 mm, but larger apertures will reveal a faint star embedded in the eastern edge.

NGC 936 ($02^h27^m.6$, -01°09'): a barred spiral (SBa) galaxy, mag. 10.1. The central area may be glimpsed with 100 mm, but the symmetrical outer regions require larger apertures.

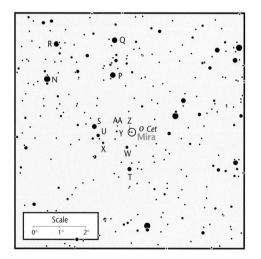

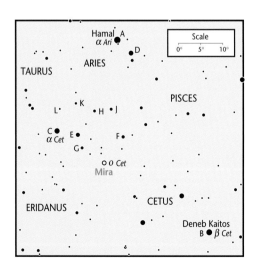

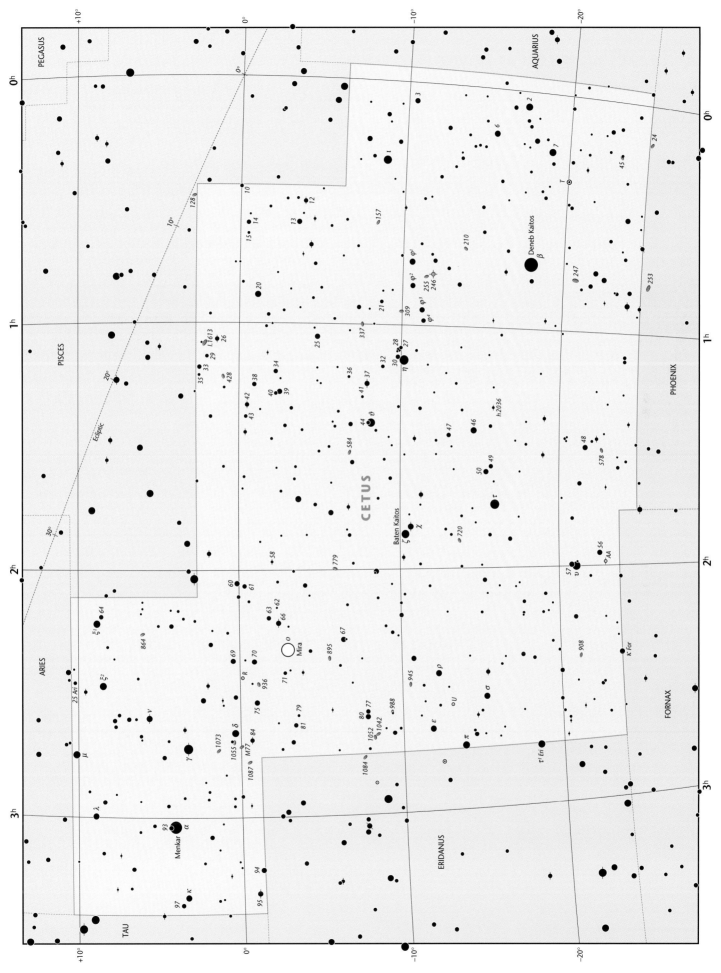

CONSTELLATIONS

Chamaeleon

CHAMAELONTIS • Cha • CHAMAELEON

Main chart(s): 20
Area: 132 sq. deg. (79th)
Culminates 00:00 local time: late February

A small constellation, introduced by Keyser and de Houtman in the late 16th century. It lies on the border of the Milky Way, and has no stars brighter than mag. 4.1.

δ¹ **Cha** (10ʰ45ᵐ.3, -80°29'): an orange (K0) giant, mag. 5.9, forms a wide (6') optical double with brighter, white (B2) δ² **Cha** (10ʰ45ᵐ.8, -80°34') mag. 4.4. It is also a binary system (mags. 6.1, 6.4; PA 84°, Sep. 0".8), requiring 200 mm to be resolved.

ε **Cha** (11ʰ59ᵐ.6, -78°13'): a very close binary (mags 5.4, 6.0; PA 203°, Sep. 0".43). Although now requiring a large aperture (300 mm or more), this binary lies in an interesting field, with another double about 2'.5

to the northeast, with a deep yellow primary and a fainter, wide companion.

NGC 3195 (10ʰ09ᵐ.5, -80°52'): a circular planetary nebula that is relatively faint (mag. 11.6), but visible with 150 mm aperture, d = 1.6 kpc (≈ 5200 l.y.).

IC 2631 (11ʰ09ᵐ.8, -76°37'), Ced 112: a bright reflection nebula surrounding a 9th mag. star, and visible with 100 mm. An aperture of 200 mm will show the spiral galaxy **NGC 3620** about 20' to the northwest, and 300 mm will allow another faint reflection nebula, Ced 110, about 45' south of IC 2631. (Ced is the abbreviation for the catalogue compiled by Cederblad in 1946.)

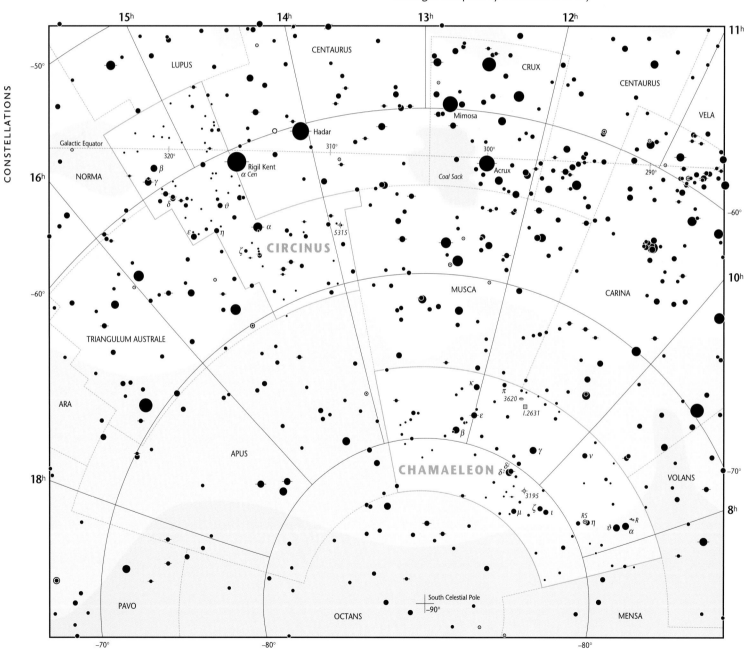

Circinus

CIRCINI • Cir • COMPASS

Main chart(s): 17, 20
Area: 93 sq. deg. (85th)
Culminates 00:00 local time: late April, early May

Another of the small constellations introduced by de La Caille, close to the bright stars α and β Centauri. (A line from α Cen prolonged beyond α Cir runs very close to the South Celestial Pole.) The constellation represents a surveyor's compass (dividers) rather than a drawing compass. (See opposite for chart.)

α **Cir** (14^{h}42^m.5, -64°59'): a long-period binary (mags. 3.2, 8.6; PA 232°, Sep. 15".7). Yellow (F0) and orange (K5) components easily resolved with 75 mm aperture.

γ **Cir** (15^{h}23^m.4, -59°19'): a binary with white (B5) and yellow (F5) components (mags. 5.1, 5.5; PA 20°, Sep. 0".7; P = 180 yrs), which requires 200 mm aperture to be resolved.

NGC 5315 (13^{h}54^m.0, -66°31'): bluish planetary nebula, mag. 9.8, clearly visible with 150 mm aperture.

Columba

COLUMBAE • Col • THE DOVE

Main chart(s): 15 (14)
Area: 270 sq. deg. (54th)
Culminates 00:00 local time: mid-December

This constellation was introduced by Petrus Plancius, the Dutch astronomer and theologian. It represents the dove that Noah sent out from the Ark to search for dry land. Lying just outside the main band of the Milky Way, it contains numerous faint galaxies. There is one globular cluster, but no open clusters.

β **755** (06^{h}35^m.4, -36°47'): a probable triple system. The principal pair (mags. 6.0, 6.8; PA 258°, Sep. 1".5) requires at least 100 mm aperture. This is accompanied by a fainter star (PA 300°, Sep. 21").

η **3857** (06^{h}24^m.0, -36°42'): a very slow binary system (mags. 5.6, 9.3; PA 256°, Sep. 12".9). An second orange-yellow star lies to the northeast at about 70" separation.

T Col (05^{h}19^m.3, -33°42'): a long-period (Mira) variable, P = 226: days. Range 6.7–12.7: and thus easily visible with binoculars at maximum.

NGC 1792 (05^{h}05^m.2, -37°59'): an elongated spiral (Sb) galaxy, mag. 10.2, visible with an aperture of about 75 mm. Its distance is about 12 Mpc (≈ 39 million l.y.).

NGC 1808 (05^{h}07^m.7, -37°31'): a barred spiral (SBa) galaxy, mag. 9.9, with elongated nuclear region, again visible with an aperture of 75 mm. It has unusual dark lanes and a starburst core, i.e., one where there has been a sudden burst of star formation.

NGC 1851 (05^{h}14^m.1, -40°03'): a strongly condensed globular cluster (mag. 7.1) that may be glimpsed in binoculars, but only begins to be resolved with an aperture of about 200 mm. Its distance is about 11 kpc (≈ 35,900 l.y.).

Coma Berenices
COMAE BERENICES • Com • HAIR OF BERENICES

Main chart(s): 5, 11 (4, 10)
Area: 386 sq. deg. (42nd)
Culminates 00:00 local time: early April

To the naked eye, this constellation appears unremarkable, because the brightest star (β) is mag. 4.2. On a clear night, the concentration of faint stars in the northeastern corner (Melotte 111 or the Coma Star Cluster) seems almost like a detached fragment of the Milky Way. However, the North Galactic Pole lies within Coma Berenices, which means that here we are looking out of the Galaxy, at right-angles to the galactic plane, with its obscuring dust and gas. Large numbers of external galaxies are found here, and in the neighbouring constellations. Near the southern border, the galaxies belong to the great Virgo Cluster, and farther north, they are part of the more distant, rich Coma Cluster.

17 Com (12ʰ28ᵐ.9, +25°54'): a wide pair of blue-white stars on the edge of the Coma Star Cluster, (mags. 5.3, 6.6; PA 251°, Sep. 145".2). There is a faint (mag. 14.5:) close companion to the fainter component, making this a triple system.

Melotte 111, the **Coma Star Cluster**, is a very loose open cluster, more than 5° across, and approximately centred on 12ʰ25ᵐ, +26°06'. It lies immediately south of orange (K2) γ Com (mag. 4.4), which is a foreground star. The cluster is best observed with low-power binoculars.

24 Com (12ʰ35ᵐ.1, +18°23'): a probable long-period binary (mags. 5.2, 6.7; PA 270°, Sep. 20"), yellow-orange (K2) and white (A7) stars, respectively. The fainter is also a spectroscopic binary, P = 7.34 days.

35 Com (12ʰ53ᵐ.3, +21°14'): a triple system. The close pair (mags 5.1, 7.2; PA 172°, Sep. 1".0) have G7 giant and F6 dwarf spectra, both appearing yellow. A preliminary period for this binary is 510 years. The wide component (mag. 9.8; PA AC 127°, Sep. 29") is relatively fixed.

R Com (12ʰ04ᵐ.0, +18°49'): Mira-type variable, P = 362.82 days, visible with binoculars at maximum (mag. 7.1). Falls to mag. 14.6 at minimum.

M53 (NGC 5024: 13ʰ12ᵐ.9, +18°10'): a fine globular cluster (mag. 7.7). Its central region is detectable with binoculars; it begins to be resolved with 100 mm aperture, and is fully resolved with 200 mm.

M64 (12ʰ56ᵐ.7, +21°40'), the Black-Eye Galaxy: a spiral (Sb) galaxy, mag. 8.5, just detectable with large binoculars under favourable conditions. The dark dust lane that gives it its popular name is visible with 150 mm and larger.

M85 (NGC 4382: 12ʰ25ᵐ.4, +18°11'): a large elliptical galaxy, mag. 9.2, easily seen with 75 mm. More details are shown with 150 mm, which also reveals **NGC 4394** (12ʰ25ᵐ.9, +18°13'), a barred spiral (SBb) galaxy, mag. 10.9, approx. 7' to the east.

M88 (NGC 4501: 12ʰ32ᵐ.0, +14°25'): a spiral (Sb) galaxy, mag. 9.5, which appears elongated even with 75 mm. Larger apertures reveal a bright core and fainter arms.

M91 (NGC 4548: 12ʰ35ᵐ.4, +14°30'): a barred spiral (SBb) galaxy, mag. 10.2, easily visible with 75 mm, but spiral arms shown only with 300 mm. Not in the position Messier recorded for M91, but the most probable candidate, allowing for a probable error in reduction of his observations.

M98 (NGC 4192: 12ʰ13ᵐ.8, +14°54'): a spiral (Sb) galaxy that is a member of the Virgo Cluster. Mag. 10.1, it requires at least 100 mm aperture, appearing spindle-shaped with 300 mm.

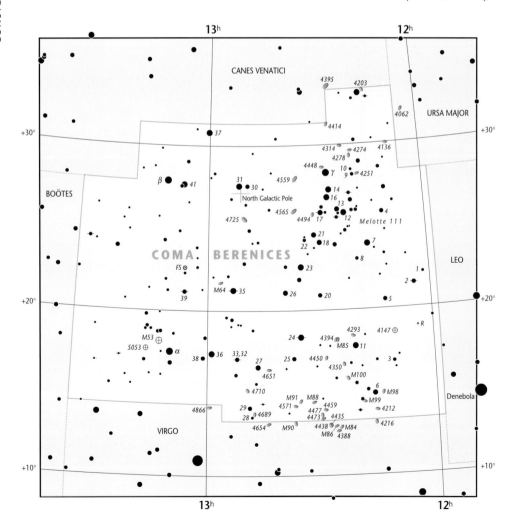

M99 (NGC 4254: 12^{h}18^m.8, +14°25'): a face-on spiral (Sc) galaxy, mag. 9.8, readily detectable with 75 mm aperture. A bright centre, but no obvious nucleus. A member of the Virgo Cluster.

M100 (NGC 4321: 12^{h}22^m.9, +15°49'): another face-on Sc spiral galaxy that is a member of the Virgo Cluster. Mag. 9.4, readily visible with 100 mm aperture.

Corona Australis
CORONAE AUSTRALIS • Cra • THE SOUTHERN CROW

Main chart(s): 18 (19)
Area: 128 sq. deg. (80th)
Culminates 00:00 local time: late June

Although this small constellation is less distinct than its northern counterpart, Corona Borealis, it has been recognized since antiquity, having been described by Ptolemy in the 2nd century. It lies close to the galactic equator, so suffers heavy obscuration from the concentrations of dust near the main plane of the Galaxy. The obscuration is so great that no external galaxies are readily visible. There are no open clusters, but the northeastern region contains various emission and reflection nebulae (one of the latter being variable), and dust clouds.

γ **CrA** (19^{h}06^m.4, -37°04'): a binary (mags. 4.8, 5.1; PA 55°, Sep. 1".3; P = 122 yrs). PA is changing rapidly (~5° per year).

ε **CrA** (18^{h}59^m.0, -37°06'): an eclipsing binary of the β-Lyrae type (EB), (mag. 4.7–5.0), with a period of just over 14 hours.

κ **CrA** (18^{h}33^m.4, -38°44'): a double (mags. 5.9, 6.5; PA 359°, Sep. 21".6) with two white stars (B8.5, B9.5). It is not known whether this is a true binary system or merely an optical double, because there has been no orbital motion since discovery by John Herschel in 1836.

NGC 6541 (18^{h}08^m.0, -43°42'): a globular cluster (mag. 6.7), visible with even the smallest instrument, but requires 150 mm before it starts to be resolved.

NGC 6729 (19^{h}01^m.9, -36°57'): a variable reflection nebula, associated with R CrA, a young, irregular (T Tauri-type) variable (mag. 9.7–13.5). There is a conspicuous double reflection nebula (**NGC 6726–6727**) surrounding two stars to the northwest. The distance of these objects is about 130 pc (≈ 424 l.y.).

IC 1297 (19^{h}17^m.4, -39°37'): a blue planetary nebula (mag. 10.7), requiring 150 mm aperture.

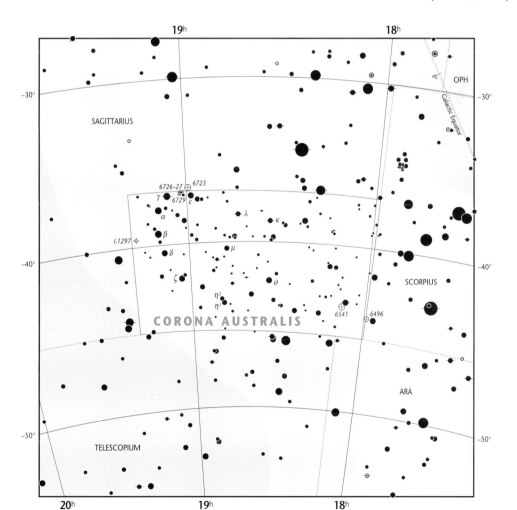

CONSTELLATIONS

Corona Borealis

CORONAE BOREALIS • Crb • THE NORTHERN CROWN

Main chart(s): 5, 6 (11)
Area: 179 sq. deg. (73rd)
Culminates 00:00 local time: mid-May

This small, highly distinctive constellation lies to the east of Boötes. Two variable stars (R CrB and T CrB) are of particular interest. The distant, rich cluster of galaxies, the Corona Borealis Cluster, is too faint for most amateur instruments.

ν **CrB** (16ʰ22ᵐ.5, +33°47'): a wide, optical binary (mags. 5.2, 5.4) with two giant stars, spectra M2 and K5, respectively.

σ **CrB** (16ʰ47ᵐ.8, +33°52'): a multiple system. Both principal components are yellow dwarfs (mags. 5.7, 6.7; PA 233°, Sep. 6".7; spectra F8, G1). The brighter star is a spectroscopic binary (P = 1.14 days), and a red dwarf, mag. 12.5, 11' southwest, is also part of the system.

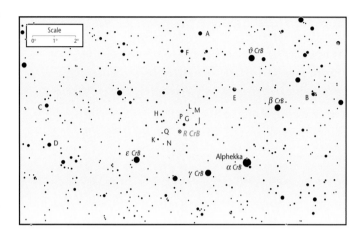

R CrB (15ʰ48ᵐ.6, +28°09'): the type star for the R Coronae Borealis variables (RCB), which are very rare, only about two dozen being known. It is an orange supergiant (spectrum C0 – a carbon star). It is normally bright, about mag. 5.9, but suddenly and unpredictably declines by between 1 and 9 magnitudes, taking days or weeks. It may remain at minimum for weeks or months, before beginning a slow recovery. Even at minimum, irregularities are present. These fades occur when carbon condenses into solid particles in the star's outer atmosphere, absorbing the light from the star.

Amateurs perform a valuable role by monitoring such stars and notifying professional astronomers when a fade occurs. R CrB is a particularly good candidate, because it is easily visible in binoculars when at maximum. There is always some variation at maximum, so alerts are triggered when the star drops below magnitude 7.

Comparisons for R CrB:

A = 5.56	F = 6.72	L = 8.60
B = 5.63	G = 7.18	M = 8.88
C = 5.94	H = 7.63	N = 9.20
D = 6.28	J = 7.93	P = 9.36
E = 6.57	K = 8.28	Q = 9.49

T CrB (15ʰ59ᵐ.5, +25°55'): a recurrent nova, normally at magnitude 10.8, which erupted in 1866 and 1946, reaching magnitude 2.0, with smaller outbursts in 1963 and 1975. As with all cataclysmics, it is a binary system, and the orbital period is 227.6 days.

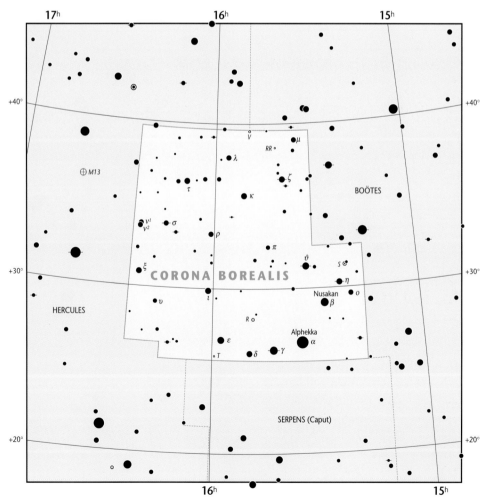

CONSTELLATIONS

Corvus

CORVI • Crv • THE CROW

Main chart(s): 11, 10 (16, 17)
Area: 284 sq. deg. (70th)
Culminates 00:00 local time: late March

The main body of this constellation consists of four stars in a trapezium and a fainter one, α Crv, which may have faded since Bayer assigned his designations. Although quite far from the galactic plane, few galaxies are visible.

δ **Crv** (12h29m.9, -16°31'): long-period binary (mags. 3.0, 9.2; PA 214°, Sep. 24".2).

Σ **1669** (12h41m.3, -13°01'): a multiple system. The principal stars (mag. 6.0, 6.1; PA 312°, Sep. 5".4) are yellow (F5) and form a long-period binary. Each component is known to be a spectroscopic binary, so the system is actually quadruple.

NGC 4038–4039 (12h01m.9, -18°52'), the Antennae: a pair of interacting galaxies, combined mag. 10.7:, requiring 150 mm to be readily visible. Consists of two spirals in collision (d ≈ 15 Mpc), and which form a powerful radio source.

NGC 4361 (12h24m.5, -18°48'): a planetary nebula (mag. 10.3:), just detectable with binoculars, but requires a larger aperture (preferably 150 mm or more) to show detail or the central star (mag. 13.7).

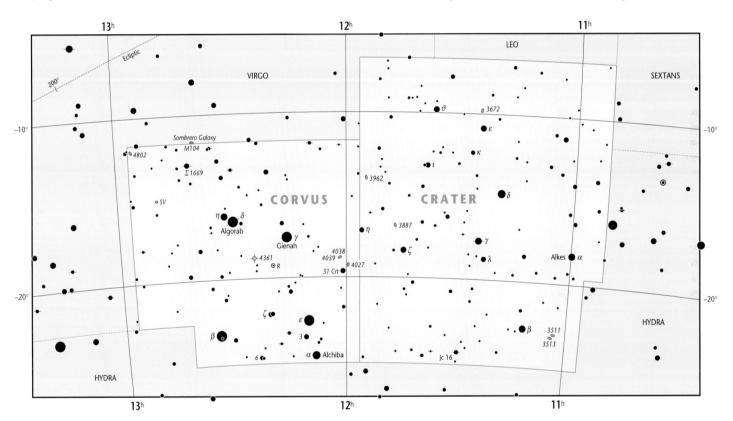

Crater

CRATERIS • Crt • THE CUP

Main chart(s): 10, 11 (16, 17)
Area: 282 sq. deg. (53rd)
Culminates 00:00 local time: mid-March

Crater, like its neighbour, Corvus, contains few objects of interest that are visible with amateur telescopes. There are a few galaxies, but the brightest is NGC 3962 at mag. 10.6. Even the variable stars are all faint, or else show low-amplitude variations that are difficult to detect.

γ **Crt** (11h24m.9, -17°41'): a long-period binary (mags. 4.1, 9.6; PA 94°, Sep. 5".3), clearly visible with 75 mm.

NGC 3887 (11h47m.1, -16°51'): a spiral (Sc) galaxy, mag. 11.0.

NGC 3962 (11h54m.7, -13°58'): an elliptical (E2) galaxy, mag. 10.6.

Jc 16 (11h29m.8, -24°29'): a very slow binary (mags 5.8, 8.8; PA 81°, Sep. 8".2), with just slight increases in position angle and separation since discovery by W.S. Jacob in 1847. The primary has a yellow (F2) dwarf spectrum.

Crux

CRUCIS • Cru • THE CROSS

Main chart(s): 17 (16, 20)
Area: 68 sq. deg. (88th)
Culminates 00:00 local time: late March

The smallest of the constellations, yet with many interesting objects, thanks to its position straddling the galactic equator. The Milky Way is particularly bright in this region, which is why the Coal Sack dark nebula appears so prominent.

α Cru (12^{h}26^m.6, -63°06'), Acrux: a multiple system, consisting of a close bright pair with a B0.5 subgiant and a B0.5 dwarf (mags. 1.4, 1.9; PA 111°, Sep. 4".1), and a more distant B4 dwarf (mag. 4.9; PA AC 202°, Sep. 90".8). The wide companion is easily visible in binoculars. The brightest star (A) is a spectroscopic binary, and the B component may also be a similar binary.

β Cru (12^{h}47^m.7, -59°41'), Mimosa: a very unequal double (mags. 1.3, 11.4; PA 321°, 44"), but notable for a deep red, unrelated star, mag. 8.6, PA 260° from primary, at 2.4' separation.

γ Cru (12^{h}31^m.2, -57°07'), Gacrux: a triple system, with a striking orange-red (M3.5) giant star, mag. 1.6. The B component has a wide separation and is readily visible (mag. 6.7; PA AB 31°, Sep. 111"), but the C component is much closer (mag. 9.5; PA AC 82°, Sep. 1".0).

μ Cru (12^{h}54^m.6, -57°11'): a probable long-period binary, consisting of a B3 subgiant and B5 dwarf (mags. 4.3, 5.3; PA 17°, Sep. 34".9).

Coal Sack (centred at approx. 12^{h}53^m, -63°): this dark nebula has dimensions of approximately 5° × 7°. Under exceptionally clear skies it is possible to see filamentary nebulosity within it. It is thought to be the closest dust cloud to the Solar System (d ≈ 555 l.y.).

NGC 4103 (12^{h}06^m.7, -61°15'): an open cluster, integrated mag. 7.4, with about 45 members (d ≈ 3900 l.y.), viewed with wide field and low power.

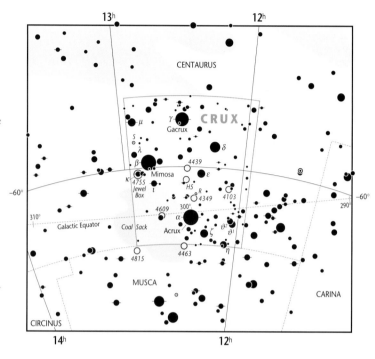

NGC 4349 (12^{h}24^m.5, -61°54'): an open cluster, mag 7.4, with 30 members (d ≈ 5545 l.y.). Visible as a hazy spot with binoculars, begins to be resolved with 100 mm.

NGC 4755 (12^{h}53^m.6, -60°20'), the Jewel Box or κ Crucis cluster: a beautiful open cluster, near κ Cru, d ≈ 7830 l.y. Integrated magnitude 4.2, but about 10' across and consists of about 50 members, including an orange-red supergiant.

Cygnus

CYGNI • Cyg • THE SWAN

Main chart(s): 7 (2, 6)
Area: 804 sq. deg. (16th)
Culminates 00:00 local time: late July

Cygnus is a large constellation lying in the Milky Way that has many objects of interest. There are numerous double stars (see the lists given with the main charts), open clusters and areas of nebulosity, but globular clusters are absent, and the only galaxies are heavily obscured and extremely faint. There have been many novae, the most notable being V1500 Cygni, which erupted in 1975, and which had the extraordinary range of over 19 magnitudes: a range resembling that found in supernovae. The area south of Deneb is sometimes known as the 'Northern Coalsack', being a dense dust cloud at the northern end of the Great Rift in Cygnus.

α Cyg (20^{h}41^m.6, +45°17'), Deneb: an exceptionally luminous blue-white (A2), supergiant star, mag. 1.3. It is about 260,000 times as bright as the Sun, and lies at a distance of some 3230 l.y. further away than any other first-magnitude star.

β Cyg (19^{h}30^m.9, +27°58'), Albireo: a striking double (mags. 3.1, 4.7; PA 54°, Sep. 34".4) that may be separated with high-power binoculars. A telescope will show the colour difference, the bright star being deep yellow (K3) and the fainter, blue-white (B8). They are not a true binary, but they are several light-years apart, at 386 and 376 l.y., respectively.

μ Cyg (21^{h}44^m.1, +28°45'): a yellow binary (mags. 4.8, 6.1; PA 320°, Sep. 1".2). Sources differ on the period, one giving a precise 507.7 yrs and another approx. 700 yrs. Clearly visible with an aperture of 75 mm.

χ Cyg (19^{h}50^m.6, +32°47'): a remarkable long-period, Mira-type (M) variable, P = 408 days, d = 346 l.y. It has an exceptional range of at least 10 magnitudes (with extremes of about mag. 3.3 and 14.2). This means that its brightness varies by about 10,000 times between maximum and minimum. Around maximum, its deep orange colour becomes apparent.

61 Cyg (21^{h}06^m.9, +38°45'): a binary (mags. 5.2, 6.1; PA 147°, Sep. 30"; P = 650 yrs). It was the first star to have its distance accurately determined (by Bessel in 1838). **61 Cyg A** is slightly nearer to the Sun (d = 11.35 l.y.). The fainter star, **61 Cyg B** (d = 11.43 l.y.), has an extrasolar planetary system. The planet's mass is about 1.7 Jupiter masses, but the orbit is extremely eccentric. In the Solar System this would take the planet from the orbit of Venus nearly to the orbit of Jupiter. It is possible that this exceptionally high eccentricity is related to the presence of the more massive star in the 61 Cygni binary system.

P Cyg (34 Cyg: 20^{h}17^m.8, +38°02'): an extremely bright, blue-white (B2) supergiant that is slightly variable and ejecting shells of material. Around 1600 it brightened to about mag. 3, but subsequently it has varied irregularly between about mags. 4.6 and 5.6. The class of stars to which it belongs, now known as the S Doradûs stars (SDOR), includes the most massive and luminous stars in any galaxy. P Cyg has an absolute magnitude of about -6.6, and a distance of 6270 l.y.

M39 (NGC 7092: 21^{h}32^m.2, +48°27'): a sparse open cluster, roughly triangular in shape, integrated mag. 4.6, best observed with low magnifications.

NGC 6826 (19^{h}44^m.8, +50°31'), the Blinking Planetary: a bluish planetary nebula (mag. 9.8). Visible with good binoculars, and the central star (mag. 10.4) may be seen with larger apertures. The popular name arises from the fact that the planetary may disappear when viewed directly, but reappear when averted vision (p. 7) is used.

NGC 6992 (20^{h}56^m.4, +31°43') and **NGC 6995** (20^{h}57^m.1, +31°13') are, together with **NGC 6960** (20^{h}45^m.7, +30°43'), patches of emission nebulae, collectively known as the Veil Nebula. All are parts of the much larger Cygnus Loop, which is the remnant of a supernova explosion that occurred about 15,000 years ago. The brightest portions may be seen with binoculars, although requiring excellent conditions. Telescopes should have a wide field and low power.

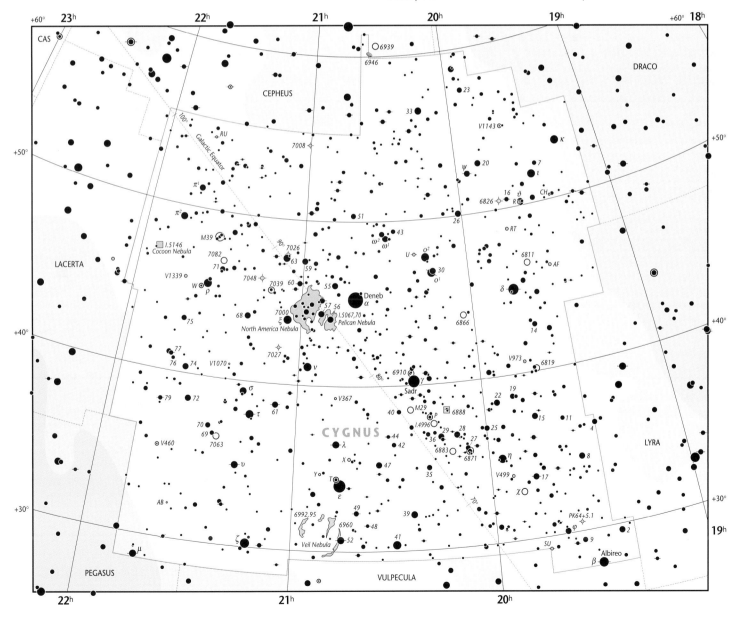

NGC 7000 (20ʰ58ᵐ.8, +44°20'), the North America Nebula: an emission nebula, just detectable with the naked eye under perfectly clear conditions. It does not stand magnification particularly well. It is part of a larger cloud of gas and dust, including **IC 5067** and **IC 5070**, the Pelican Nebula, to the west. The outline of the 'East Coast' and the 'Gulf of Mexico' are formed by an intervening dust cloud.

α-**Cygnids** (radiant 21ʰ00ᵐ, +48°): a meteor shower active for a long time (at a low rate) throughout July and August. Two maxima, July 21, and Aug. 21, with a zenithal hourly rate of 5.

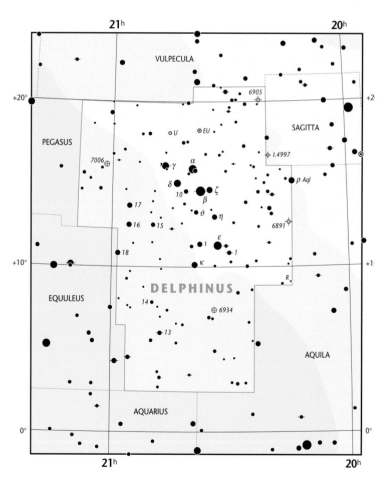

Delphinus
DELPHINI • Del • THE DOLPHIN

Main chart(s): 13 (6, 7, 12)
Area: 189 sq. deg. (69th)
Culminates at 00:00 local time: late July

Although this small, distinctive constellation lies on the borders of the Milky Way, it has no open clusters or gaseous nebulae. There are two interesting planetary nebulae, and two globular clusters. It was the site of the remarkable slow nova HR Del, which erupted in 1967, but had a very slow rise to maximum. An initial rise of about 6 mags. lasted about 30 days, followed by fluctuations which eventually took the star to mag. 3.7. It remained close to maximum for nearly a year.

β **Del** (20ʰ37ᵐ.5, +14°36'): a close yellow binary (mags. 4.0, 4.9; PA 150°, Sep. 0".6; P = 26.6 yrs). Requires at least 200 mm aperture. At maximum separation in 2004.

γ **Del** (20ʰ46ᵐ.7, +16°07'): a fine, long-period binary (mags. 4.5, 5.5; PA 268°, Sep. 9".6; spectra G5, F8).

1 **Del** (20ʰ30ᵐ.3, +10°54'): a suspected binary (mags. 6.1, 8.1; PA 346°, Sep. 0".9). Visible with 150 mm aperture.

NGC 6905 (20ʰ22ᵐ.4, +20°07'), the Blue Flash Nebula: a rather faint planetary nebula (mag. 11.1), which may be detected with 100 mm, but really requires at least 150 mm. With 200 mm or more, the blue colour becomes visible.

NGC 6934 (20ʰ30ᵐ.2, +07°24'): a globular cluster (mag. 8.9, d ≈ 49,000 l.y.), detectable with small apertures, but really requires more than 200 mm. An unrelated star (mag. 9.0:) appears in the same field.

NGC 6981 (20ʰ15ᵐ.2, +12°42'): a bluish planetary nebula (mag. 10.5), approx. 12' in diameter.

NGC 7006 (21ʰ01ᵐ.5, +16°11'): a globular cluster (mag. 10.6), just visible with 100 mm, but really requires a larger aperture. It is extremely remote, lying at about 114,000 l.y.

Dorado

DORADÛS • Dor • **THE DORADO**

Main chart(s): 15 (20)
Area: 179 sq. deg. (72nd)
Culminates 00:00 local time: early December

This small constellation was introduced by Pieter Keyser and Frederick de Houtman in the late 16th century and there is often confusion over the meaning of its name. A dorado is a tropical oceanic fish with iridescent colouring. It is sometimes called a 'dolphin', but has no connection with marine mammals. (Delphinus is a true dolphin.) It is certainly not a 'swordfish', nor a 'goldfish'.

Dorado includes the major portion of the Large Magellanic Cloud, the remainder lying in Mensa. There is a group of more distant galaxies in the northwestern area of the constellation.

Large Magellanic Cloud (LMC): a satellite of our Milky Way galaxy, sometimes known as 'Nubecula Major', lying at 50 kpc (≈ 163,000 l.y.). Its apparent size is about 8°, and it is about 6 kpc (≈ 20,000 l.y.) across. It is a rewarding object for any instrument. Formerly classed as irregular, it is now considered to show some spiral structure as well as an incipient bar. It contains many open and globular clusters, and gaseous nebulae. Being so close, some of the remarkable objects within it are easier to study than corresponding objects in our own galaxy, which are often obscured by stars, gas and dust. One example is SN 1987A, a supernova that reached mag. 2.8, and remained visible to the naked eye for nearly a year. The stellar precursor was found to have been a blue supergiant, contrary to the then accepted view that such supernovae originated in red supergiants. Many of the young clusters in the LMC are so compact that they resemble the older globular clusters found in our own galaxy.

R Dor (04^{h}36.8^m, -62°05'): a long-period variable (class M). A red giant, (range mag. 4.8–6.6; P = 338: days; M8 spectrum). At maximum it is a deep orange-red colour, in striking contrast to the fainter stars in its vicinity.

S Dor (in LMC, 05^{h}18.2^m, -69°15'): a highly luminous irregular variable, and the type star for its class (SDOR). Such stars are at least 30 times as massive as the Sun, and have about 1 million times the luminosity. S Dor itself varies from approximately mag. 9.0 to 11.5, and is surrounded by an expanding shell of material ejected from the star. Within NGC 1910, there is a faint companion (mag. 12.1; PA 110°, Sep. 13".4).

NGC 1549 (04^{h}15.7^m, -55°36') and **NGC 1553** (04^{h}16.2^m, -55°47'): a pair of interacting elliptical galaxies (mags. 9.9 and 9.5, respectively). Part of the Dorado Group of galaxies, which includes some galaxies in Reticulum.

NGC 1566 (04^{h}20^m, -54°56'): an active spiral galaxy, mag. 9.4, clearly visible with 100 mm. A Seyfert galaxy with active central region and energetic radio emission.

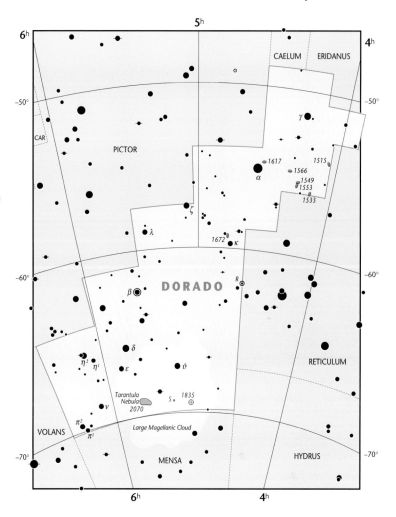

NGC 1835 (in LMC, 05^{h}05.2^m, -69°24'): a small condensed globular cluster, mag. 9.9. One of the few 'old' globulars in LMC.

NGC 1850 (05^{h}09^m.2, -68°48'): a bright, easily resolved open cluster, mag. 8.4, roughly circular in shape and about 2' in diameter. The fine field includes two other clusters, **NGC 1854**, a small compact group about 7' to the southeast; and **NGC 1858**, about 4' to the south. The last is slightly nebulous in appearance and very rich in stars. All three clusters are clearly visible with 100 mm aperture.

NGC 1866 (in LMC, 05^{h}13.5^m, -65°28'): a highly condensed young cluster, mag. 8.9, that resembles a globular cluster. One of the so-called 'blue globulars' that have no counterpart in the Galaxy, with an estimated age of 150 million years. Detectable with small apertures, and begins to be resolved with 300 mm.

NGC 1910 (in LMC, 05^{h}17.2^m, -69°18'): a concentration of stars (a 'star cloud') about 6' × 4' in size, and accompanied by two unresolved clusters, NGC 1903 and NGC 1916. S Dor lies in the southern portion. Although visible with smaller apertures, at least 150 mm is required to do it justice.

CONSTELLATIONS

NGC 1935–1936 (in LMC, 05ʰ21ᵐ.9, -67°58'): a stellar association, consisting of five bright young stars, with a nearby, triangular cloud of stars and related emission nebulosity.

NGC 2004 (in LMC, 05ʰ30.7ᵐ, -67°17'): one of the 'blue globulars', a young cluster (mag. 9.0) that has an estimated age of just 20 million years.

NGC 2070 (in LMC, 05ʰ38ᵐ.7, -69°06'), 30 Dor, the Tarantula Nebula: this magnificent emission nebula is so large – much larger than any similar nebula in the Galaxy – that it is readily visible to the naked eye. If it were located in the same position as the Orion Nebula (M42) it would be about 30° across, and so bright that it would cast shadows. There are emission regions, dust lanes, and a central cluster of young blue stars, whose radiation excites the overall emission. The surrounding area contains numerous clusters and nebulous patches.

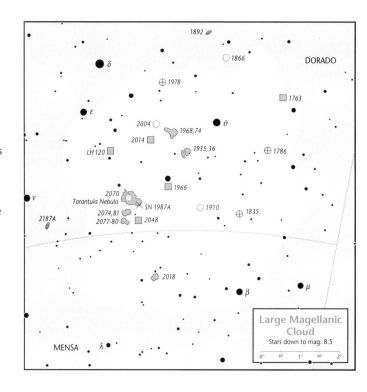

Draco

DRACONIS • Dra • THE DRAGON

Main chart(s): 6, 1 (4, 7)
Area: 1083 sq. deg. (8th)
Culminates 00:00 local time: late May

This fairly large constellation runs roughly half-way round the sky near the North Celestial Pole. It does not contain any diffuse nebulae, nor any open or globular clusters, but does have a large number of galaxies. Unfortunately, most of these are faint. There is one particularly notable planetary nebula.

ε **Dra** (19ʰ48ᵐ.2, +70°16'): a fairly close binary (mags 3.8, 7.4; PA 15°, Sep. 3".1). The primary has a G8 giant spectrum, and a recent source suggests that both stars may be slightly fainter (4.0 and 7.6).

ν **Dra** (17ʰ32ᵐ, +55°11'): a binocular double, consisting of a pair of almost identical white stars (mags. 4.9, 4.9; PA 311°, Sep. 62".3).

ψ¹ **Dra** (17ʰ41ᵐ.9, +72°09'): an optical double (mags. 4.9, 6.1; PA 15°, Sep. 30".3), resolved with binoculars under good conditions. Yellowish-white (F5) and yellow (G0) stars.

16 Dra (16ʰ36ᵐ.2, +52°54') and **17 Dra** (16ʰ36ᵐ.3, +52°55'): a wide, probable binary (mags. 5.5, 5.4). 16 Dra itself is a binary (mags. 5.4, 6.4; PA 106°, Sep. 3".2) and requires 75 mm to be resolved.

39 Dra (18ʰ23ᵐ.9, +58°48'): a complex multiple system. Binoculars show the principal pair (mags 5.0, 8.0; PA 351°, Sep. 3".1). The brighter has a close companion (C, mag. 7.4, PA AC 21°, Sep. 88".9). Two more components are visible in moderate-sized telescopes: E, mag. 10.8, PA AE 67°, Sep. 199".3; F, mag. 11.1:, PA AF 81°, Sep. 152".9. There is no component D. Two more stars, both mag. 14.1, are also part of this system.

UX Dra (19ʰ21ᵐ.6, +76°34'): a semiregular variable, range mag. 5.9–7.1, and therefore easily covered with binoculars. It exhibits a fairly marked periodicity of 168 days, although both the amplitude and period are subject to considerable fluctuations.

NGC 4125 (12ʰ08ᵐ.1, +65°11'): a moderately bright (mag. 9.8), elliptical (E5) galaxy.

NGC 4236 (12ʰ16ᵐ.7, +69°28'): a barred spiral (SB) galaxy, mag. 9.7. Quite a difficult object, requiring low magnification. It is visible with a magnification of about × 15 with 100 mm aperture, or × 25 with 200 mm.

NGC 6543 (17ʰ59ᵐ.6, +66°38'), the Cat's Eye Nebula: a planetary nebula, (mag. 8.8). Visually, this planetary has a bluish tint, unlike the vibrant red and green tones shown in the image obtained by the Hubble Space Telescope. The central star (mag. 9.5) is readily visible with large binoculars or a small telescope. It exhibits a hot (O7 + Wolf-Rayet) spectrum, with a temperature of 47,000 K.

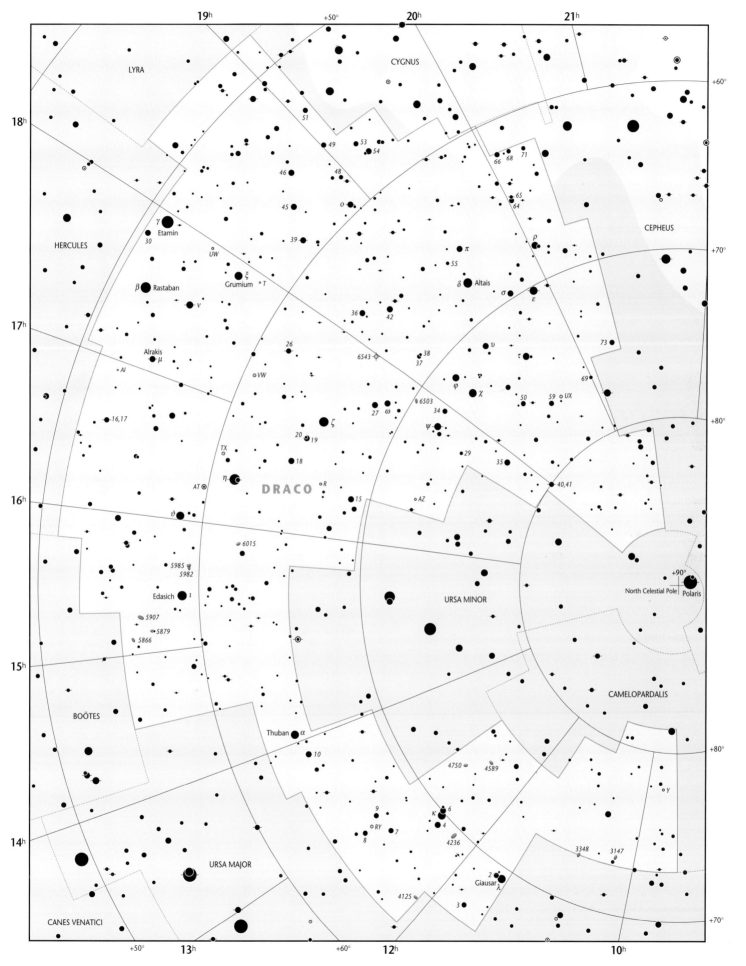

19h
20h
21h
+50°
+60°

LYRA

CYGNUS

CEPHEUS

51

49
53
54
66 68 71

46
48
65
64

45
O

γ
Etamin
30
39
π
55
ρ

HERCULES

UW
δ Altais
σ
ε

β Rastaban
ξ
Grumium
T
ν

36
42
ν
τ

73

Alrakis
μ
AI
26
6543
38
37

VW
τ

69

16,17
27
ω
6503
34
φ
χ
50
59 UX

20
19
ζ

ψ
35

TX
18
29
40,41

η
R
AZ

AT
15

DRACO
ϑ

URSA MINOR
North Celestial Pole

6015

5985
5982

Edasich ι

5907
5879
5866

CAMELOPARDALIS

BOÖTES

Polaris
+90°

Thuban α

10
4750
4589

γ

9
κ 6
4

URSA MAJOR
RY
7
4
4236

8
2
Giausar

CANES VENATICI
4125
λ
3348 3147

3

Equuleus

EQUULEI • Equ • THE LITTLE HORSE

Main chart(s): 13
Area: 72 sq. deg. (87th)
Culminates 00:00 local time: early August

This very small constellation (second only to Crux in smallest area) appears to have been introduced by Ptolemy, the famous Greek astronomer, who lived and worked in the 2nd century BC. There are no clusters, nebulae or galaxies.

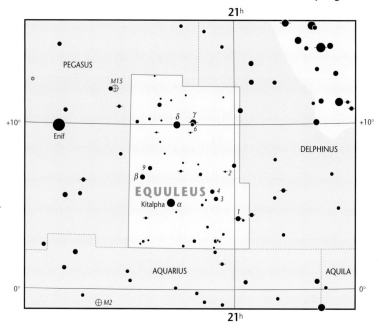

γ **Equ** (21^{h}10^m.3, +18°08'): a wide optical double (mags. 4.7, 5.9; PA 153°, Sep. 352".5). These are identified as components A and D, however, because A is a triple system (BC mags. 11.5, 12.5; PA AB 268°, Sep. 1".9; PA AC 5°, Sep. 47".7).

1 Equ (ε Equ: 20^{h}59^m.1, +10°08'): a quadruple system, with the main pair consisting of yellow stars (mags. 6.0, 6.3; PA 284°, 0".8, but closing; P = 101.4 yrs). The third component (C, mag. 7.4; PA AC 67°, Sep. 10".3) has a long, unknown period. A is a spectroscopic binary.

Eridanus

ERIDANI • Eri • (THE RIVER ERIDANUS)

Main chart(s): 8, 9, 14, 15
Area: 1138 sq. deg. (6th)
Culminates 00:00 local time: mid-October to mid-November

Eridanus is a very large constellation, with a great range in declination, and may only be seen in its entirety from about 30°N to 90°S. The constellation originally included the stars that now form Fornax, and ended at θ Eridani, Acamar (formerly named Achernar). The constellation was subsequently extended to the south, and the name transferred to what is now α Eridani, a blue-white star of mag. 0.5 in the far south. Both Acamar and Achernar arise from the same Arabic linguistic root, and mean 'End of the River'.

There are many double stars, but no open clusters and the only known globular is too faint for amateur instruments. There are numerous galaxies, including many in the Eridanus Cluster.

ε **Eri** (03^{h}33^m.1, -09°27'): a yellow-orange star (K2), mag. 3.7, d = 10.49 l.y. The tenth closest star or system to the Sun, it is also the closest known extrasolar planetary system. The planet is probably a gas giant, with a mass 0.8 times that of Jupiter, orbiting at a distance of about 3 AU from the star. (Jupiter orbits at 5.2 AU in our own Solar System.)

o² **Eri** (04^{h}15^m.2, -07°39'): a multiple system, consisting of a yellow-orange (K1) dwarf, mag. 4.4, and a white dwarf companion (mag. 9.5; PA 106°, Sep. 88".4). After the white dwarf components of α CMa and α

CMi, and Van Maanen's Star in Pisces, this is the nearest white dwarf to the Solar System (d = 16.45 l.y.), and the easiest to detect, visible with 75 mm. A slightly fainter red dwarf near the white dwarf also belongs to the same system, and there are a further two 12th-magnitude components.

NGC 1291 (03^{h}17^m.3, -41°08'): a barred spiral (SBa) galaxy, mag. 8.5, visible with binoculars, and revealing increasing detail with larger instruments. A very large outer region is visible with 300 mm.

NGC 1532 (04^{h}12^m.1, -32°52'): an elongated spiral (Sb) galaxy, mag. 11.1. The same field includes **NGC 1531**, an E6 elliptical galaxy, with the long axis approximately perpendicular to the axis of NGC 1532. Both are visible with 100 mm, although larger apertures will reveal considerably more detail.

NGC 1535 (04^{h}14^m.2, -12°44'): a bluish planetary nebula, mag. 9.6, readily visible in small instruments, even binoculars. In a rather sparse star field, so requires some effort to locate. Large apertures will reveal its bluish or bluish-green tint, with the central star (mag. 12) becoming visible with 200–250 mm aperture.

IC 2118 (05^{h}06^m.9, -07°13'), the Witch Head Nebula: large but rather faint reflection nebula (an old supernova remnant) illuminated by β Ori (Rigel). Visible to the naked eye under exceptional conditions, and brightest about 1° south of β Eri. Wide fields and low magnification are required for it to be detectable with any optical equipment.

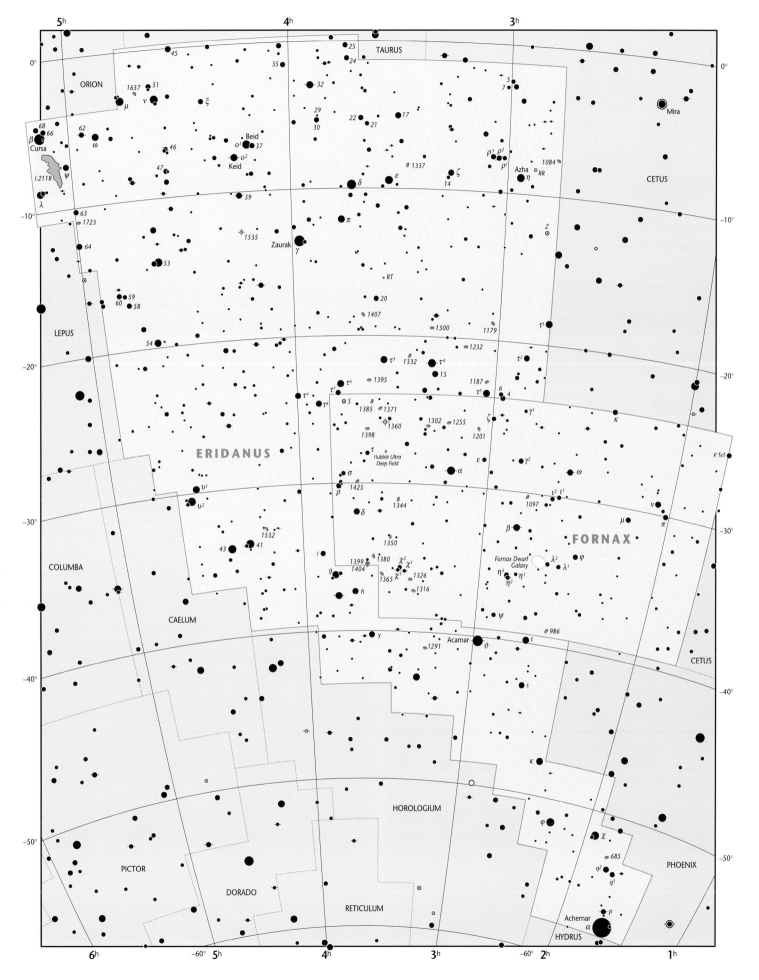

Fornax

FORNACIS • For • THE FURNACE

Main chart(s): 14 (8, 15)
Area: 398 sq. deg. (41st)
Culminates 00:00 local time: early November

This small constellation, introduced by Nicolas de La Caille as Fornax Chemica (the Chemical Furnace), is star-poor, but galaxy-rich. It contains, in particular, the Fornax Cluster of galaxies, the centre of which lies 23 Mpc (75 million l.y.) away. It also contains a small satellite of the Galaxy, the Fornax Dwarf, at a distance of about 153,000 parsecs (500,000 l.y.), which is, however, of such low surface brightness that it is not readily detectable with amateur equipment. The Hubble Ultra Deep Field was obtained in this area.

α **For** (03^h12^m.1, -28°59'): a fine binary system (mags. 4.0, 7.0 var.; PA 299°, Sep. 5".1; P = 314 yrs), pale yellow (F6) and yellow (G7) stars. An easy object with small telescopes.

ω **For** (02^h33^m.8, -28°14'): a pair of white stars (B9 and A5 spectra) that probably form a long-period binary (mags. 5.0, 7.7; PA 244°, Sep. 10".8).

NGC 1097 (02^h46^m.3, -30°17'): a barred spiral (SBb) galaxy, mag. 9.3, with a companion galaxy, NGC 1097A to the northeast, visible with 200 mm aperture.

NGC 1316 (03^h22^m.7, -37°12'): a barred spiral (SB0) galaxy, appearing elliptical in form, mag. 8.9. Interacting with **NGC 1317** (approx. mag. 11.1), 6.5' north, and giving rise to the strong radio source Fornax A. Both visible with 100 mm.

NGC 1360 (03^h33^m.3, -25°51'): a large, but diffuse planetary nebula, mag. 9.4, elliptical in appearance. A 9th-magnitude star lies east of the centre, but it is unknown whether it is associated with the nebula or happens to lie on the line of sight.

NGC 1365 (03^h33^m.6, -36°08'): a fine barred spiral (SBb) galaxy, mag. 9.5. The bright central region is visible with 150 mm.

▼ **Hubble Deep Field North** ($12^h36^m49^s$.4, +62°12'58".0) was the first of the extremely deep images obtained by the Hubble Space Telescope to probe the very early stages of the universe. In effect, the telescope kept one tiny area of sky in view for 10 days, making exposures through various filters. The images were then combined to produce a true-colour image. The faintest galaxies recorded – the pale red dots – have a magnitude of about 30, and are seen as they were less than 1,000 million years after the Big Bang. See constellation on pp. 148–149.

▼ **Hubble Deep Field South** ($22^h32^m56^s$.22, -60°33'02".69) complements the earlier Hubble Deep Field obtained in the Northern Hemisphere (in Ursa Major), and serves as a check to ensure that the northern field was truly representative of the early universe. It was also specifically chosen to include a quasar (the brilliant centre of an active galaxy). Quasars are not only significant in themselves but also enable information to be gleaned about intervening intergalactic gas clouds, important for the study of the growth and evolution of galaxies. As with the first Deep Field, the faintest galaxies are seen less than 1,000 million years after the Big Bang. See Tucana on p. 147.

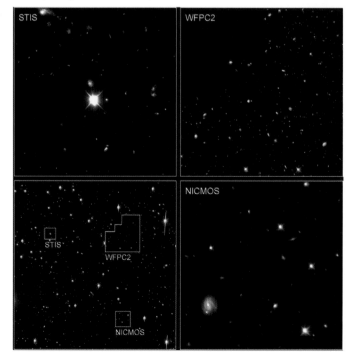

▲ **Hubble Ultra Deep Field** (3ʰ32ᵐ40ˢ.0, -27°48'00") actually consists of images obtained with two different instruments: the Advanced Camera for Surveys (ACS) and the Near Infrared Camera and Multi-Object Spectrometer (NICMOS).

The faintest objects detected on the ACS image, shown here, have ages of about 800 million years after the Big Bang. The NICMOS infrared images show objects as young as 400 million years after the Big Bang.

Among the galaxies of all sizes, shapes and colours that may be seen in this field, many appear very similar to the familiar images of spiral and elliptical galaxies that lie close to us. What is particularly striking, however, is that there are also large numbers of galaxies exhibiting extraordinary shapes. Some appear to be interacting, others are extremely elongated, and yet others look like links of a chain. This ultra-deep field has finally taken us back to a time when galaxies had yet to develop the familiar order and structure that we observe in galaxies and clusters of galaxies in the nearby universe. At this distant epoch, galaxies were in the early stages of formation, and changes occured very rapidly. These images therefore provide a rich source of data for understanding how the very early universe evolved.

Gemini

GEMINORUM • Gem • THE TWINS

Main chart(s): 3 (4, 9, 10)
Area: 514 sq. deg. (30th)
Culminates 00:00 local time: early January

The eastern end of Gemini lies just on the galactic equator, and the constellation has a number of open clusters, although only one is particularly interesting. There are neither globular clusters nor readily detectable galaxies, but there is one notable planetary nebula. Fittingly, Gemini contains double and binary stars, and also the radiant for a major meteor shower.

α **Gem** (07ʰ34ᵐ.6, +31°53'), Castor: a remarkable multiple star, d = 42 l.y. The blue-white star (apparent mag. 1.6) consists of two components (mags. 1.9, 2.9; PA 75°, Sep. 3".1), with an orbital period of 467 years.

Each component is a spectroscopic binary (P = 9.213 days and 2.928 days, respectively). A red-dwarf companion (YY Gem) is an eclipsing binary formed by dwarf M stars (P = 0.814 days), so the overall system consists of six individual stars.

δ **Gem** (07ʰ20ᵐ.1, +21°59'), Wasat: a slow binary (mags 3.5, 8.2; PA 226°, Sep. 5".8), and yellow F0 subgiant primary, and orange-red (K3) secondary. The primary is a spectroscopic binary with a period of 6.13 years.

ζ **Gem** (07ʰ04ᵐ.1, +20°34'): a multiple system and a variable. The brightest star, a yellow supergiant, is a Cepheid variable (range mag. 3.6–4.2, P = 10.1 days) and forms a binary system with component B (mag. 10.5;

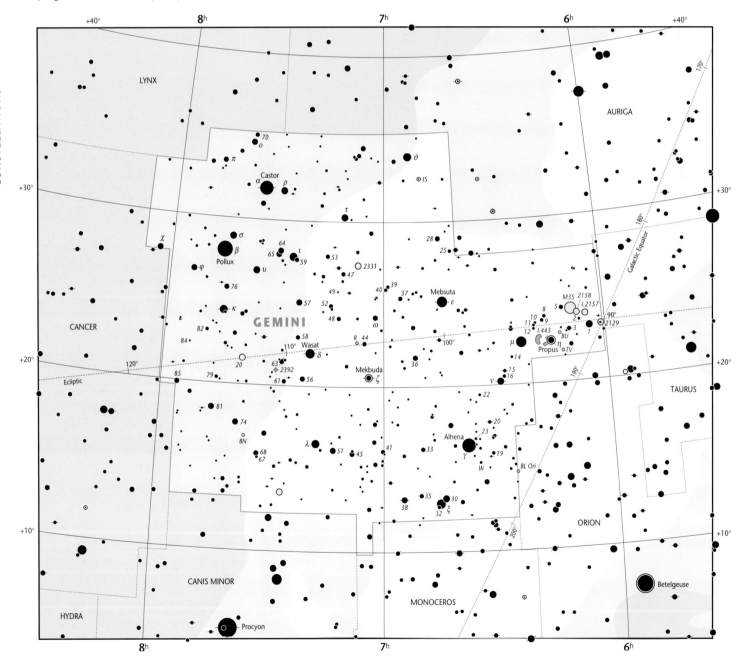

PA 84°, Sep. 87"). There is an unrelated companion, designated C (mag. 7.6; PA 350°, Sep. 96".5) and two other 12th- and 13th-magnitude components.

η **Gem** (06ʰ14ᵐ.9, +22°30'), Propus: a triple system with two visible components: a red (M3) giant semiregular variable (mag. 3.2–3.9), and a yellow (G0) giant (mag. 6.5; PA 257°, Sep. 1".6; P = 473.7 yrs). The red semiregular occasionally shows moderately marked periodicity of 233 days. It is also a spectroscopic and eclipsing binary 293.8 days.

κ **Gem** (07ʰ44ᵐ.4, +24°24'): a long-period binary (mags 3.7, 8.2; PA 240°, Sep. 7".2). The primary is a G8 giant, and the secondary is white.

λ **Gem** (07ʰ18ᵐ.1, +16°32'): a long-period binary (mags 3.6, 10.3; PA 320°, Sep. 1".2). The bright primary has a yellowish A7 dwarf spectrum and is also a spectroscopic and eclipsing binary. The secondary appears white and is shown with 100 mm aperture.

38 Gem (06ʰ54ᵐ.6, +13°11'): a long-period binary (mags. 4.7, 7.7; PA 145°, Sep. 7".1; spectra F0, G6). A fine pair even with small apertures.

M35 (NGC 2168: 06ʰ08ᵐ.9, +24°20'): a large open cluster (mag. 5.1, d = 2840 l.y.), visible to the naked eye, and with some stars resolved in binoculars, but most effective with slightly larger apertures.

NGC 2392 (07ʰ29ᵐ.2, +20°55'), the Eskimo Nebula: a bright planetary nebula, mag. 9.1. The central star is clearly visible.

> **Geminids** (radiant at 07ʰ32ᵐ, +33°): a fine meteor shower, rich in bright events and excellent for photography. Visible Dec. 7–16, with maximum in the early morning of Dec. 14 with a zenithal hourly rate of about 100. They are associated with the small minor planet 3200 Phaethon, which is probably the inert remnant of a former short-period comet.

Grus

GRUIS • Gru • THE CRANE

Main chart(s): 19 (14, 18, 20)
Area: 366 sq. deg. (45th)
Culminates 00:00 local time: late August

This is another of the constellations introduced by Pieter Keyser and Frederick de Houtman, and was first shown in Bayer's *Uranometria* atlas of 1603. It is fairly distant from the galactic plane so there are no open clusters, globular clusters, or diffuse nebulae. Although there are a number of galaxies, particularly towards the northeast and the border with Sculptor, none are brighter than mag. 10.

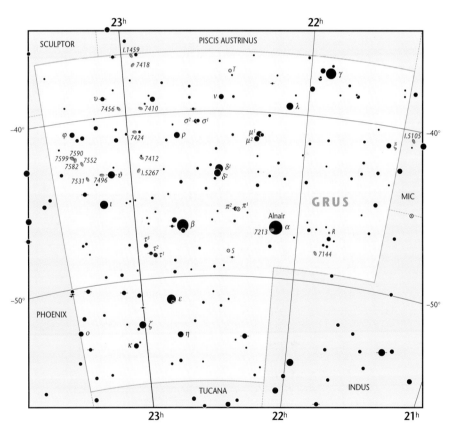

ϑ **Gru** (23ʰ06ᵐ.9, -43°31'): a probable binary of unknown period (mags. 4.5, 7.0; PA 75°, Sep. 1".1).

υ **Gru** (23ʰ06ᵐ.9, -38°54'): a binary system of unknown period. White components (mags. 5.7, 8.0; PA 211°, Sep. 1".1). Visible with 150 mm.

NGC 7213 (22ʰ09ᵐ.3, -47°10'): a bright (mag. 10.4) barred spiral galaxy (SBb), which may be seen with an aperture of 75 mm. However, α Gruis (Al Nair), mag. 1.7, is just 16' to the northwest, making observation difficult.

NGC 7552 (23ʰ16ᵐ.4, -42°33'): a barred spiral (SBb) galaxy, mag. 10.7. 100 mm reveals the nucleus and a faint hazy outline, 150 mm shows the elongated bar, which is the brightest part of the galaxy.

NGC 7582 (23ʰ18ᵐ.6, -42°20'): a barred spiral (SBb) galaxy, mag. 10.2. Two other galaxies appear in the same field: **NGC 7590**, mag. 11.5, and **NGC 7599**, mag. 11.4. All are visible with 100 mm.

π **Gru** (22ʰ22ᵐ.7, -45°56'): a wide optical double, consisting of an orange-red (S5 spectrum) semiregular variable (π¹ **Gru**), mag. 5.4–6.7, with a periodicity of approximately 150 days (d = 500 l.y.). This star is one of the brightest stars in the sky with this rare type of spectrum. The second star (π² **Gru**) is a blue-white (F0) subgiant, mag. 5.68, that is much closer (d ≈ 130 l.y.). It has a faint binary companion (mag. 11.3; PA 214°, Sep. 4".6), visible with 150 mm.

Hercules

HERCULIS • Her • (HERCULES)

Main chart(s): 6, 12 (5, 7, 11)
Area: 1225 sq. deg. (5th)
Culminates 00:00 local time: mid-June

Although Hercules lies outside the immediate vicinity of the Milky Way, its galaxies are all faint, even those in the Hercules Cluster (also known as Abell 2151). Three globular clusters are readily visible, including M13, the finest in the northern sky. The two planetary nebulae tend to be neglected, but there are numerous interesting doubles.

α Her (17ʰ14ᵐ.6, +14°23'), Ras Algethi: a red (M5Ib) supergiant semiregular variable, range mag. 2.7–4.0. Also a multiple system, where the B component is a bright giant (mag. 5.4; PA 106°, Sep. 4".6) and spectroscopic binary. The fourth component is a close companion to A, not visible with amateur equipment.

ζ Her (16ʰ41ᵐ.3, +31°36'): a binary system (d = 33 l.y.) with one G0 subgiant and one G7 dwarf component (mags. 2.9, 5.4; PA 12°, 0".8; P = 34.5 yrs). The stars were closest in 2001 and are now separating.

κ Her (16ʰ08ᵐ.1, +17°03'): a fairly close double, visible in binoculars, with yellow-orange components of mags. 5.3 and 6.5.

μ Her (17ʰ46ᵐ.5, +27°43'): a triple system (d = 29 l.y.) consisting of a yellow (G5) subgiant and red dwarf (M4) components. The AB pair is a slow binary (mags. 3.4, 10.1; PA 247°, Sep. 33".8). The BC pair (C mag. 10.0; PA 10.5°, Sep. 0".5–1".6; P = 43.2 yrs) was closest in 2001.

ρ Her (17ʰ23ᵐ.7, +37°09'): a multiple system with visible B9.5 giant and A0 dwarf stars (mags. 4.6, 5.6; PA 316°, Sep. 4".1). The primary is also a very close binary system.

68 Her (u Her: 17ʰ17ᵐ.3, +33°06'): an eclipsing binary that shows continuous changes in brightness, range mag. 4.7–5.4, P = 2.05 days.

AC Her (18ʰ30ᵐ.3, +21°52'): an interesting semiregular variable of the RV Tauri type, with alternating deep and shallow minima. Its range is mag. 6.6–9.1, and the period (deep minimum to deep minimum) is 75 days.

X Her (16ʰ02ᵐ, +47°14'): a semiregular variable (mag. 5.5–7.7), with a deep red (M6) spectrum. It shows intervals with a poorly expressed periodicity of about 95 days, interspersed with slow, irregular variations.

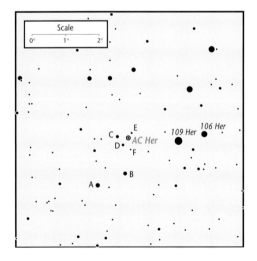

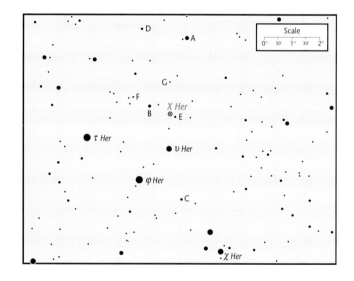

Comparisons for AC Her:

A	6.4	D	7.4
B	6.5	E	8.1
C	7.0	F	8.6

Comparisons for X Her:

A	5.9	E	7.4
B	6.6	F	7.6
C	6.9	G	8.0
D	7.0		

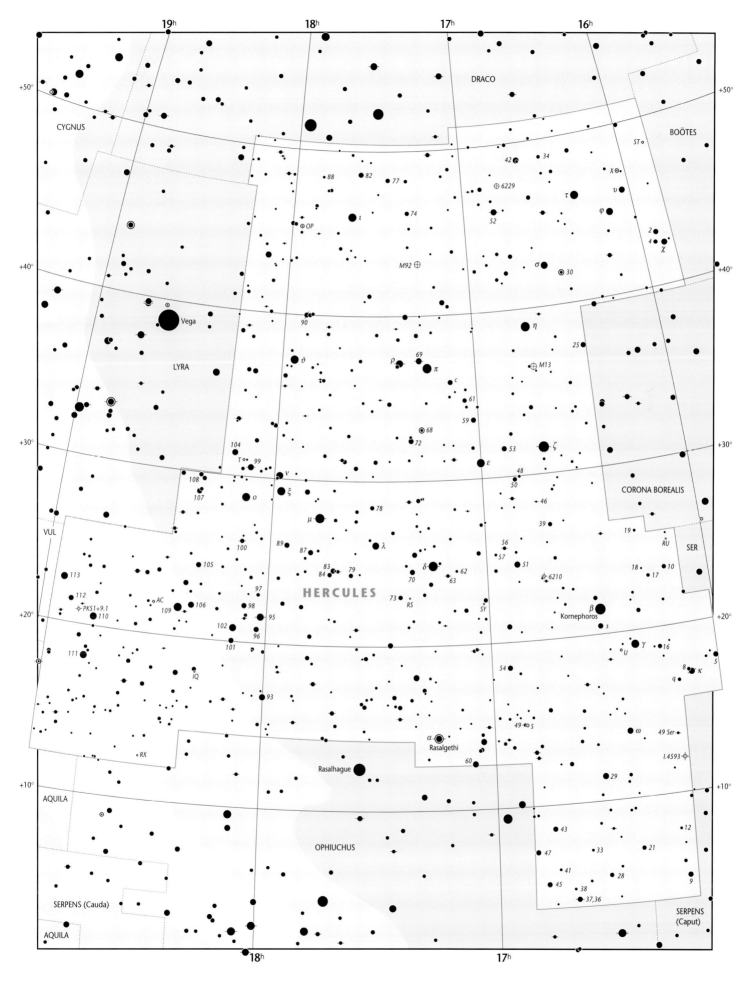

Horologium

HOROLOGII • Hor • THE (PENDULUM) CLOCK

Main chart(s): 14 (15, 20)
Area: 249 sq. deg. (58th)
Culminates 00:00 local time: late November

An extremely inconspicuous constellation introduced by de La Caille in 1752. The brightest star is α Hor, mag. 3.8. There are neither open clusters nor diffuse nebulae, and few double stars. One globular, NGC 1261, is fairly bright, but the other, AM1, is about mag. 15. This is the most distant globular cluster known in the Galaxy, at 120,000 pc (≈ 390,000 l.y.).

NGC 1261 (03h12m.3, -55°13'): a strongly condensed globular cluster, mag. 8.4, d = 16,000 pc (≈ 52,000 l.y.). Visible in 75 mm, begins to be resolved with 200 mm, and fully resolved with 300 mm.

NGC 1433 (03h42m.0, -47°13'): a barred spiral (SBa) galaxy, mag. 10.0. Only the nucleus is visible in 100 mm.

NGC 1512 (04h03m.9, -43°21'): a barred spiral (SBa) galaxy, mag. 10.6. Just visible with 100 mm, and really requires 300 mm. Interacting with NGC 1510, 5' to the southwest.

NGC 1448 (03h44m.5, -44°39'): an edgewise spiral (Sc) galaxy. Sources differ regarding its magnitude, quoted as mag. 10.8 and 11.3. The elongated nature of the galaxy is detectable with 150 mm aperture, but really requires a larger telescope.

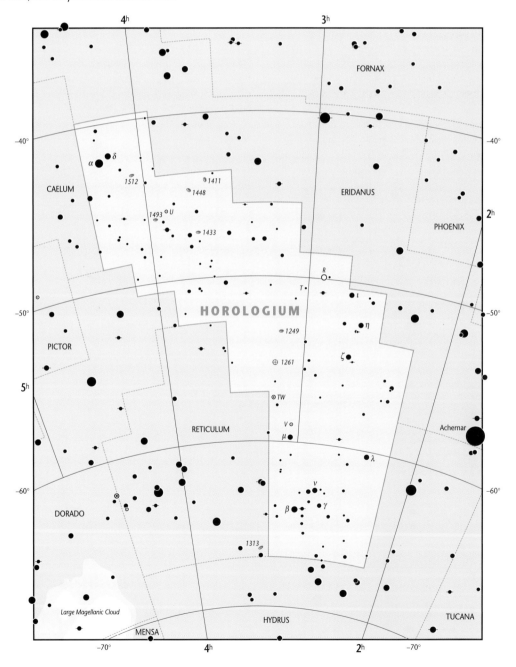

Hydra

HYDRAE • Hya • (HYDRA)

Main chart(s): 10, 16, 17 (11)
Area: 1303 sq. deg. (1st)
Alphard (α Hya) culminates 00:00 local time: early February

This ancient constellation is the largest and longest in the sky, covering seven hours of right ascension. It largely consists of faint stars, and the only conspicuous portion is in the west – with the head, an asterism of six stars, actually at very different distances (from 135 to 466 l.y.) – and α Hya (Alphard). There are many galaxies, including the Hydra 1 Cluster, although none are particularly bright. There are also numerous double stars, only a few of which are included here.

ε **Hya** (08ʰ46ᵐ.8, +06°25'), the northernmost star of the 'head' of Hydra: a quintuple system, where the A and B components (mags. 3.4, 4.7; P = 15.1 yrs; G5 giant and A9 subgiant spectra) are not readily distinguished even at maximum separation of 0".27. They are currently closing. The AC pair are obvious (mags. 3.4, 7.8; PA 289°, Sep. 2".0), with C being an F7 dwarf spectroscopic binary (P = 9.90 days). A fifth component (mag. 12.7; PA 196°, Sep. 19") is also part of the system.

27 Hya (09ʰ20ᵐ.5, -09°33'), near α Hya (Alphard): a wide double with yellowish and white components (mags. 5.0, 6.9; PA 211°, Sep. 229".4), easily detectable in binoculars, with a further fainter component (mag. 9.1; PA BC 198°, Sep. 9".3).

54 Hya (14ʰ46ᵐ.0, -25°27'): a possible binary (mags. 5.1, 7.1; PA 126°, Sep. 8".6; F0, G1 spectra), readily visible with small apertures.

59 Hya (14ʰ58ᵐ.7, -27°39'): a binary system with two white components (mags. 6.3, 6.6; PA 80°, Sep. 0".3; P = 339.6 yrs; A4, A6 spectra). Requires about 250 mm to be resolved.

R Hya (13ʰ29ᵐ.7, -23°17'): a red giant and long-period variable, range mag. 3.5–10.9 at minimum, P = 389 days. The colour is extremely noticeable at maximum. There is a nearby star (mag. 12.0; PA 324°, Sep. 21"), but it is not known whether they form a binary system.

U Hya (10ʰ37ᵐ.6, -13°23'): an interesting semiregular variable, with a deep red (C5) spectrum. Range mag. 4.7–5.2, periodicity 450 days, and other intervals of more irregular activity.

M48 (NGC 2548: 08ʰ13ᵐ.8, -05°47'): a very large open cluster (about 30' across), just visible to the naked eye and a fine object in binoculars. Rather difficult to locate in a sparsely populated region.

M68 (NGC 4590: 12ʰ39ᵐ.5, -26°45'): an 8th-magnitude globular cluster, detectable in binoculars. Large apertures reveal an uneven core and faint halo.

M83 (NGC 5236: 13ʰ37ᵐ.0, -29°52'): a face-on spiral (Sc) galaxy, easily seen in binoculars (mag. 8.2).

NGC 2784 (09ʰ12ᵐ.3, -24°10'): a lenticular (S0) galaxy, mag. 10.1, only the elliptical centre of which is visible with 150 mm. Faint extensions may become visible with a larger aperture.

NGC 3242 (10ʰ24ᵐ.8, -18°39'), Ghost of Jupiter: a planetary nebula, d ≈ 1960 l.y., named from its resemblance to the planet. Detectable at low magnifications with just 50 mm, but about 300 mm required to show detail.

NGC 3109 (10ʰ03ᵐ.1, -26°09'): an edge-on irregular (Irr) galaxy, mag. 10.4. Its general shape is apparent even with just 150 mm aperture, but becomes distinct with 300 mm, when a 12th-magnitude foreground star may be seen near its centre. It lies just outside the Local Group of galaxies at a distance of approximately 1.3 Mpc (≈ 4,240,000 l.y.).

NGC 3309 (10ʰ36ᵐ.6, -27°31') and **NGC 3311** (10ʰ36.7ᵐ, -27°32'): two giant elliptical (E0) galaxies that actually share a common envelope, although this is not visible with amateur equipment. There are two other galaxies in the same field: **NGC 3308** (10ʰ36ᵐ.4, -27°26'), 6' northwest (S0), and **NGC 3312** (10ʰ37ᵐ.0, -27°34'), 7' southeast (Sb). All are members of the Hydra 1 Cluster (Abell 1060) and fairly faint (mags. 11–12), but visible with 150 mm.

NGC 3621 (11ʰ18ᵐ.3, -32°49'): a spiral (Sc) galaxy, mag. 9.9, elliptical central region easily visible, although rather faint, with 75 mm.

NGC 5061 (13ʰ18ᵐ.1, -26°50'): an elliptical (E2) galaxy, mag. 10.2. The nucleus is clearly visible with apertures of 100 mm and more. Some sources erroneously state that it is a spiral galaxy. About 2.5' to the east is β 246, a close binary (mags 9.1, 9.3; PA 129°, Sep. 0".63), requiring at least 250 mm to be resolved.

NGC 5694 (14ʰ39ᵐ.6, -26°31'): a distant, but relatively bright, globular cluster: mag. 10.2. It appears as a hazy patch with 100 mm, but requires a much larger aperture (300 mm or more) for it to start to be resolved. Its distance is approximately 37.4 kpc (≈ 122,000 l.y.).

CONSTELLATIONS

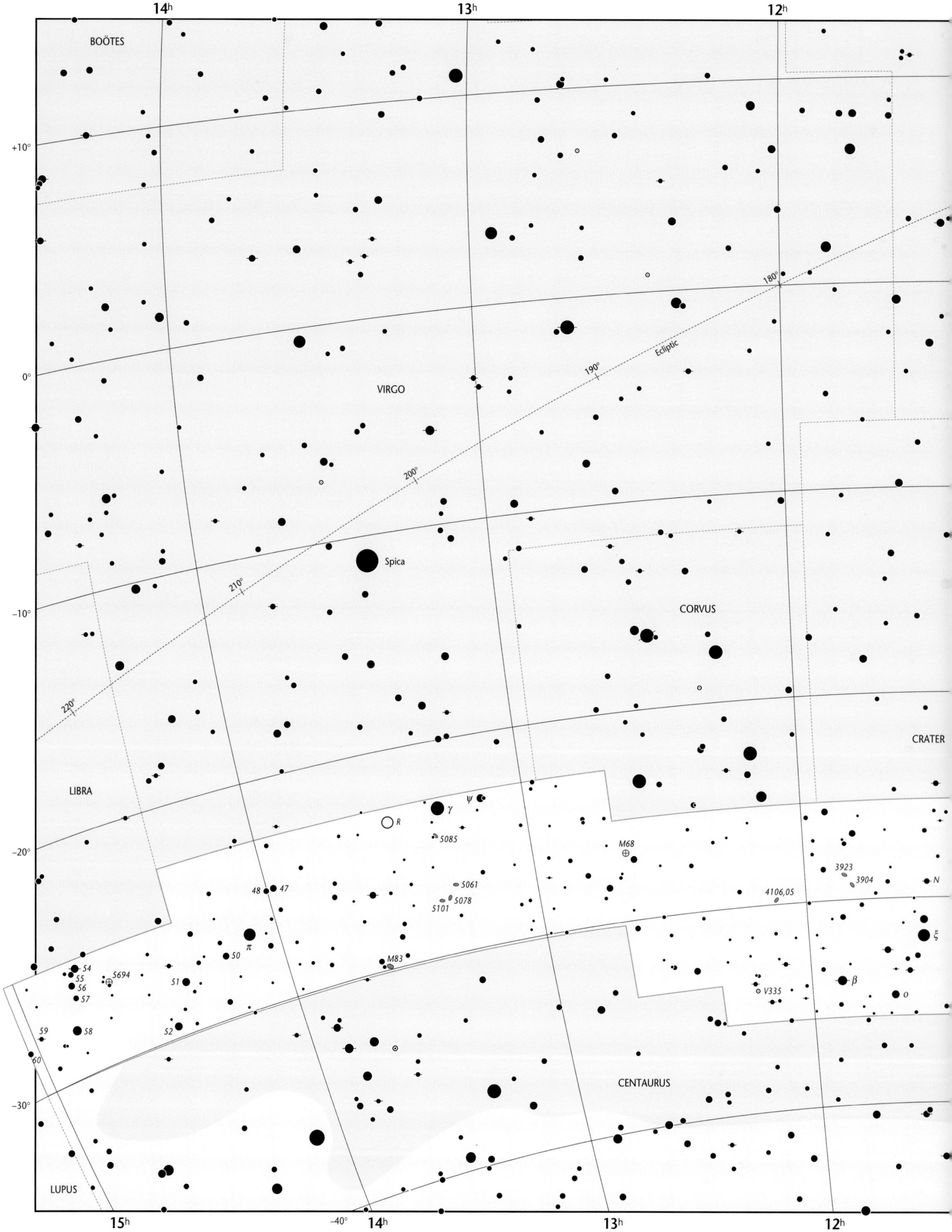

14h

13h

12h

12h

BOÖTES

+10°

0°

180°

Ecliptic

190°

VIRGO

200°

Spica

210°

−10°

CORVUS

220°

CRATER

LIBRA

ψ

γ

R

5085

M68

−20°

3923

3904

48 47

5061

4106,05

N

5078

5101

ξ

π

50

M83

β

54

55 5694

51

V335

o

56

57

59 58

52

60

CENTAURUS

−30°

LUPUS

15h

−40° 14h

13h

12h

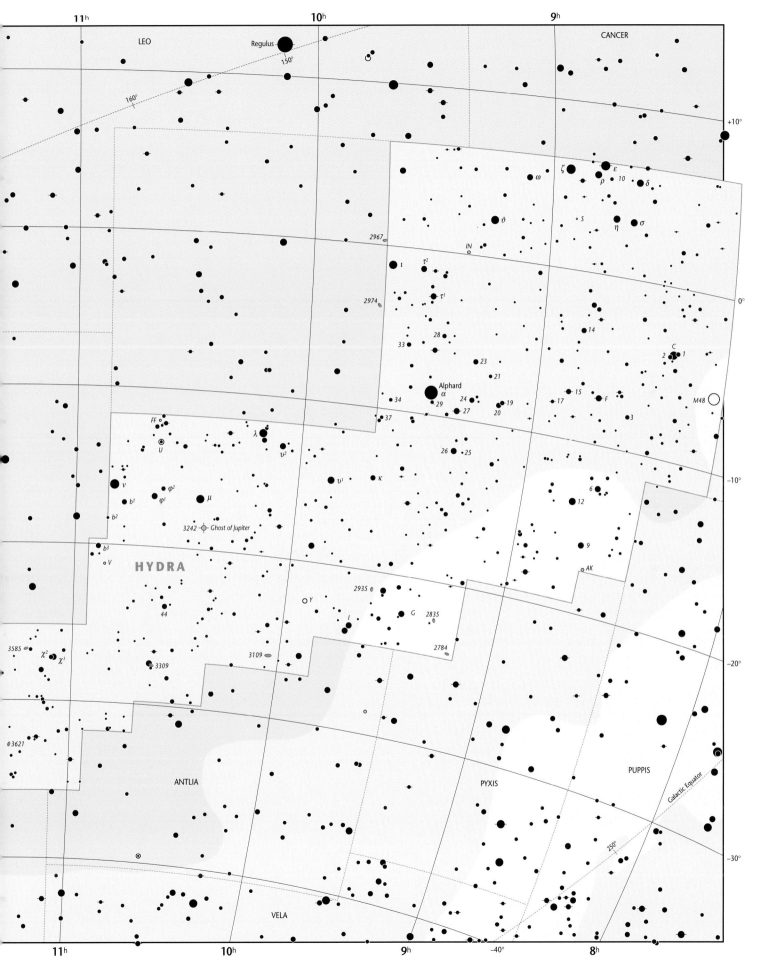

Hydrus
HYDRI • Hyi • THE WATER SERPENT

Main chart(s): 20 (15, 19)
Area: 243 sq. deg. (61st)
Culminates 00:00 local time: late October

This small constellation (another of those introduced by Pieter Keyser and Frederick de Houtman) is in a rather barren area of sky and contains few objects of interest. There are a few galaxies, but these are all faint. Two doubles discovered by John Herschel (whose catalogue is identified by the letter 'h') are given. To variable-star observers, the constellation is known for VW Hydri, an interesting cataclysmic variable.

VW Hyi (04^h09^m.1, -71°18'): a relatively bright U Geminorum star (dwarf nova), which has outbursts of a few magnitudes with a mean period of 27.3 days, but 'supermaxima' that are brighter than normal. The latter have a mean period of 179 days. The orbital light-curve (P = 0.0742711 day ≈ 1 hr 46 min.) displays a 'hump', the period of which changes during supermaxima. The period of 'superhumps' is then 0.0769 day (≈ 1 hr 51 min). The star's extreme range is mag. 8.4–14.4.

BM Hyi (03^h07^m.4, -78°58'): a binary system (mags. 5.7, 9.3; PA 226°, Sep. 15".2). Previously thought to be a low-amplitude variable of the δ Scuti (DSCT) type, and given a variable-star identification. It is now believed that the variability arises from its binary nature.

η 3475 (01^h55^m.3, -60°19'): a probable binary system with yellow stars (mags. 7.2, 7.3; PA 71°, Sep. 2".3; F1, F2 spectra). An easy object for small apertures.

η 3568 (03^h07^m.5, -78°59'): a suspected long-period binary, containing a yellow (F0) giant and a white companion (mags. 5.7, 7.8; PA 222°.5, Sep. 15".2).

NGC 602 (012^h9^m.6, -73°34'): a small cluster and associated emission nebulosity, easily visible with 150 mm. Thought to be outlying nebulosity of the Small Magellanic Cloud.

Indus
INDI • Ind • THE INDIAN

Main chart(s): 19, 20 (18)
Area: 294 sq. deg. (68th)
Culminates 00:00 local time: late February, early March

Yet another of the faint southern constellations introduced by Pieter Keyser and Frederick de Houtman. Its brightest star (α Ind) is an orange giant, mag. 3.1.

ε Ind (22^h03^m37s, -56°46'04"): an orange (K5) dwarf, mag. 4.7, and one of the closest stars to the Sun (d = 11.8 l.y.). Infrared observations have recently shown that it is accompanied by a remarkable pair of faint, low-temperature, brown dwarf stars. These stars (ε Indi Ba and ε Indi Bb), of spectral class T, form a true binary system, with a separation of approximately 12 AU, and an orbital period of about 10 years. Their magnitudes are 16.9 and 18.4, and their temperatures about 1240 K and 850 K, respectively.

ϑ Ind (21^h19^m.9, -53°27'): a binary system consisting of two dwarf stars (mags. 4.5, 7.0; PA 275°, Sep. 6"; A5, G0 spectra).

T Ind (21^h20^m.2, -45°01'): a deep red, semiregular variable, range mag. 5.5–6.5, P = 320: days, with a carbon (C7) spectrum.

NGC 7049 (21^h19^m.0, -48°34'): a lenticular (S0) galaxy, mag. 10.7, which appears as an elliptical patch in 150 mm and requires larger apertures.

NGC 7090 (21^h36^m.5, -54°33'): a barred spiral (SBc) galaxy, mag. 10.7, that appears as a faint streak with 150 mm, but is much better shown with 200 mm or larger.

NGC 7205 (22^h08^m.5, -57°25'): a spiral (Sb) galaxy, mag. 11.1. Faintly visible with 150 mm, but its shape becomes apparent only with 200 mm.

IC 5152 (22^h02^m.9, -51°17'): a dwarf irregular galaxy, mag. 10.6. A nearby star (mag. 8.0:) may mask the light from the galaxy.

Lacerta
LACERTAE • Lac • THE LIZARD

Main chart(s): 7 (1, 2, 6)
Area: 201 sq. deg. (68th)
Culminates 00:00 local time: late August

This small constellation was introduced in 1687, like Canes Venatici, by Johannes Hevelius. It consists of a zig-zag of moderately faint stars lying between Cygnus and Andromeda. The northern portion of the constellation lies in the Milky Way, so the constellation has a number of open clusters, but there are no emission nebulae or globular clusters. None of the eight planetary nebulae is brighter than mag. 11.

8 Lac (22^h35^m.9, +39°38'): a complex multiple system (d = 640 l.y.), believed to have no fewer than 7 components. The principal pair (AB) consists of two white stars (mags 5.7, 6.5; PA 186°, Sep. 22".4) and may be resolved with binoculars under good conditions. Three more

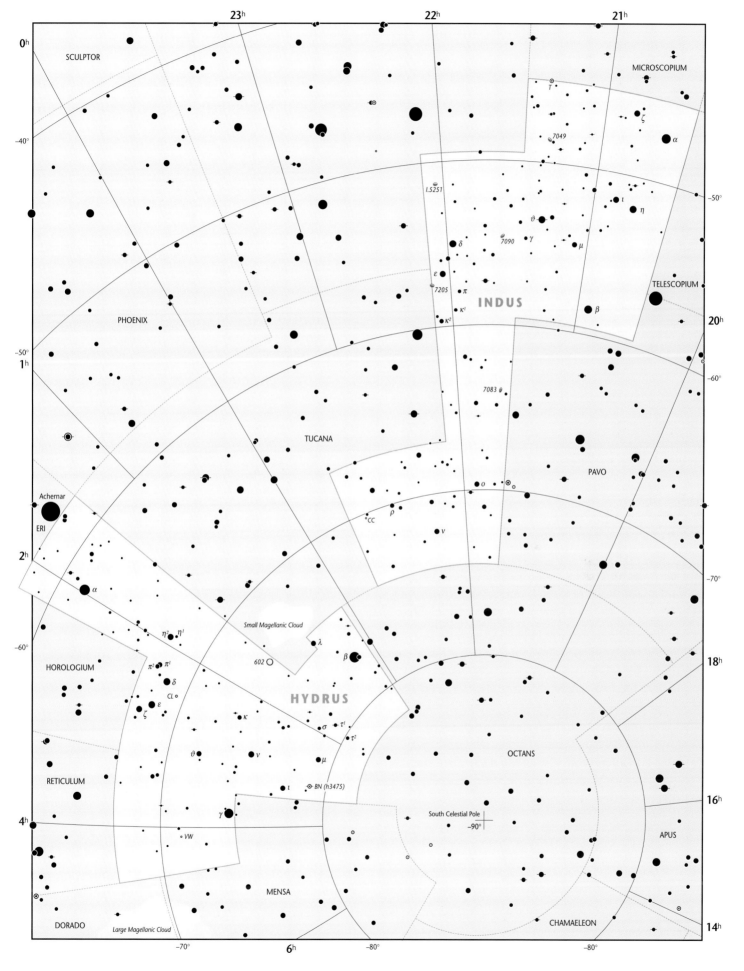

23ʰ 22ʰ 21ʰ

0ʰ

SCULPTOR

MICROSCOPIUM

−40°

T

ζ

I.5251

7049

ι

α

ϑ

η

δ

7090

γ

μ

ε

7205

π

PHOENIX

κ¹

INDUS

κ²

TELESCOPIUM

β

−50°

20ʰ

1ʰ

−60°

7083

TUCANA

PAVO

−50°

o

ρ

CC

ν

Achernar

2ʰ

ERI

−70°

α

Small Magellanic Cloud

η²   η¹

HOROLOGIUM

π²   π¹

602

λ

−60°

δ

β

CL

HYDRUS

18ʰ

ε

ζ

κ

σ   τ¹

τ²

ϑ

ν

OCTANS

μ

RETICULUM

ι

BN (h3475)

16ʰ

γ

South Celestial Pole

−90°

APUS

4ʰ

VW

MENSA

CHAMAELEON

14ʰ

DORADO   Large Magellanic Cloud

−70°   6ʰ   −80°   −80°

components are visible in small instruments: C (mag. 10.5; PA AC 169°, Sep. 48".8); D (mag. 9.3; PA AD 144°, Sep. 81".8); and E (mag. 7.8; PA AE 239°, Sep. 336".6). The two faint possible components are identified as R (mag. 14.6; PA CR 255°, Sep. 1".4) and S (mag. 13.3; PA DS 226°, Sep. 9".5).

AR Lac (22^{h}08^m.7, +45°45'): an eclipsing binary (EA), range mag. 6.1–6.8 (and thus always readily seen with binoculars), P = 1.98 days.

Σ 2894 (22^{h}18^m.9, +37°46'): a wide probable binary, with yellow and red stars (mags. 6.1, 8.3; PA 193°, Sep. 15".6).

Σ 2906 (22^{h}26^m.8, +37°27'): an unequal, and poorly known pair (mags. 6.5, 10.1; PA 1°, Sep. 4".4) with white stars, and which may be a true binary. Visible with 100 mm.

Σ 2942 (22^{h}44^m.1, +39°28'): a long-period binary (mags. 6.1, 8.3; PA 279°, Sep. 2".8; K4 and K1 giant spectra). Visible with 75 mm.

NGC 7209 (22^{h}05^m.2, +46°30'): an irregular, sparsely populated, open cluster (mag. 6.7, d ≈ 2940 l.y.). Binoculars show just a few stars against an apparently nebulous background.

NGC 7243 (22^{h}15^m.3, +49°53'): an irregularly shaped, sparse open cluster (mag. 6.4, d ≈ 3300 l.y.), visible in binoculars.

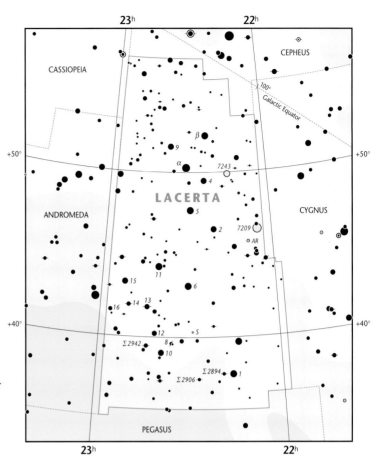

Leo

LEONIS • Leo • THE LION

Main chart(s): 10 (4, 5, 11)
Area: 947 sq. deg. (12th)
Culminates 00:00 local time: late February, early March

Leo lies away from the galactic plane and does not contain any globular or open clusters, nor diffuse nebulae. There are, however, many galaxies, including two of the dwarf spheroidal satellites of the Milky Way, Leo I and Leo II. The constellation also contains the radiant for the Leonids, a major meteor shower. Although too faint to be shown here, it also contains at a distance of 7.8 l.y., the fourth nearest star or system to the Sun (after Proxima Centauri, the A and B components of α Centauri, and Barnard's Star in Ophiuchus). This is CN Leo, also known as Wolf 359, an M6 dwarf flare star (UV Ceti type) like Proxima Centauri.

α Leo (10^{h}08^m.4, +11°58'), Regulus: a blue-white (B7) star, mag. 1.4, that forms a wide double with an orange (K1) mag. 7.7 companion (PA 307°, Sep. 176".9), easily detectable with 75 mm.

γ Leo (10^{h}20^m.0, +19°51'), Algiebra: a multiple system. The principal pair is a binary consisting of orange (K1), and yellow (G7) giants (mags. 2.2, 3.5; PA 125°, Sep. 4".4; P = 618.6 yrs), visible with small apertures. There are two very wide, fainter components: C (mag. 9.2; PA AC 291°, Sep. 259".9) and D (mag. 9.6; PA AD 302°, Sep. 333".0).

ω Leo (09^{h}28^m.5, +09°03'): a close binary (mags. 5.9, 6.5; PA 84°, Sep. 0".6; P = 118.2 yrs).

R Leo (09^{h}47^m.6, +11°26'): a long-period variable of the Mira type. It rises to mag. 5.9 at normal maxima, but may occasionally become much brighter, reaching as much as mag. 4.4, when it appears strongly red (M8 giant spectrum). Minimum generally about mag. 10, but may go even lower. Its period is 310 days.

Leo I (U5470: 10^{h}08^m.4, +12°18'): a dwarf spheroidal galaxy (classified as dE3), with a nominal magnitude of 9.8, but with low surface brightness. This galaxy lies 20' north of α Leonis (Regulus) and is visible only if the extremely bright star is excluded from the field. At least 200 mm is required for the galaxy to be seen.

M65 (NGC 3623: 11^{h}18^m.9, +13°05'): an edgewise spiral (Sb) galaxy (mag. 9.3), just detectable in large binoculars under good conditions.

M66 (NGC 3627: 11^{h}20^m.2, +12°59'): another spiral (Sb) galaxy, slightly easier to detect than M65.

M95 (NGC 3351: 10^{h}44^m.0, +11°42'): a barred spiral (SBb) galaxy, mag. 9.7, just visible with 100 mm. Details of the nucleus and outer regions need 300 mm. M95, M96, M105, and NGC 3384 are the brightest members of a small group of galaxies about 10 Mpc (≈ 33 million l.y.) distant.

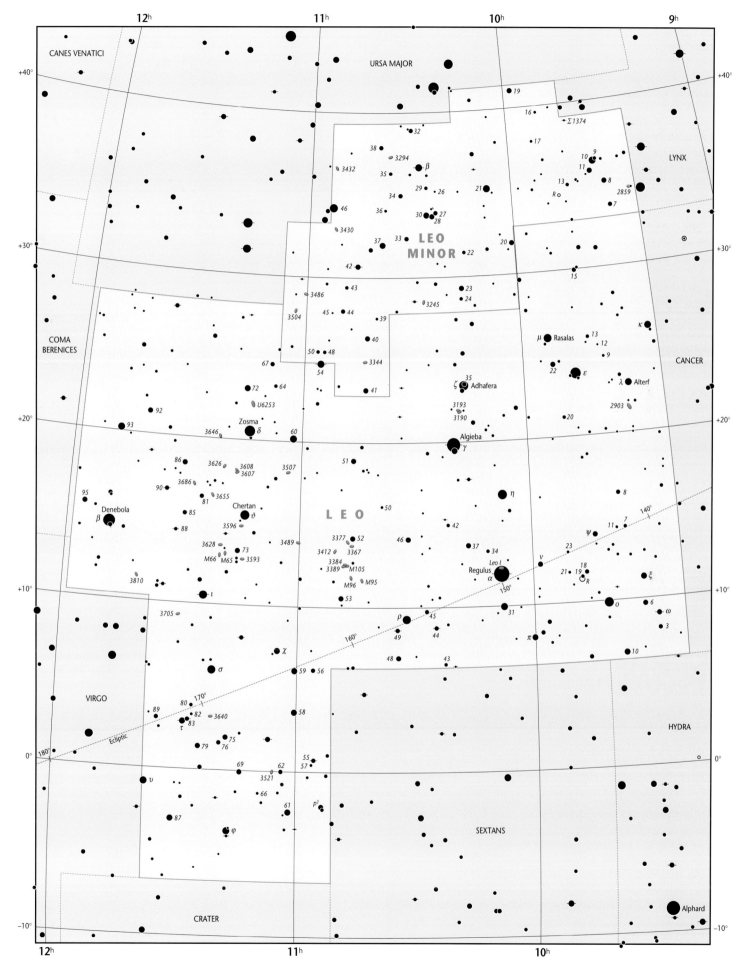

M96 (NGC 3368: $10^h46^m.8$, $+11°49'$): a spiral (Sb) galaxy, mag. 9.2, visible with 75 mm. The inner regions become clear with larger apertures.

M105 (NGC 3379: $10^h47^m.8$, $+12°35'$): an elliptical (E1) galaxy, mag. 9.3, clearly visible with 75 mm, as is **NGC 3384** ($10^h48^m.3$, $+12°38'$) about 7' to the northeast. This is also an elliptical galaxy, but the type (E7) with the greatest flattening. It has a magnitude of 10.0. About 10' southeast of M105 is **NGC 3389** ($10^h48^m.5$, $+12°32'$): a fainter spiral (Sc) galaxy, requiring an aperture of at least 150 mm.

NGC 2903 ($09^h32^m.2$, $+21°30'$): a bright spiral (Sb) galaxy, mag. 8.9, d ≈ 7 Mpc (≈ 22.8 million l.y.), visible with just 75 mm. Its elongation is visible with any optical aid, but it, and the off-centred nucleus, require about 300 mm to be clearly seen.

NGC 3521 ($11^h05^m.8$, $-00°02'$): another spiral (Sb) galaxy, mag. 8.9, d = 9 Mpc (≈ 29.4 million l.y.), easily seen with 75 mm.

Leonids (radiant at 10^h08^m, $+22°$): a fascinating meteor shower. The stream of particles is associated with Comet Tempel-Tuttle and tends to give exceptionally high rates at intervals of 33 years, the period of the parent comet. Major displays occurred in the years around 1999, the predicted date of return. That year the maximum hourly rate reached about 2500–3000, much lower than the extreme rate observed in 1966, which was estimated at a phenomenal 100,000 per hour. Generally, the hourly rate is approximately 100. The meteors are fast and tend to leave persistent trains. The shower is visible over the period Nov. 15–20, with maximum on Nov. 17.

Leo Minor
LEO MINORIS • Lmi • THE LITTLE LION

Main chart(s): 4 (5)
Area: 232 sq. deg. (64th)
Culminates 00:00 local time: late February

This small constellation was another that was introduced by Hevelius in 1687. It is extremely inconspicuous, and contains few objects of interest. Because of an error when the stars were given designations, α was omitted, so the brightest star is actually 46 LMi (mag. 3.8), and the second brightest is β (mag. 4.2). There are three galaxies and two double stars that are perhaps worthy of study.

β **LMi** ($10^h27^m.9$, $+36°42'$): a very close binary (mags. 4.4, 6.1; PA 240°, Sep. 0".2; P = 37 yrs). This system changes rapidly and is difficult to resolve.

Σ **1374** ($09^h41^m.4$, $+38°57'$): a binary system with yellow and white stars (mags. 7.3, 8.6; PA 304°, Sep. 3".0). Easily detectable with 75 mm.

NGC 3245 ($10^h27^m.3$, $+28°30'$): a moderately flattened (E5) elliptical galaxy, mag. 10.8. Just detectable with 100 mm under excellent conditions, but really requires at least 300 mm to show the extended envelope.

NGC 3344 ($10^h45^m.5$, $+24°55'$): a spiral (Sc) galaxy, integrated magnitude 10.0. Because of its structure, at least 100 mm, and preferably a larger aperture, is required for it to be detected.

NGC 3486 ($11^h00^m.4$, $+28°58'$): another spiral (Sc) galaxy, integrated magnitude 10.3. This galaxy also requires at least 150 mm aperture to be detectable.

Lepus
LEPORIS • Lep • THE HARE

Main chart(s): 9 (15)
Area: 290 sq. deg. (51st)
Culminates 00:00 local time: mid-December

This constellation, due south of Orion, tends to be overlooked by many amateurs, who concentrate on its brilliant neighbour. It does, however, contain some interesting objects. The name Arneb for the brightest star, α Leporis (an F0 bright supergiant), is Arabic for 'the hare'.

β **Lep** ($05^h28^m.2$, $-20°46'$): an unequal binary (mags. 2.8, 7.3; PA 346°, Sep. 2".3). The difference in magnitude means that this system requires good conditions, when it is visible with 150 mm.

γ **Lep** ($05^h44^m.5$, $-22°27'$): a wide binary, consisting of two yellow stars (mags. 3.7, 6.3; PA 350°, Sep. 97"; spectra F6, K2), readily visible in binoculars.

κ **Lep** ($05^h13^m.2$, $-12°57'$): a binary with an extremely long period (mags. 4.5, 7.4; PA 357°, Sep. 2".3). Both stars appear white, and the primary has a B9 dwarf spectrum. Clearly visible with an aperture of 75 mm.

R Lep ($04^h59^m.6$, $-14°48'$), Hind's Crimson Star: a long-period (Mira-type) variable, range mag. 5.5–11.7, P = 427 days, temperature ≈ 3000 K. At maximum, when it is just visible to the naked eye, it appears intensely red when viewed with any optical aid. John Russell Hind described it as 'intense smoky red' and it has also been likened to 'a drop of blood on a black field'.

M79 (NGC 1904, $05^h24^m.5$, $-24°31'$): a globular cluster that may be detected in binoculars under favourable conditions. The outermost stars are visible with 100 mm, and larger apertures will resolve stars at its centre. Its distance is about 13 kpc (≈ 42,400 l.y.).

NGC 2017 (05ʰ39ᵐ.4, -17°51'): a group of stars, six visible with 75 mm, of differing colours. These may appear to form an open cluster, but are actually at differing distances. The bluish star towards the southeast is a double (mags. 8.5, 9.2; PA 357°, Sep. 1".5). The brightest star is a binary (β 321: mags. 6.4, 7.9; PA 156°, Sep. 0".6), requiring at least 250 mm to be resolved.

IC 418 (05ʰ27ᵐ.5, -12°42'): a bright, bluish planetary nebula, mag. 9.3. The central star is mag. 10.6, and is visible with 75 mm.

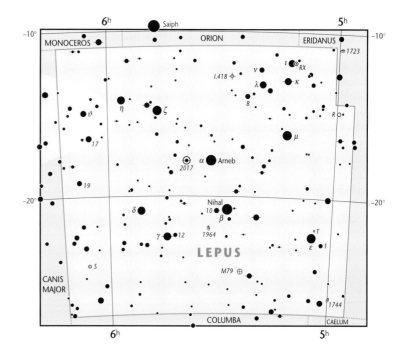

Libra
LIBRAE • Lib • THE SCALES

Main chart(s): 11 (17)
Area: 538 sq. deg. (29th)
Culminates 00:00 local time: early May

Despite its size, none of the stars in this constellation are brighter than third magnitude. Most of its area lies outside the Milky Way, so there are no open clusters or emission nebulae. There is one reasonably bright globular cluster and one planetary nebula, catalogued by Merrill (Me 2-1), but the few galaxies are all faint.

At one time the autumnal equinox lay in this constellation, which was one reason for it to be associated with a balance (between summer and winter). Although precession caused the equinox to move into Virgo in the 8th century BC, by analogy with the First Point of Aries, the autumnal equinox is occasionally known as the First Point of Libra.

α **Lib** (14ʰ50ᵐ.9, -16°03'), Zubenelgenubi: a wide double star: α², α¹ (mags 2.7, 5.2; PA 314°, Sep. 231".0; spectra A3, F3).

δ **Lib** (15ʰ01ᵐ.1, -08°31'): an Algol-type (EA) eclipsing variable, range mag. 4.9–5.9, P = 2.327 days.

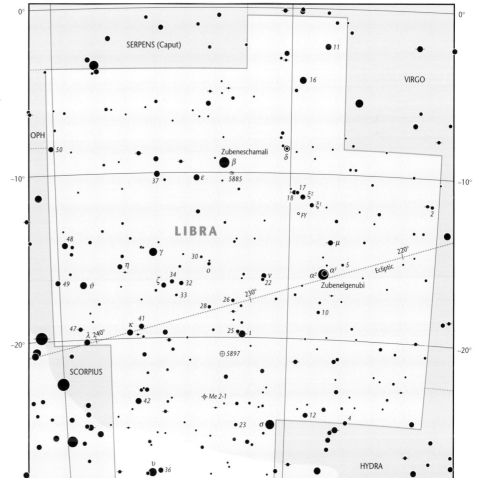

CONSTELLATIONS

ι **Lib** (15^{h}12^m.2, -19°47'): mag. 4.5, forms a wide binocular double with 25 Lib, mag. 6.1. The pair are sometimes known as ι¹ and ι² Librae. ι¹ Lib (brighter) is actually a multiple star, with component B (PA AB 106°, Sep. 60") appearing as mag. 9.4, but actually consisting of an equal pair (mags. 10.6, 10.6; PA 15°, Sep. 1".9), which are difficult to resolve with less than 150 mm. Component A is a very close binary (P = 23.4 yrs), which cannot be resolved. There is spectroscopic evidence for another star in this system, meaning that ι¹ Lib may be quintuple.

Lupus

LUPI • Lup • WOLF

Main chart(s): 17, 18
Area: 334 sq. deg. (46th)
Culminates 00:00 local time: early May

Lupus lies in the Milky Way, nearly reaching the galactic equator. The region is heavily obscured by dust, so there are not as many striking 'deep sky' objects as its position might lead one to expect. All the galaxies are faint, and although there are a few open clusters, just one is readily visible, together with three globular clusters. In compensation, there are some interesting double stars.

γ **Lup** (13^{h}35^m.1, -41°10'): a binary system consisting of two white (B2) subgiants (mags. 3.5, 3.6; PA 282°, Sep. 0".74; P ≈ 190 yrs). Gives an elongated image in most amateur-sized equipment, but maximum separation will occur in 2014.

κ **Lup** (15^{h}11^m.9, -48°44'): an extremely long-period binary (mags. 3.9, 5.8; PA 144°, Sep. 26".8). The actual period is unknown, because the system has shown no change since discovery. The yellow components have identical proper motions, suggesting they are a true binary.

μ **Lup** (15^{h}18^m.5, -47°53'): a triple system, where AB (mags. 5.1, 5.2; PA 142°, Sep.1".2) is just resolved with 150 mm. For the more distant component, we have (mag. 7.2; PA AC 130°, Sep. 23".7).

π **Lup** (15^{h}05^m.1, -47°03'): a binary, or possibly multiple system (mags. 4.6, 4.7; PA 73°, Sep. 1".4). There are indications that both components may be spectroscopic binaries.

ξ **Lup** (15^{h}56^m.9, -33°58'): a suspected binary system (mags. 5.3, 5.8; PA 49°, Sep. 10".4; A2.5 and A1 spectra). Common proper motion suggests that they are gravitationally bound, even though no orbital motion has been evident since discovery in 1837.

CG Lup (15^{h}32^m.2, -23°53'): a bright β Lyrae-type (EB) eclipsing binary, range mag. 5.5–6.0; P = 2.164175 days.

Barnard 228 (15^{h}45^m.5, -34°24'): a dark nebula, readily visible in binoculars, lying between ψ and χ Lupi.

NGC 5822 (15^{h}05^m.2, -54°21'): a large open cluster, integrated mag. 6.5, at a distance of approx. 760 pc (2480 l.y.). Because of its size (about 40' across), it requires a wide field.

NGC 5824 (15^{h}04^m.0, -33°04'): a very condensed globular cluster, mag. 9.0, easily visible with 75 mm, but begins to be resolved only with about 300 mm. Its distance is approx. 32 kpc (≈ 104,400 l.y.).

NGC 5897 (15^{h}17^m.4, -21°01'): a conspicuous but poorly condensed globular cluster, mag. 8.6. The cluster is not resolved with 100 mm, but shows some signs of granularity. It is resolved with 150 mm or more.

Me 2-1 (15^{h}22^m.3, -23°38'): a small but relatively bright planetary nebula, mag. 11.6. It appears as a point of light in 75 mm, about 1' east of a 10th-magnitude orange-yellow star. In larger apertures it appears as a tiny, bluish disk.

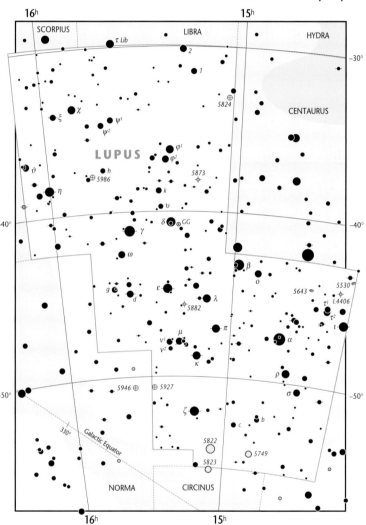

NGC 5882 (15^{h}16^m.8, -45°39'): a relative easy planetary nebula, mag. 10.5, visible even with 75 mm. As with many planetaries, it appears bluish when observed with a large aperture.

NGC 5927 (15^{h}28^m.0, -50°40'): a very rich globular cluster, mag. 8.3, d = 7.6 kpc (≈ 24,800 l.y.). Visible as a hazy object with 75 mm, its stars begin to be resolved with 150 mm.

NGC 5986 (15^{h}46^m.1, -37°47'): a compact globular cluster, mag. 7.1, d = 10.5 kpc (≈ 34,250 l.y.). Although, like NGC 5927, it appears hazy with small instruments, it is resolved with 150 mm.

Lynx

LYNCIS • Lyn • THE LYNX

Main chart(s): 3, 4
Area: 545 sq. deg. (28th)
Culminates 00:00 local time: late January

Another constellation that was introduced in 1687 by Johannes Hevelius to fill the large, relatively blank area between Ursa Major, Auriga, and Gemini. It is larger than Gemini, but poorly known, with the brightest star (α) only mag. 3.1. There are a few galaxies, none particularly bright or easy to study.

The original representations of constellations did not have rigid boundaries. When these were defined formally by the International Astronomical Union in 1930, some stars, previously given specific designations, were found to lie on the 'wrong' side of the boundaries. In this area, the stars 10 UMa and 41 Lyn are cases in point, because they now lie within Lynx and Ursa Major, respectively.

5 Lyn (06ʰ27ᵐ.2, +58°25'): a triple system. Binoculars reveal the AC pair (mags. 5.2, 8.1; PA 272°, Sep. 95".1), and a larger aperture will show the B component (mag. 9.8; PA AB 140°, 31".5).

38 Lyn (09ʰ18ᵐ.8, +36°48'): a bright, long-period binary (mags. 3.9, 6.6; PA 229°, Sep. 2".7; A3, A4 spectra). Readily visible with 75 mm. The fainter star is a spectroscopic binary.

NGC 2419 (07ʰ38ᵐ.1, +38°53'): an extremely distant globular cluster (mag. 10.4). It lies far out in intergalactic space at about 84.2 kpc (≈ 275,000 l.y.) from the galactic centre. Such clusters are sometimes known as 'intergalactic tramps'.

NGC 2683 (08ʰ52ᵐ.7, +33°25'): an edge-on spiral (Sb) galaxy, mag. 9.7, only just detectable with 150 mm.

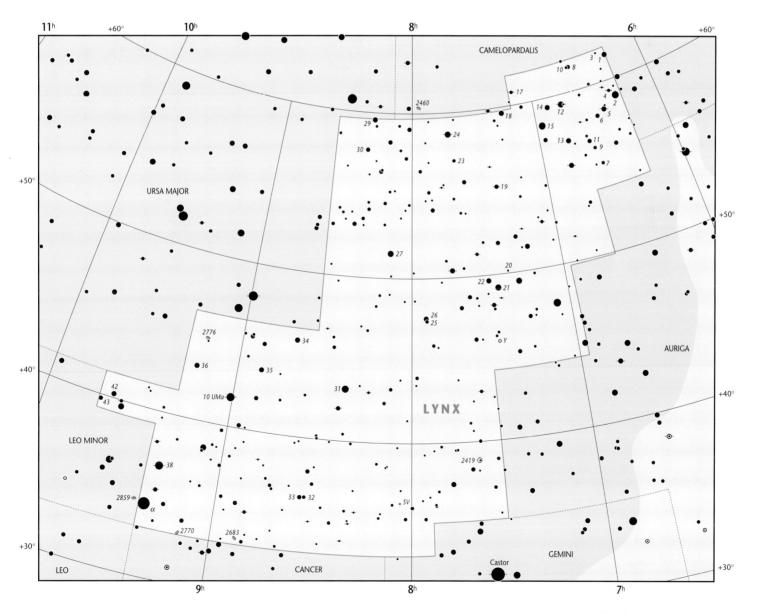

Lyra

LYRAE • Lyr • THE LYRE

Main chart(s): 6 (7)
Area: 286 sq. deg. (52nd)
Culminates 00:00 local time: early July

Although part of Lyra lies in the Milky Way, there is only one open cluster, Steph 1, close to β Lyr, and one globular cluster. There are a few galaxies, but all are too faint to be included on the main charts or here. There are, however, some interesting double stars.

α **Lyr** (18h36m.9, +38°47'), Vega. This brilliant, white (A0) dwarf star, mag. 0.033, forms an optical double with a wide companion (mag. 10.5; PA 173°, 63") visible with 150 mm aperture. The stars are unrelated, however, lying at different distances, that of Vega being 7.756 pc (≈ 25.3 l.y.). When the magnitude scale was put on a mathematical and scientific basis by Norman Pogson in 1856, Vega was used as the zero point, being assigned a magnitude of exactly 0.0. Subsequent research has adjusted this zero point slightly, with Vega now being considered to be of mag. 0.033.

β **Lyr** (18h50m.1, +33°22'), Sheliak: the prototype for eclipsing stars that show continuous variations, even outside eclipses (EB). It has a period of 12 days 22 hours and varies between mags. 3.3 and 4.3. There is also a wide companion (mag. 7.2; PA 149°, Sep. 46").

Comparisons for β Lyr:

A =	γ Lyr	3.23	F = ρ Her	4.17
B =	μ Her	3.42	G = κ Lyr	4.34
C =	ξ Her	3.71	H = ν Her	4.41
D =	θ Her	3.86	J = η Lyr	4.46
E =	ζ Lyr	4.09		

δ **Lyr** (18h54m.5, +36°54'): a wide double visible with the naked eye or binoculars and consists of a pair of unrelated stars of mag. 4.3 (δ² Lyr) and 5.7 (δ¹ Lyr). The brighter star is a red (M4) bright supergiant that is slightly variable, and the fainter a white (B2.5) dwarf. The star is part of the Steph 1 open cluster, with about 15 members.

ε **Lyr** (18h44m.4, +39°40'), the Double Double: sometimes seen as double by people with keen eyesight, readily revealed with binoculars. The fainter star, ε¹ Lyr, is mag. 6.1, and the brighter star, ε² Lyr, mag. 5.2. Each star is a binary, visible with larger apertures (60–75 mm). For ε¹ Lyr, the AB pair, we have (mags. 5.1, 6.0; PA 354°, Sep. 2".5; spectra A4, F1), and for ε² Lyr, the CD pair (mags. 5.1, 5.4; PA 98°, Sep. 2".4; spectra A8, F0). All are dwarf stars. Component C is now known to be an extremely close binary, so the overall system is quintuple.

η **Lyr** (19h13m.8, +39°09'): an optical double (mags 4.4, 9.1; PA 81°, Sep. 28"; spectra B2.5 dwarf, and A0, respectively). There is a third

component (mag. 11.1; PA AC 150°, Sep. 160"), which does not appear to be related to either of the other two stars.

RR Lyr (19h25m.3, +42°47'): the prototype (and brightest member) of the RR-Lyrae class of variables, which resemble Cepheids, but have lower luminosities and shorter periods. (They were once known as 'cluster variables', from their occurrence in globular clusters.) Typical periods are 0.2–1.2 days. For RR Lyr itself it is 0.567 days, and the range is mag. 7.06–8.12.

M56 (NGC 6779: 19h16m.6, +30°11'): a poorly condensed globular cluster, mag. 8.2. Visible with 100 mm, and resolved with 200 mm.

M57 (NGC 6720: 18h53m.6, +33°02'), the Ring Nebula: nominal mag. 9.7, d = 330 pc (1080 l.y.), visible with 75 mm. Its elliptical form is also easily seen (PA 80°). The central star (mag. 14.8) is not an easy object, even with large apertures.

Lyrids (radiant at 18h08m, +32°): a meteor shower that normally exhibits a low hourly rate of about 10 meteors per hour, but may display greater activity on rare occasions. Associated with Comet Thatcher. Active April 19–25, maximum April 22.

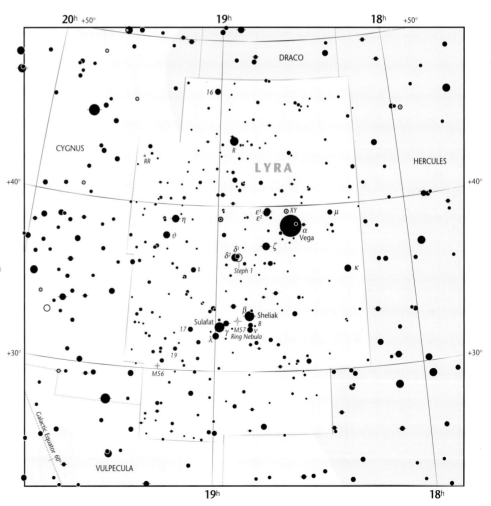

Mensa

MENSAE • Men • TABLE (MOUNTAIN)

Main chart(s): 20 (15)
Area: 153 sq. deg. (75th)
Culminates 00:00 local time: mid-December

This small, inconspicuous constellation was another introduced by de La Caille. Its stars are all faint, the brightest, α Men, being mag. 5.1. The only object of interest is the southern portion of the Large Magellanic Cloud, but this contains no conspicuous clusters or star clouds, unlike the region within Dorado. There are two binocular variables, one rather faint double, discovered by R.T.A. Innes, one globular cluster and one galaxy (both faint).

U Men (04ʰ09ᵐ.6, -81°51'): a semiregular variable, mag. 7.6–10.7, with occasional periodicity of 407.28 days.

TZ Men (05ʰ30ᵐ.2, -84°47'): an Algol-type (EA) eclipsing binary, mag. 6.2–8.7, P = 8.569 days.

I 277 (05ʰ35ᵐ.3, -71°08'): a faint double, viewed against the background of the LMC (mags. 7.8, 11.0; PA 190°, Sep. 3".9). The primary is an orange (K2) giant.

NGC 1841 (04ʰ45ᵐ.2, -84°00'): a faint, rather irregular globular cluster, mag. 11.0, detectable as a dim, hazy spot with 150 mm, but requiring at least 300 mm to show its form. Its distance is about 45 kpc (≈ 147,000 l.y.), and it is an outlying cluster of the LMC.

IC 2051 (03ʰ52ᵐ.0, -83°50'): an elongated spiral galaxy, mag. 11.4, detectable in 150 mm, but really requiring a larger aperture.

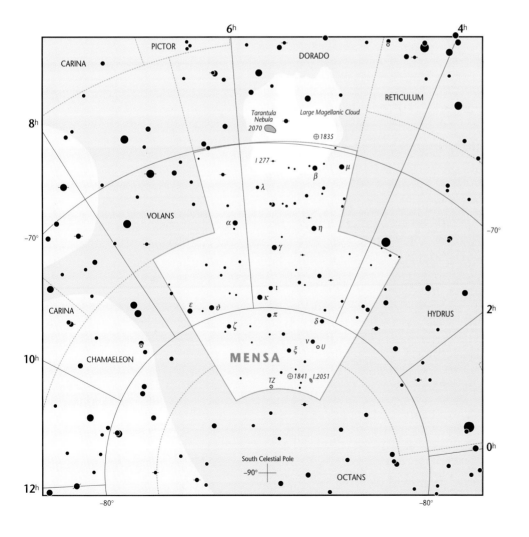

Microscopium

MICROSCOPII • Mic • THE MICROSCOPE

Main chart(s): 19 (18)
Area: 210 sq. deg. (66th)
Culminates 00:00 local time: early August

Yet another of de La Caille's faint constellations, with no stars brighter than mag. 4.7 (γ and ε). There are a few galaxies, but only one readily detectable with amateur-sized equipment.

α **Mic** (20h50m.0, -33°47'): a probable binary system (mags. 5.0, 10.0; PA 166°, Sep. 20".5). The bright star is a yellow (G7) giant. Readily separated with 75 mm.

MlbO 6 (21h27m.0, -42°33'): an unequal probable binary (mags. 5.6, 8.2; PA 149°, Sep. 2".9), clearly visible with 75 mm. The spectra are magnetic A for the brighter star and deep yellow (F8) for the fainter. The designation indicates that the star was discovered at the Melbourne Observatory by Ellery in the late 19th century.

NGC 6925 (20h34m.3, -31°59'): an edgewise spiral (Sb) galaxy, mag. 11.3, appearing elongated with 150 mm.

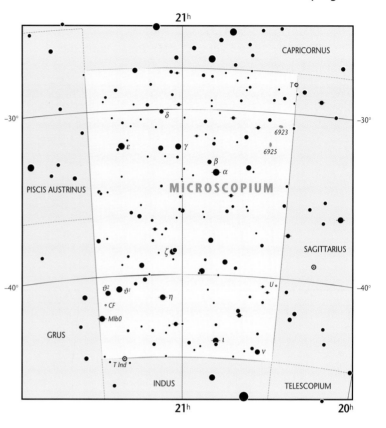

Monoceros

MONOCEROTIS • Mon • THE UNICORN

Main chart(s): 9 (10)
Area: 482 sq. deg. (35th)
Culminates 00:00 local time: early January

Although its introduction is normally attributed to Petrus Plancius, the first representation of this constellation dates back to the previous (16th) century. It lies across the galactic equator, and contains over 50 clusters. There are several diffuse nebulae, but, as might be expected, any galaxies are faint. There is one extraordinary multiple system (15 Mon) with 16 known components.

β **Mon** (06h28m.8, -07°02'): a fine multiple system. The stars in the visible triplet all have B3 dwarf spectra: AB (mags. 4.7, 5.2; PA 132°, Sep. 7".3); BC (mag. 6.1; PA 124°, Sep. 10"). A is a spectroscopic binary and C is thought to have a very close companion.

15 Mon (06h41m.0, +09°54'): a highly complex system with 16 known components, six of which are detailed here. AB (mags. 4.7, 7.5; PA 213°, Sep. 2".8); C (mag. 9.8; PA AC 13°, Sep. 16".6); D (mag. 9.6; PA AD 308°, Sep. 41".3); E (mag. 9.9; PA AE 139°, Sep. 41".3); F (mag. 7.7; PA AF 222°, Sep. 156"). The additional components range from mag. 8.2 to 12.5.

V640 Mon (06h37m.6, +06°08'), Plaskett's Star: an extraordinary system, being the second most massive binary known. It has an apparent magnitude of 6.1 (which is slightly variable), and consists of two blue-white (O8) supergiants. One estimate places the masses at 43 and 51 times that of the Sun, and another calculates the total mass of the system as about 110 solar masses. (Recent observations show that WR 20a in Carina is a binary and that each star is about 80 solar masses.)

M50 (NGC 2323: 07h03m.4, -08°20'): a fine open cluster, consisting of nearly 100 stars, d = 910 pc (≈ 2970 l.y.). The brightest may be resolved in binoculars.

NGC 2232 (06h26m.6, -04°44'): a loose open cluster around 10 Mon, consisting of about 20 stars, d = 400 pc (≈ 1305 l.y.), readily visible in binoculars.

NGC 2237–2239 (06h32m.3, +05°03'), the Rosette Nebula: surrounds the open cluster NGC 2244. Under good conditions the bright outer region of the nebula is detectable in binoculars. Its estimated age is about 500,000 years and star formation is probably still taking place within it.

CONSTELLATIONS

NGC 2244 (06ʰ32ᵐ.4, +04°52'): an open cluster that is just detectable with the naked eye under good conditions (integrated mag. 4.8), and excellent in binoculars. It is surrounded by NGC 2237, the Rosette Nebula.

NGC 2261 (06ʰ39ᵐ.2, +08°44'), Hubble's Variable Nebula: a triangular emission and reflection nebula, illuminated by R Mon, an irregular variable, range mag. 11.0–13.8. The nebula is just visible with 75 mm.

NGC 2264 (06ʰ41ᵐ.1, +09°52'), the Christmas Tree: another open cluster that is associated with nebulosity, in this case with the Cone Nebula, which is difficult to detect. The cluster is visible to the naked eye, mag. 3.8, especially because it contains the bright, blue-white star S Mon, at about mag. 4.7, which is a low-amplitude irregular variable.

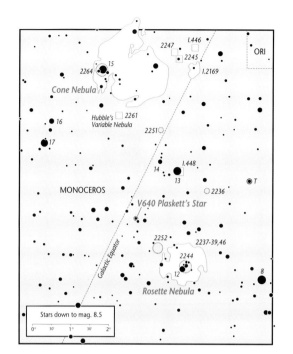

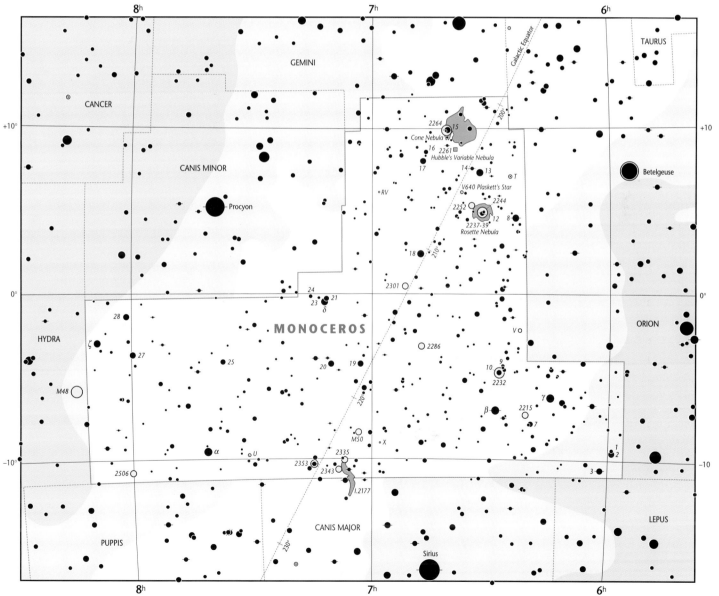

Musca

MUSCAE • Mus • THE FLY

Main chart(s): 20 (17)
Area: 138 sq. deg. (77th)
Culminates 00:00 local time: late March

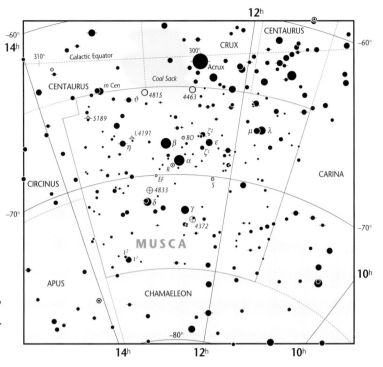

This constellation was originally introduced (as Apis, the Bee) by Bayer, only subsequently becoming known as Musca. Immediately south of Crux, it is not far from the galactic equator, but its open clusters are not particularly interesting. There are two globular clusters, one fairly bright planetary nebula, and some double stars.

β **Mus** (12^{h}46^m.3, -68°06'): a bright white (B2 & B2.5) long-period binary (mags. 3.7, 4.0; pa 35°, Sep. 1".0). Slowly closing, currently requires about 125 mm to be resolved.

ϑ **Mus** (13^{h}08^m.1, -65°18'): a bright binary (mags. 5.7, 7.3; PA 187°, Sep. 5".3). The primary is a spectroscopic binary (P = 18.4 days) consisting of a hot Wolf-Rayet star (WC5) and a B0 hypergiant. The secondary is an O9 subgiant.

NGC 4372 (12^{h}25^m.8, -72°40'): a large globular cluster, mag. 7.8, partially obscured by a dust lane, d = 5.8 kpc (≈ 18,900 l.y.). If a bright star approx. 5' to the northwest is hidden, many faint stars are revealed, even with 75 mm.

NGC 4833 (12^{h}59^m.6, -70°53'): a compact globular cluster, mag. 7.4, d = 6 kpc (≈ 19,600 l.y.). Fully resolved with 100 mm.

NGC 5189 (13^{h}33^m.5, -65°59'): a planetary nebula, mag. 10.3, d = 1.3 kpc

(≈ 4240 l.y.), surrounding three stars. Visible with 75 mm, and shows considerable structure with larger apertures.

Norma

NORMAE • Nor • LEVEL (SQUARE)

Main chart(s): 17, 18
Area: 165 sq. deg. (74th)
Culminates 00:00 local time: late May

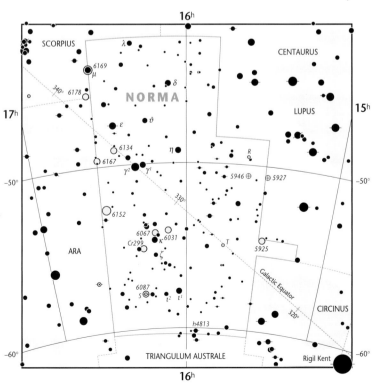

Unlike most of the other constellations introduced by de La Caille, this one lies squarely across the galactic equator. However, there are no bright stars and the designations α and β are missing. The brightest star, γ², is mag. 4.0, so any pattern of stars is lost against the background of the Milky Way. Due its location, there are no visible galaxies, and none of the open clusters is particularly striking. Although there are some interesting planetary nebulae, all are faint (below mag. 12).

ε **Nor** (16^{h}27^m.2, -47°33'): a wide binary (mags. 4.8, 7.5; PA 33°4, Sep. 23"). The brighter star may be a spectroscopic binary.

h 4813 (15^{h}55^m.5, -60°11'): a probable binary (based on the components having identical proper motions), with a bright yellow (F9.5) star and white (Am) companion (mags. 5.9, 8.5; PA 100°, Sep. 3".9).

NGC 5946 (15^{h}35^m.5, -50°40'): a small globular cluster, mag. 9.6, in a heavily obscured region, where the absorption is estimated to be about 1.7 magnitudes. Its distance is about 11 kpc (≈ 36,000 l.y.). Just detectable with 100 mm, but resolved with 200 mm.

CONSTELLATIONS

NGC 6067 (16ʰ13ᵐ.2, -54°13'): a rather scattered open cluster, northwest of κ Nor, mag. 5.6, d = 2100 pc (≈ 6850 l.y.).

NGC 6087 (16ʰ18ᵐ.9, -57°54'): another very scattered open cluster, mag. 5.4, d = 900 pc (≈ 2940 l.y.). The central star is **S Nor**, a yellow supergiant and Cepheid variable, range mag. 6.1–6.8, P = 9.754 days.

Octans
OCTANTIS • Oct • THE OCTANT

Main chart: 20
Area: 291 sq. deg. (50th)
Southern circumpolar: always visible

Another faint constellation introduced by de La Caille. The brightest star is ν Oct, mag. 3.7. The constellation contains the South Celestial Pole, but the closest naked-eye star is σ Oct, mag. 5.5, about 1° away from the Pole. There are one or two doubles, but the only galaxies are too faint for ready observation.

λ **Oct** (21ʰ50ᵐ.9, -82°43'): a long-period binary, consisting of a deep yellow (G6) giant, and white (A) star (mags. 5.4, 7.7; PA 70°, Sep. 3".1).

μ² **Oct** (20ʰ41ᵐ.7, -75°21'): a wide, probable binary system (mags. 7.1, 7.6; PA 17°, Sep. 17".4; spectra G1V).

R **Oct** (05ʰ26ᵐ.1, -86°23'): a long-period (M) variable, mag. 6.4–13.2, P = 405.6 days.

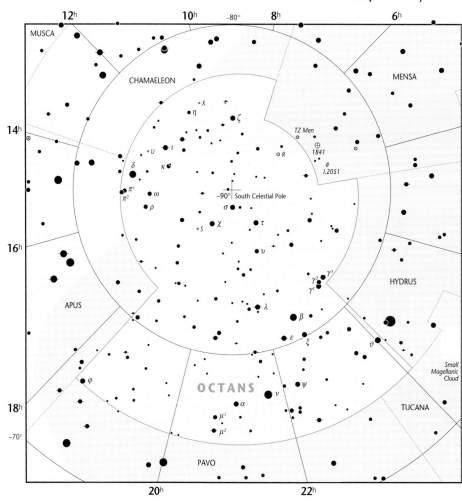

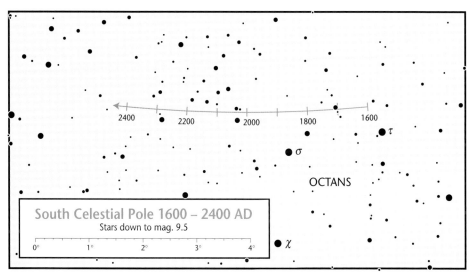

South Celestial Pole 1600 – 2400 AD
Stars down to mag. 9.5

CONSTELLATIONS

Ophiuchus

OPHIUCHI • Oph • THE SERPENT BEARER

Main chart(s): 12 (18)
Area: 948 sq. deg. (11th)
Culminates 00:00 local time: mid-June

Ophiuchus is a very large but not particularly distinctive constellation, the southern portion of which extends to the galactic plane. (The galactic centre is just over the border, in Sagittarius.) The whole of the southern area is filled with gas and dust, giving rise to all three types of diffuse nebulae. There are several open clusters, and about 25 globular clusters. Only a selection of these may be described here. There are a number of double stars and, given its location, it is not surprising that numerous novae have erupted in the constellation. Particularly interesting is the recurrent nova RS Oph, as is Kepler's Star, the last supernova to be seen in our own galaxy.

ρ Oph ($16^h25^m.6$, -23°27'): a long-period binary of yellow (B2) stars (mags. 5.1, 5.7, PA 339°, Sep. 3".1), resolved with 75 mm. The system is surrounded by bluish reflection nebulosity. Two other bright stars form a triangle with ρ Oph. The star to the west is β 1115, another binary (mags. 6.8, 8.2; PA 350°, Sep. 0".8), which may be resolved with 200 mm.

These stars are in the centre of a vast area of dust and gas, approximately 5° in RA and 3° in dec. (16^h20^m to 16^h40^m; -22°50" to -25°50"), which is generally devoid of stars. This large area of nebulosity lies at a distance of about 160 pc (≈ 520 l.y.).

Some of the extensive dark nebulosity in this region is visible to the naked eye, particularly the two portions of the Pipe Nebula, Barnard 59, 65–67 (approx. 17^h21^m, -27°23'), and Barnard 78 (approx. 17^h33^m, -26°30'). With a telescope both reveal intricate detail.

τ Oph ($18^h03^m.1$, -08°11'): a binary system, consisting of a pair of yellow (F2) stars (mags. 5.2, 5.9; PA 283, Sep. 1".7; P = 280 yrs). The separation is decreasing and is currently at about the limit for 75 mm, really requiring a larger aperture.

Barnard's Star ($17^h57^m.8$, +04°41'36"), a red dwarf (spectrum M4), mag. 9.6. The third closest star to the Sun (after Proxima and α Centauri), d = 5.94 l.y., and the star with the largest proper motion, 10".36 per year.

Kepler's Star ($17^h30^m.6$, -21°29'): the last supernova observed in our galaxy. It erupted in 1604 – just before the invention of the telescope – reached mag. -3 and was visible for nearly a year. It was a supernova of Type Ia, i.e., the explosion of one star in a close binary system.

RS Oph ($17^h50^m.2$, -06°43'): a recurrent nova, with outbursts in 1898, 1933, 1958, 1967, and 1985. Normally about mag. 12.5, it has reached mag. 4.3 during an outburst. Another member of this interesting class is T Pyxidis.

M9 (NGC 6333: $17^h19^m.2$, -18°31'): a large globular cluster with an integrated magnitude of about 7.8, d = 8.2 kpc (≈ 26,700 l.y.). It lies towards the centre of the Galaxy where there is obscuration by dust, but is readily visible with 75 mm.

M10 (NGC 6254: $16^h57^m.1$, -04°06'): a large, bright globular cluster, mag. 6.6, d = 4.4 kpc (≈ 14,000 l.y.), clearly visible in binoculars, and beginning to be resolved with 75 mm.

M12 (NGC 6218: $16^h47^m.2$, -01°57'): another large, bright globular cluster, again mag. 6.6. Slightly smaller and less concentrated than M10. The surrounding field is rather barren, because the area is moderately obscured, but d = 4.9 kpc (≈ 16,000 l.y.).

M14 (NGC 6402: $17^h37^m.6$, -03°15'): a globular cluster, slightly fainter than M10 and M12 (about mag. 7.6), d = 8.9 kpc (≈ 30,000 l.y.). It is visible, and appears slightly elongated, in binoculars, but only starts to be resolved with 200 mm.

M19 (NGC 6273: $17^h02^m.6$, -26°16'): a fine globular cluster, mag. 7.2, that appears distinctly elongated, even in binoculars. It begins to be resolved with 150 mm aperture.

M62 (NGC 6266: $17^h01^m.2$, -30°07'): a globular cluster, mag. 6.6, which although visible with small apertures, again requires about 150 mm to be resolved. It lies on the southernmost border of the constellation, and there is such heavy absorption that its distance is difficult to determine, but is about 6 kpc (nearly 20,000 l.y.).

M107 (NGC 6171: $16^h32^m.5$, -13°03'): the faintest globular cluster included here, mag. 8.1. It suffers from absorption, being so close to the galactic centre, with d = 6.4 kpc (≈ 21,000 l.y.). Appears as a faint patch in 75 mm, but the outer regions start to be resolved with 150 mm.

NGC 6572 ($18^h12^m.1$, +06°51'): a bright planetary nebula, mag. 8.1, d = 570 pc (≈ 1860 l.y.), and is visible with 75 mm aperture.

NGC 6633 ($18^h27^m.7$, +06°34'): a bright open cluster, integrated magnitude 4.6 and thus visible with the naked eye, d = 320 pc (≈ 1044 l.y.). Well worth examining with binoculars.

IC 4665 ($17^h46^m.3$, +05°43'): a large, sparse open cluster not far from β Oph, d = 430 pc (≈ 1400 l.y.). It is readily seen in binoculars and small apertures (and even with the naked eye), but does not bear magnification.

Ophiuchids (radiants at 17^h56^m, -23° & 17^h20^m, -20°): a shower with weak activity from several radiants. Active May 19 to Jly.; maxima Jun. 09 and Jun. 19 for southern and northern radiants, respectively. Zenithal hourly rate 5 at maximum.

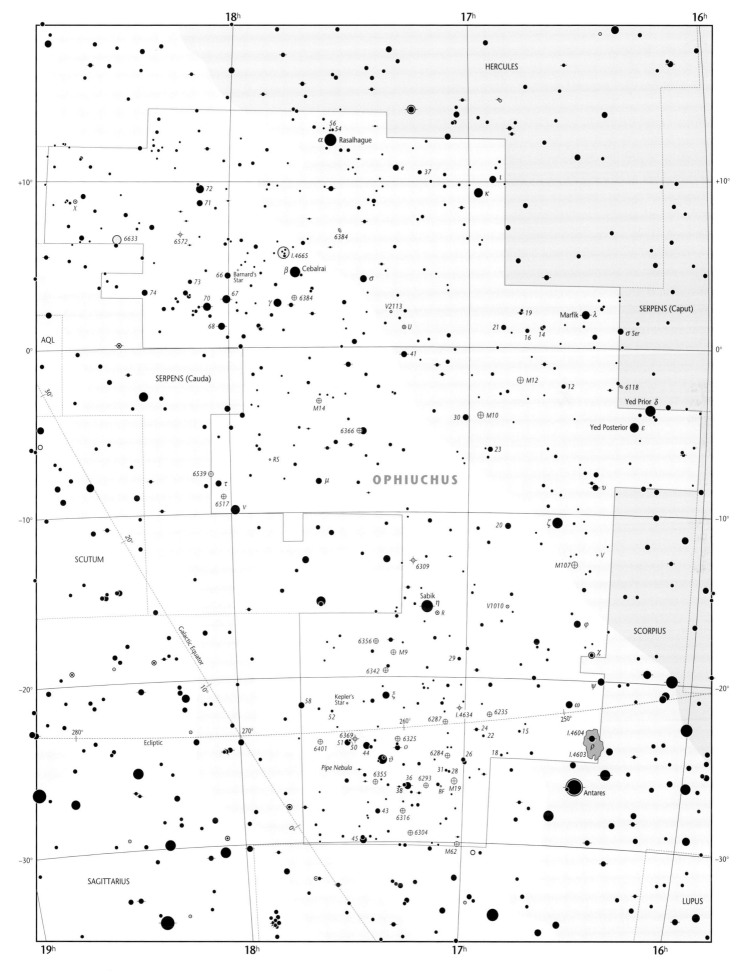

18ʰ   17ʰ   16ʰ

HERCULES

56
54
α Rasalhague

e
37

ι
κ

72
71

6633
6572
6384

I.4665

β Cebalrai
66 Barnard's Star
73
74
70
67
68
γ

6384
σ

V2113
U

19
Marfik λ
21
16 14

SERPENS (Caput)

σ Ser

41

M12
12

6118

Yed Prior δ

AQL

SERPENS (Cauda)

M14

6366

30
M10

Yed Posterior ε

23

OPHIUCHUS

6539
τ
6517
υ
V

RS

μ

20
ζ

υ
M107

SCUTUM

6309

V
Galactic Equator

Sabik
η
R

V1010

φ

SCORPIUS

χ

6356
M9

29

ψ

6342
ω

58
Kepler's Star
ξ
52

6287
I.4634
6235

24
22
15

250°
I.4604
ρ
I.4603

260°
270°
280°
Ecliptic

6369
51 50
44
ϑ
O
6325
6401

6284
26
18

Pipe Nebula
6355
36 6293
38 BF M19
31 28

Antares

43
6316

45
6304
M62

SAGITTARIUS

LUPUS

19ʰ   18ʰ   17ʰ   16ʰ

+10°
0°
−10°
−20°
−30°

30°
20°
10°

CONSTELLATIONS

Orion

ORIONIS • Ori • (ORION)

Main chart(s): 9 (3)
Area: 594 sq. deg. (26th)
Culminates 00:00 local time: mid-December

This striking constellation, well-known to people in both hemispheres, dominates the winter skies for those in the north. Many of the stars visible to the naked eye are young, blue or blue-white, with the exception of red Betelgeuse in the northeast. The three bright stars of Orion's belt, the 'Sword' and the hazy spot of the Great Orion Nebula are readily visible. The latter is merely a tiny fraction of a vast molecular cloud, the site of active star formation. The northeastern region lies in the Milky Way, and there some interesting clusters, although there are also two enormous star associations (groups of related stars) that are far too large to be viewed as a whole, one surrounding the stars in Orion's belt, and the other centred on λ Ori. There are no globular clusters and the few galaxies are faint.

α **Ori** (05h55m.2, +07°24'), Betelgeuse: a red supergiant, about 800 times the diameter of the Sun, d = 427 l.y. It is slightly variable, range mag. 0.3–1.2, and occasionally shows intervals with a periodicity of about 2335 days (approximately 7 years). It is difficult to estimate visually, because of its colour, and because comparision stars are some distance away, and of different colours.

β **Ori** (05h14m.5, -08°12'), Rigel: a complete contrast to Betelgeuse, being a much hotter, blue (B8), extreme supergiant (hypergiant) about 50,000 times as bright as the Sun, mag. 0.2, d = 773 l.y. It is also a binary, with a white companion (mag. 6.8; PA 203°, Sep. 9".5), which itself is a spectroscopic binary, consisting of two B5 dwarf stars, P = 9.86 days.

ϑ **Ori**: a wide, bright double consisting of ϑ¹ and ϑ², both of which have magnitudes of about 5.1. ϑ¹ **Ori** (05h35m.5, -05°23'), the Trapezium, is a multiple system that illuminates the centre of the Orion Nebula. Although named the Trapezium for the four brightest stars, there are two others: E, readily visible with 100 mm, and F, seen with 150 mm. The A, B, C, and D components are labelled in order of RA, as shown on the small chart, position angles and separations being measured from A. Component A is an Algol-type (EA) eclipsing variable, V1016 Ori (mag. 6.7–7.7; P = 65.43 days). Component B (PA AB 31°, Sep. 8".8; B3 spectrum) is another eclipsing (EA) variable, BM Ori (mag. 8.0–8.5; P = 6.47 days). Component C (PA AC 132°, Sep. 12".8; O6 spectrum) is the brightest, at mag. 5.1. It is extremely young, possibly only a few thousand years old, and is exceptionally hot (≈ 45,000 K), emitting most of its radiation in the ultraviolet region. Finally, we have component D (mag. 6.7; PA AD 96°, Sep. 21".5; B2 spectrum). Components E and F are both about mag. 10.0, and 4".5 from A and C respectively.

ϑ² **Ori** (05h35m.4, -05°25'): a double (mags. 5.1, 6.4; PA 92°, Sep. 52".5), visible in binoculars.

ι **Ori** (05h35m.4, -05°55'): a double star at the southern edge of M42 (mags. 2.8, 6.9; PA 141°, Sep. 11".3; spectra O9, B7) at a distance of

1326 l.y. It lies in the same field as another double, Σ **747** (mags. 4.8, 5.7; PA 226°, Sep. 36").

σ **Ori** (05h38m.7, -02°36'): a remarkable group of stars. The bright star (mag. 3.7) is a very close binary (AB), separable only with large apertures. It is accompanied by three other stars: C (mag. 10.3; PA AC 239°, Sep. 11".3), D (mag. 7.5; PA AD 82°, Sep. 11".2), and E (mag. 6.5; PA AE 58°, 40".4). Only 3.5' to the northwest lies Σ **761**, which is a triple system: AB (mags. 7.9, 8.2; PA 202°, Sep. 68") and C (mag. 8.7; PA BC 267°, Sep. 9".0).

Other interesting binaries are δ **Ori** (Mintaka); ζ **Ori** (Alnitak); η **Ori**; λ **Ori**; ρ **Ori**; τ **Ori**; and Flamsteed **14, 33, 42,** and **52**.

U **Ori** (05h55m.8, +20°10'): a long-period (Mira) variable, range mag. 4.8–13.0. Its period is slightly more than 368 days.

M42 (NGC 1986, 05h35m, -05°26' approx.), the great Orion Nebula: a diffuse nebula, visible to the naked eye, and as a hazy spot in binoculars and small telescopes. The visible region, illuminated by the hot, young stars of the Trapezium (ϑ¹ Ori) is a tiny portion of a vast interstellar molecular cloud that covers most of the constellation. The glowing hydrogen gas has a highly distinctive pinkish colour that is evident in any photographs, even those taken with exposures of just a few seconds. Visually, however, the colour is detectable only with large apertures, when the nebulosity has a faint greenish tint. Individual areas of M42 are bluish, being reflection nebulosity illuminated by nearby hot blue stars.

M43 (NGC 1982: 05h35m.6, -05°16'): a small patch of nebulosity just north of the main body of M42 and visible under good conditions in binoculars. In fact it is merely part of the whole Orion Nebula complex.

M78 (NGC 2068: 05h46m.7, +00°03'): a reflection nebula, approximately mag. 8.0, illuminated by two hot B-type stars, all visible with 75 mm.

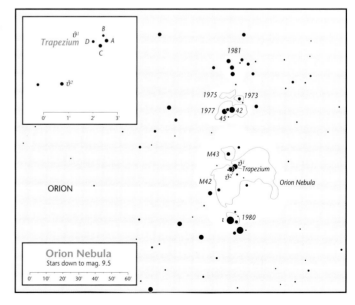

NGC 1981 (05ʰ35ᵐ.2, -04°26'): a sparse open cluster, detectable with the naked eye, but with so few stars that it does not bear much magnification.

NGC 2024 (05ʰ40ᵐ.7, -01°51'): a gaseous nebula with dark dust lanes, very close to ζ Ori (Alnitak), which should be kept outside the field of view. The emission is detectable with binoculars, and the dark lanes with 100 mm.

NGC 2169 (06ʰ08ᵐ.4, +13°57'): a small, bright open cluster, mag. 5.9, consisting of about 30 stars.

Orionids (radiant at 06ʰ24ᵐ, +15°): a moderately active meteor shower, with a peak zenithal hourly rate of about 25. They are active Oct. 16–27 and reach a flat maximum on Oct. 20.

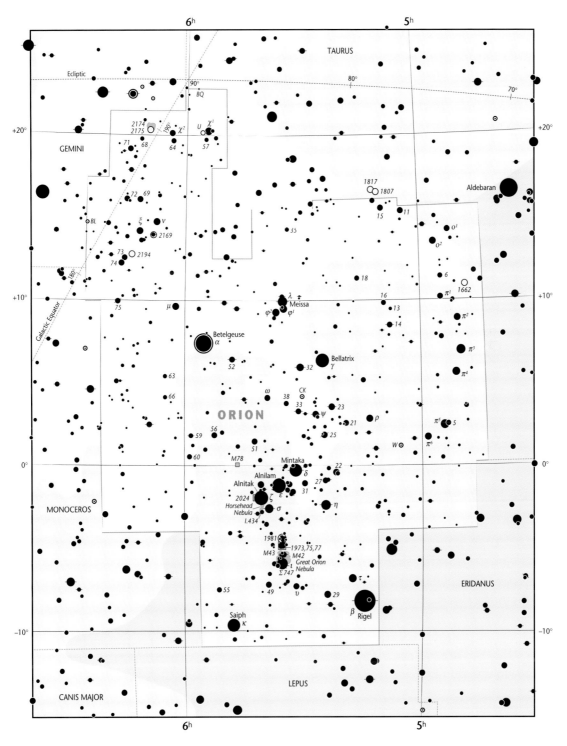

Pavo

PAVONIS • Pav • THE PEACOCK

Main chart(s):18, 20
Area: 378 sq. deg. (44th)
Culminates 00:00 local time: mid-July

A fairly unremarkable constellation introduced by Pieter Keyser and Frederick de Houtman. The only bright star, α Pavonis (Peacock), mag. 1.9, is on the northern boundary of the constellation. Although the western portion lies on the outer edge of the Milky Way, there are no open clusters, but there is one fine globular cluster. The constellation also contains the Pavo Cluster of galaxies, but most of these are faint.

ξ **Pav** (18^{h}23^m.2, -61°30'): a binary system (mags. 4.4, 8.6; PA 154°, Sep .3".3), visible with 75 mm. The bright component is a spectroscopic binary (P = 6.1 yrs.)

NGC 6684 (18^{h}49^m.0, -65°11'): a barred spiral (SB) galaxy, mag. 11.4, clearly visible with 150 mm, although there is some interference from the bright star ϑ Pav.

NGC 6744 (19^{h}09^m.8, -63°51'): a fairly bright barred spiral (SBb) galaxy, mag. 9.0, clearly visible with 100 mm under good conditions. Its distance is about 7 Mpc (≈ 23 million l.y.).

Pegasus

PEGASI • Peg • (PEGASUS)

Main chart(s): 13 (7, 2, 8)
Area: 1121 sq. deg. (7th)
Culminates 00:00 local time: early September

Although Pegasus is a large constellation, it has no open clusters, and just one bright globular cluster, albeit a fine one. Interestingly, the brightest galaxies lie just outside the borders of the Milky Way, and those further away are fainter. There are, however, many double stars.

β **Peg** (23^{h}03^m.8, +28°05'), Scheat: an irregular bright giant variable, range mag. 2.3–2.7.

ε **Peg** (21^{h}44^m.2, +09°53'), Enif: a wide double star, just detectable with good-quality binoculars under good conditions. One star, a yellow (K0) supergiant is mag. 2.4 and the second is approximately mag. 8.0.

κ **Peg** (21^{h}44^m.6, +25°39'): a multiple system, with the principal components forming a close binary (mags. 4.1, 10.6; PA 291°, Sep. 14".2; P = 11.6 yrs). Both stars appear to be spectroscopic binaries. The fifth star (mag. 11.0) visible in the same field is unrelated and merely happens to lie on the line of sight.

51 Peg (22^{h}58^m, +20°47'): a faint star (mag. 5.5) that is apparently very similar to the Sun. It is an extrasolar planetary system, of the 'hot

Jupiter' type, with a large planet (0.45 Jupiter-masses) that orbits just 0.05 AU from the star, and has a period of just 4.23 days. (An even more extreme example of a 'hot Jupiter' system is τ Boötes.)

M15 (NGC 7078: 21ʰ30ᵐ.0, +12°10'): one of the finest northern globular clusters, easily visible in binoculars, mag. 6.4. It is noticeably asymmetric when viewed with larger apertures. It is one of the rare globular clusters that contains a planetary nebula, but this is detectable only with apertures of 300 mm or more.

AG Peg (21ʰ51ᵐ.0, +12°38'): interesting variable star, readily visible in binoculars. A very slow nova, it had an outburst in 1870 and slowly declined, with erratic behaviour ever since, including intervals when the binary system's orbital period of 820 days is detectable.

NGC 7332 (22ʰ37ᵐ.4, +23°48'): a greatly flattened (E7) elliptical galaxy, mag. 10.9, just detectable with 100 mm. About 5' east is **NGC 7339** (22ʰ37ᵐ.8, +23°47'), a fainter (mag. 11.9), edge-on galaxy, visible with 200 mm aperture. It is uncertain whether this is a normal spiral (Sb) or a barred spiral (SBb).

NGC 7331 (22ʰ37ᵐ.1, +34°25'): a spiral (Sb) galaxy, mag. 9.5, which appears elongated in binoculars. A much greater aperture will reveal its elliptical form with a bright nucleus.

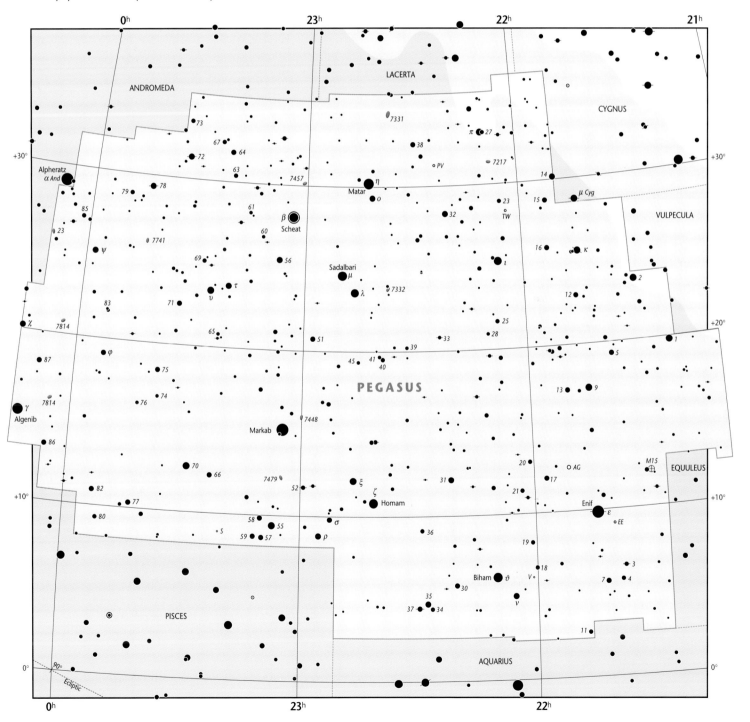

Perseus

PERSEI • Per • (PERSEUS)

Main chart(s): 2 (1, 3)
Area: 615 sq. deg. (24th)
Culminates 00:00 local time: early November

Most of this constellation lies in the Milky Way, but it has no globular clusters and only one major diffuse nebula. There are numerous open clusters however, most notably the famous Double Cluster, rivalled only by NGC 6231 in Scorpius. There are relatively few double stars, but some interesting variables, including the best-known eclipsing variable, Algol, β Persei. Of a number of novae that have erupted in the constellation, the most notable is perhaps GK Per (03^{h}31^m.2, +43°54'), Nova Per 1901, which reached mag. 0.2. It was the first nova in which a light echo was observed – where the light from the outburst illuminates surrounding material – and (some 40 years later) the first where material ejected in the outburst was detected.

β **Per** (03^{h}08^m.2, +40°58'), Algol: a famous variable star, the prototype for the EA class of eclipsing variables. Only the primary eclipse (when the bright star is hidden by the fainter star) is observable with normal amateur equipment. During eclipse (every 2.87 days) it drops from mag. 2.1 to mag. 3.4. Each eclipse lasts approximately 10 hours.

Comparisons for β Per:

α Per = 1.80	γ Per = 2.94	α Tri = 3.44
γ And = 2.10	β Tri = 3.00	ν Per = 3.77
ζ Per = 2.86	δ Per = 3.03	κ Per = 3.81
ε Per = 2.89		

ζ **Per** (03^{h}54^m.1, +31°53'), Atik: a multiple system with five components: AB (mags 2.9, 9.5; PA 208°, Sep. 12".9); C (mag. 11.3; PA AC 286°, 32".8); D (mag. 9.5; PA AD 195°, 94".2); E (mag. 10.2; PA AE 185°, 120".3).

η **Per** (02^{h}50^m.7, +55°54'): a multiple system with three components. In the principal pair (mags. 3.8, 8.5; PA 300°, Sep. 28".3), component A is an orange K0 supergiant with a radius of 2 AU. The third component is mag. 9.8 (PA AC 268°, Sep. 66".6).

ρ **Per** (03^{h}05^m.2, +38°50'): a semiregular red giant variable. It varies from mags. 3.3 to 4.0, and occasionally exhibits periodicity of about 50 days.

X **Per** (03^{h}55^m.4, +31°03'): an unusual and extremely interesting variable. It consists of an unequal binary with a young O9.5 supergiant star and a tiny neutron star, perhaps 20–30 km across. The supergiant undergoes outbursts like those of γ Cassiopeiae, and there are X-ray bursts from the neutron star. Amateurs play a vital role in monitoring this star and alerting professional astronomers when outbursts occur.

Comparisons for X Per:

40 Per	5.04	Y	5.73	Z	6.36
42 Per	5.10	A	6.1	C	6.6
W	5.48	B	6.23	12	8.0

M34 (NGC 1039: 02^{h}42^m.0, +42°47'): a fine open cluster, visible with the naked eye, and rather scattered. An excellent object for binoculars or wide-field telescopes.

h Per and χ **Per** (02^{h}19^m, +57°09' and 02^{h}23^m, +57°07', respectively), the Double Cluster, also known as NGC 869 and NGC 884. Although both of these open clusters are large (roughly the size of the Moon), not everyone finds them easily visible with the naked eye. They are a magnificent sight in binoculars and wide-field telescopes. **h** (NGC 869) – the closer to Cassiopeia – is slightly brighter, contains about 200 stars and is about 6 million years old. χ (NGC 884) consists of about 150 stars, and is younger, at about 3 million years old. Their distances are 7500 and 7100 light-years, respectively.

M76 (NGC 6501: 01^{h}42^m.4, +51°34'), the Little Dumbbell Nebula: a relatively faint (mag. 10.1) planetary nebula that is distinctly asymmetrical. Requires about 150 mm for the shape to start to become apparent.

NGC 1023 (02^{h}40^m.4, +39°04'): an extremely flattened (E7) elliptical galaxy, mag. 9.5. The shape is visible with 150 mm, and larger apertures will show the bright central region.

NGC 1499 (04^{h}00^m.7, +36°37'), the California Nebula: a large, faint emission nebula. A rather difficult object because of its size and low surface brightness. It requires a rich-field telescope and a nebular filter to be readily visible.

Perseids (radiant at approximately 03^{h}04^m, +58°): one of the most consistent meteor showers, active Jly. 23 to Aug. 20, maximum Aug. 12–13. Maximum zenithal hourly rate about 80. Many Perseid meteors are bright (ideal for photography) and often leave trains.

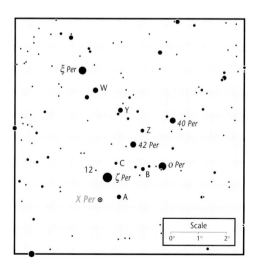

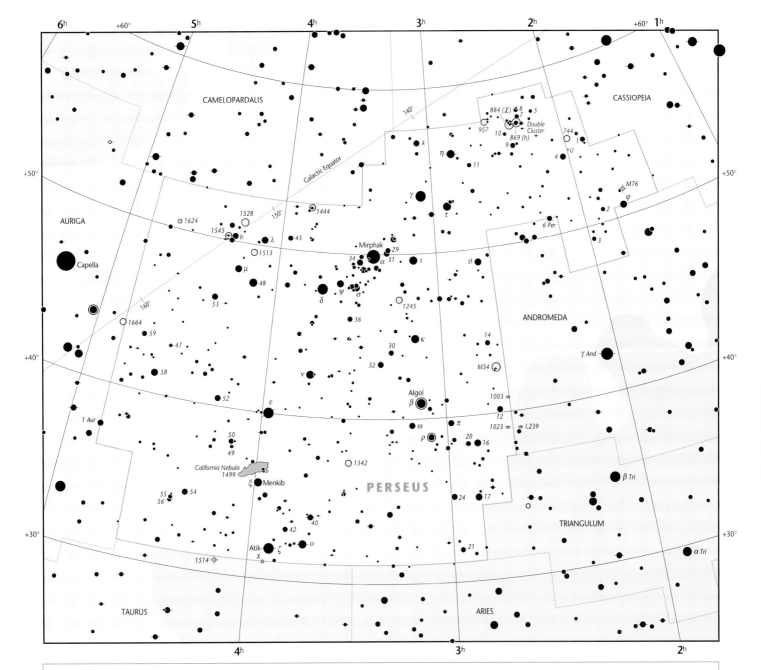

Associations The arms of spiral galaxies contain groups of stars that formed together, generally less compact than normal open clusters. Some stellar associations include recognized open clusters. The stars disperse rapidly, and some associations are the sources of runaway stars: stars with extremely high velocities, probably arising from the disruption of a binary system, perhaps when one component became a supernova.

OB associations consist of massive, young, hot stars of spectral classes O and B, and about 100 are known in our galaxy. In Perseus, the Per OB1 association includes h and χ Per, and has about 65 OB stars that have absolute magnitudes greater than -6.0. The α Persei Association (Per OB3), also known as Melotte 20, includes α and δ Per as well as other hot stars. The Orion Association (Ori OB1) contains the Trapezium (ϑ Ori), NGC 1981, and Collinder 70 clusters, and most of the naked-eye stars in Orion, with the exception of α Ori, Betelgeuse. It spawned the runaway stars AE Aur, μ Col, and 53 Ari. In Monoceros, NGC 2244 and Plaskett's Star are part of the Mon OB2 association. The Antares Cluster (Sco OB2), with α, β2, and δ Sco, and the runaway star ζ Oph, are a portion of the larger Sco-Cen Association. This is the nearest association, the main body of which extends from Scorpius to Crux, including such stars as α CMa, α Car, β and δ Cen, α and β Cru, and α Eri.

T associations are regions of active star formation, embedded in the giant molecular clouds that are stellar nurseries. The stars have yet to settle down to steady hydrogen fusion within their cores and are irregular variables of the T Tauri type (after which T associations are named). They are often so heavily obscured by dust clouds that they are detectable at infrared wavelengths alone. In the giant, nearby Taurus-Auriga association, for example, the stars are of visual mag. 11–19.

Phoenix

PHOENICIS • Phe • PHOENIX

Main chart(s): 14 (19)
Area: 469 sq. deg. (37th)
Culminates 00:00 local time: early October

This constellation was introduced by Keyser and de Houtman and first depicted by Johannes Bayer. Its brightest star (α Phe, Ankaa) is an orange (K0) giant, mag. 2.4. It has no open or globular clusters nor any diffuse nebulae. Despite lying well away from the galactic plane, it has just a few galaxies, and only one that is moderately bright.

β **Phe** (01ʰ06ᵐ.1, -46°43'): a long-period, close binary (mags. 4.0, 4.2; PA 307°, Sep. 0".7; yellow G8 giant spectra). The stars are closing, and 200 mm aperture is currently needed to resolve them.

ζ **Phe** (01ʰ08ᵐ.4, -55°15'): a multiple system. The primary (AB) is an eclipsing binary (mag. 3.9–4.4; P = 1.67 days), with B6 and B8 spectra. The third component is (mag. 8.0; PA 243°, Sep. 6".5; spectrum A7).

ϑ **Phe** (23ʰ39ᵐ.5, -46°38'): a probable binary (mags 6.5, 7.3; PA 276°, Sep. 3".9; A7 giant and A9 dwarf spectra). The extremely slow changes since discovery in 1835 suggest that it may be a true binary system.

NGC 625 (01ʰ35ᵐ.1, -41°26'): an elongated galaxy, mag. 11.0, visible with 150 mm. Sources differ as to its type, some classifying it as irregular, and others as a barred spiral. Its distance is approx. 4 Mpc (≈ 13 million l.y.).

ESO 245-G5 (01ʰ45ᵐ.1, -43°36'): a dwarf irregular galaxy, one of the satellites of the Milky Way. It is just detectable with 250 mm aperture, with integrated mag. 12.3. It lies at about the same distance as **NGC 625**.

ESO 245-G7 (01ʰ51ᵐ.2, -44°27'), the Phoenix Dwarf Galaxy, a close satellite of the Milky Way at a distance of about 500 kpc (≈ 1,630,000 l.y.). It is very faint at mag. 13.0, but is just detectable with 300 mm aperture under good conditions. (See also Fornax and Sculptor.)

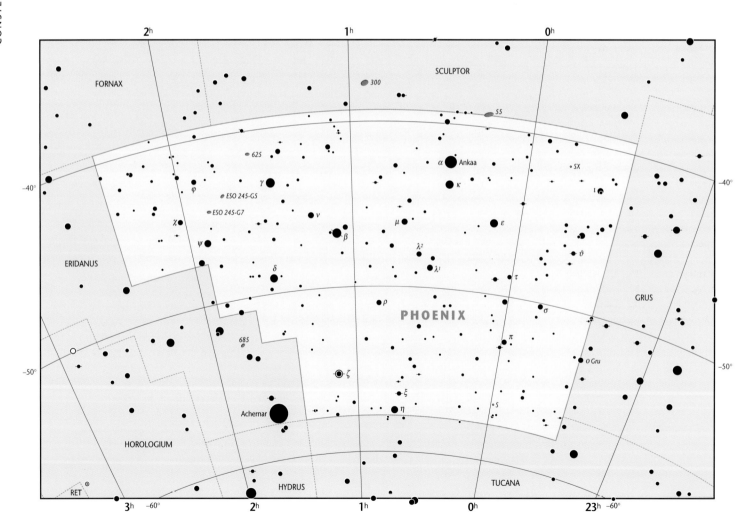

Pictor

PICTORIS • Pic • THE PAINTER

Main chart(s): 15 (16)
Area: 247 sq. deg. (59th)
Culminates 00:00 local time: mid-December

This small, insignificant constellation is yet another of those introduced by de La Caille. It is overshadowed by brilliant Canopus (α Car), mag. -0.62, immediately to its east. The name, originally Equuleus Pictoris, 'The Painter's Easel', was subsequently shortened.

α **Pic** (16ʰ18ᵐ.2, -61°57'): the brightest star in the constellation at mag. 3.24. It has a pale yellow (A7) subgiant spectrum and lies at a distance of 30.3 pc (≈ 100 l.y.). The data obtained by the Hipparcos satellite suggest that the star may be a low-amplitude variable.

β **Pic** (05ʰ47ᵐ.4, -51°04'): an A3 dwarf star (mag. 3.9), d = 63 l.y. Infrared observations reveal a disk of dust and gas around the star, which appears to be warped, suggesting that a large planetary body has formed within it.

η¹ **Pic** (05ʰ02ᵐ.9, -49°09'): a difficult binary because of the great difference in magnitudes (mags 5.4, 13.0; PA 199°, Sep. 10.7"). The primary has an F2 dwarf spectrum.

ι **Pic** (04ʰ50ᵐ.9, -53°28'): a probable binary consisting of two yellow stars (mags. 5.6, 6.5; PA 58°, Sep. 12".5; spectra F0, F4). The stars have large and identical proper motions. The primary may be a spectroscopic binary.

ϑ Pic (05ʰ24ᵐ.8, -52°19'): a multiple system, although only the two principal components may be resolved (mags. 6.3, 6.8; PA 330°, Sep. 38".2). The brighter component is a close binary where the separation has decreased since discovery so that currently it cannot be resolved visually.

μ **Pic** (06ʰ32ᵐ.0, -58°45'): a relatively static pair of white stars (mags. 5.8, 9.3; PA 231°, Sep. 2".4; spectra B9, A8).

Kapteyn's Star (05ʰ11ᵐ.7, -45°01'): a red dwarf, mag. 8.9, d = 12.8 l.y., with the second largest proper motion (after Barnard's Star in Ophiuchus), of 8".67 per year.

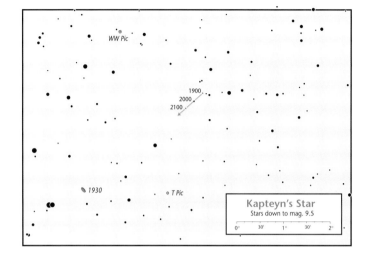

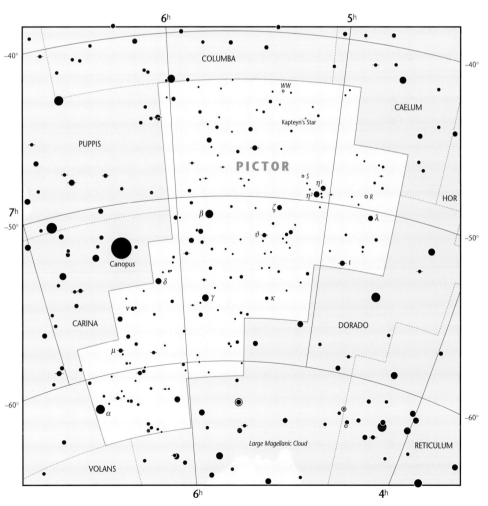

CONSTELLATIONS

Pisces

PISCIUM • Psc • THE FISHES

Main chart(s): 8 (2, 13)
Area: 889 sq. deg. (14th)
Culminates 00:00 local time: late September

This zodiacal constellation is a large but relatively sparsely populated area. There are no open clusters or globular clusters and most of the galaxies are faint. Precession has carried the spring (vernal) equinox – still known as the First Point of Aries – well into Pisces, where it now lies south of the star ω Psc.

Van Maanen's Star (00ʰ49ᵐ.1, +05°25'): a white dwarf (mag. 12.3), d = 13.8 l.y. (the third closest after α CMa B and α CMi B).

α Psc (02ʰ02ᵐ.0, +02°46'), Alrescha: a long-period (P = 933.1 yrs) binary system (mags. 4.2, 5.1; PA 272°, Sep. 1".8; A0, A3 spectra), resolved easily with 75 mm. Both stars are small-amplitude magnetic variables of the α CVn type, and the brighter may also be a spectroscopic binary.

ζ Psc (01ʰ13ᵐ.7, +07°35'): multiple system consisting of a moderately wide double (mags. 5.6, 6.5; PA 63°, Sep. 23".0; A7, F7 spectra), visible with binoculars in good conditions. A is suspected of being a binary, and B is an undoubted spectroscopic binary, P = 9.075 days, the other component having a G7 spectrum. B also has another companion (mag. 12.2; PA 79°, Sep. 1".5), with an orbit lying close to the line of sight. It may possibly be resolved with large apertures.

κ Psc (23ʰ27ᵐ.1, +01°16') and **9 Psc** form a wide binocular double, consisting, respectively, of an A0 dwarf, mag. 4.9, and an unrelated G7 giant, mag. 6.3. **ρ Psc** (01ʰ26ᵐ.5, +19°11'), an F2 dwarf, mag. 5.4, forms a similar double with orange K1 giant **94 Psc**, mag. 5.5.

M74 (NGC 628: 01ʰ36ᵐ.7, +15°47'): a face-on spiral (Sc) galaxy (mag. 9.2), that may sometimes be glimpsed with binoculars under favourable conditions. Because of the widespread arms, even 100 mm shows only a dim hazy spot, and even larger apertures are really required for successful observation.

NGC 524 (01ʰ24ᵐ.8, +932'): a very slightly flattened (E1) elliptical galaxy, mag. 10.6, visible with 150 mm.

Piscids (multiple radiant: 00ʰ36ᵐ, +07°; 00ʰ24ᵐ, +00°; 01ʰ44ᵐ, +14°): a complex meteor shower, active September–October, maxima for the three radiants: Sep. 08, Sep. 21, and Oct. 13, respectively; rates: 10, 5, and unknown, respectively.

Piscis Austrinus

PISCIS AUSTRINI • Psa • THE SOUTHERN FISH

Main chart(s): 19 (13)
Area: 245 sq. deg. (60th)
Culminates 00:00 local time: late August

This ancient constellation was described by Ptolemy. There are no open or globular clusters, and most of the galaxies are faint.

α PsA (22ʰ57ᵐ.9, -29°36'), Fomalhaut: a blue-white (A3) dwarf star, mag. 1.2. The name is Arabic for 'mouth of the fish'. It is a relatively close neighbour, lying at a distance of almost 25 l.y. Like β Pictoris, Fomalhaut is encircled by a disk of dust and gas, within which planetary formation is thought to be occurring.

β PsA (22ʰ31ᵐ.5, -32°21'): a probable binary (mags. 4.9, 7.9; PA 172°, Sep. 30".3), in a very sparse field. No orbital motion is apparent, but both stars have identical proper motions. A similar situation occurs with **δ PsA** (22ʰ55ᵐ.9, -32°32') which consists of a G7 giant and G5 dwarf (mags. 4.2, 9.9; PA 243°, Sep. 4".9).

γ PsA (22ʰ52ᵐ.5, -32°53'): a slow binary (mags. 4.5, 8.0; PA 262°, Sep. 4".2) consisting of a B9.5 sub-giant, and a F5 dwarf.

NGC 7172 (22ʰ02ᵐ.0, -31°52'), **NGC 7173** (22ʰ02ᵐ.1, -31°59'), and **NGC 7176** (22ʰ02ᵐ.2, -31°59'): three faint galaxies in the same field (mags. 11.9, 12.1, and 12.6, respectively) with uncertain classifications: S:, E2:, and S:. Requires 300 mm or more.

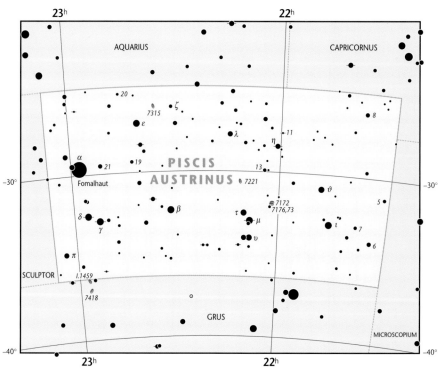

NGC 7314 (22ʰ35ᵐ.8, -26°03'): a spiral (Sc) galaxy, mag. 10.9, just visible with 150 mm. Its shape becomes clearly detectable with 200 mm.

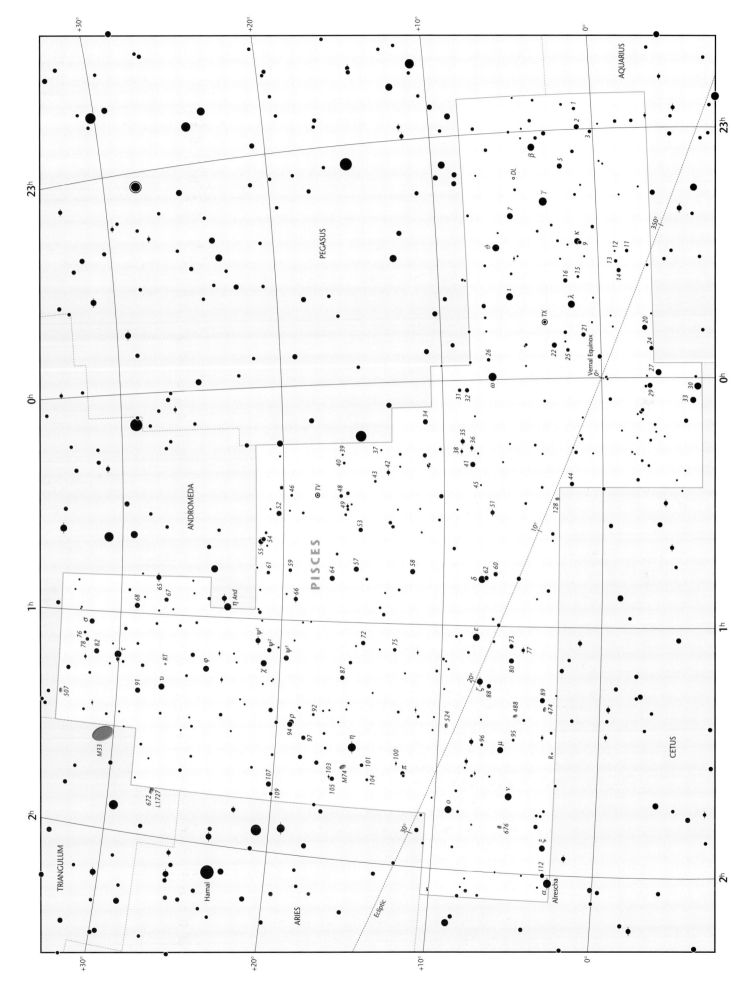

CONSTELLATIONS

Puppis

PUPPIS • Pup • THE POOP

Main chart(s): 15, 16 (9, 10)
Area: 673 sq. deg. (20th)
Culminates 00:00 local time: early January

This constellation was one of four that were part of the constellation Argo. (The others being Carina, Pyxis, and Vela.) The brightest stars with Greek-letter designations in Bayer's original constellation now lie in Carina.

Puppis contains part of the gigantic Gum Nebula, the largest emission nebula in the sky, which is actually centred (at approximately 08^h30^m, -45°) in the neighbouring constellation of Vela. This gigantic structure, named after its discoverer Colin Gum, is about $30° \times 40°$ across. Its distance is thought to be about 1300 l.y., which implies a diameter of about 800 l.y., and it is still expanding at about 20 km/s. It is the result of a supernova explosion about one million years ago.

Puppis lies across the Milky Way, which is particularly rich in this region. It contains about 70 open clusters, although many of these do not stand out clearly against the rich star fields. There are various planetary nebulae, just one globular cluster, one bright emission nebula, but (as might be expected), all the galaxies are faint.

σ **Pup** (07^h29^m.2, -43°18'): a multiple system, consisting of a visual binary (mags. 3.3, 9.4; PA 74°, Sep. 22".3; K5 giant and G5 dwarf spectra). The primary is a spectroscopic binary, and the additional component is also a giant.

ξ **Pup** (07^h49^m, -28°58'), Aspidiske: a very wide binary, consisting of two yellow stars, of magnitudes 3.3 and 5.3.

L² **Pup** (07^h13^m.5, -44°39'): a semiregular variable, range 2.6–6.2 and occasional periodicity of 140.5 days. It has a red (M5) spectrum, d ≈ 200 l.y., and it forms a wide visual double with L¹ **Pup**, a blue-white (A) star which is a low-amplitude variable of the α CVn type, approximately mag. 4.9, with d ≈ 182 l.y.

V **Pup** (07^h58^m.2, -49°15'): naked-eye b-Lyrae (EB) eclipsing binary in the extreme southeast of the constellation, mag. 4.4–4.9, P = 1.45 days.

KQ **Pup** (07^h33^m.8, -14°31'): one of the largest stars, with a radius of 7.4 AU, equal to the size of the supergiant component in VV Cephei, and second in size to μ Cephei only. It is an irregular variable, mags. 4.8–5.2.

M46 (NGC 2437: 07^h41^m.8, -14°48'): an open cluster, mag. 6.5, which appears as a large unresolved glow in binoculars. A larger aperture (100–150 mm) will reveal a bluish planetary nebula, **NGC 2438** (07^h41^m.8, -14°44'), mag. 10.1, in the northeastern portion of the cluster. The planetary nebula is at a distance of about 1 kpc (≈ 3,260 l.y.), and the cluster itself is farther away at about 1.7 kpc (≈ 5,540 l.y.).

M47 (NGC 2422: 07^h36^m.6, -14°29'): a bright (mag. 4.3) open cluster, visible to the naked eye, and a magnificent object in binoculars.

Predominantly white stars in a field approximately 30' across, with an orange star on the western side.

M93 (NGC 2447: 07^h45^m, -23°51'): a bright globular cluster (mag. 6.5). Some of its brightest stars may be resolved with binoculars, but an aperture of about 100 mm with a wide field is more-or-less ideal. This cluster has two orange stars at its southwestern edge. Its distance is about 1.1 kpc (≈ 3600 l.y.).

NGC 2298 (06^h49^m.0, -36°00'): a small, slightly irregular globular cluster, mag. 9.3, d = 12 kpc (≈ 39,000 l.y.). Easily seen with 100 mm, but requires 150 mm to begin to be resolved.

NGC 2451 (07^h45^m.5, -37°57'): a large, rather sparse, open cluster (mag. 3.7), d = 220 pc (≈ 720 l.y.). It surrounds the orange (K2.5) supergiant c Pup, mag. 3.6. The cluster is visible with the naked eye and resolved in binoculars, but requires a wide field with larger apertures.

NGC 2477 (07^h52^m.3, -38°32'): an open cluster, mag. 5.8, d = 1.3 kpc (≈ 4,250 l.y.). It contains an exceptionally large number of stars, but these are unresolved in binoculars, so that it appears more like a globular, rather than an open, cluster. It is particularly fine with an aperture of about 150 mm, when the stars are well resolved.

NGC 2546 (08^h12^m.4, -37°38'): a large, scattered, open cluster (mag. 5.2), which covers approximately 40', and therefore requires a large field of view and is suitable for small apertures. The stars do not exhibit any condensation towards a centre, but there is an irregular, elongated concentration on its northern edge, towards **h 4051** (described below).

h 4038 (08^h02^m.7, -41°19'): a fine pair of stars (mags 5.5, 8.5; PA 346°, Sep. 27") with the brighter having a B9.5 dwarf spectrum. It is not known whether these stars are merely a visual double or a true binary system. There has been little change since discovery by John Herschel in 1837, hence the uncertainty as to its true status.

h 4046 (08^h05^m.7, -33°34'): possible binary (mags 6.2, 8.9; PA 88°, Sep. 22") with third component to the north (mag. 9.5; PA AC 58°, Sep. 28"). A faint close pair lies to the west, visible with 200 mm. Primary is a yellow-orange (G1) supergiant, and the close companion is white.

h 4051 (08^h11^m.0, -37°18'): a triple system consisting of one bright, white (B0), giant and two much fainter stars (mags AB, 6.4, 13.4; PA 265°, Sep. 18"; mag. C, 13.6; PA AC 206°, Sep. 17"), visible with 200 mm. The brighter companion may be seen with 150 mm. Part of a fine field which includes an irregular grouping that is part of **NGC 2546**. The companions are believed to be field stars.

Puppids-Velids (radiants at 09^h00^m, -48°, and 09h20m, -65°): a complex stream with several radiants in Puppis, Carina, and Vela, active between November 27 and January. Maxima for the radiants given: Dec. 09 and Dec. 26, respectively, with zenithal hourly rates of 15.

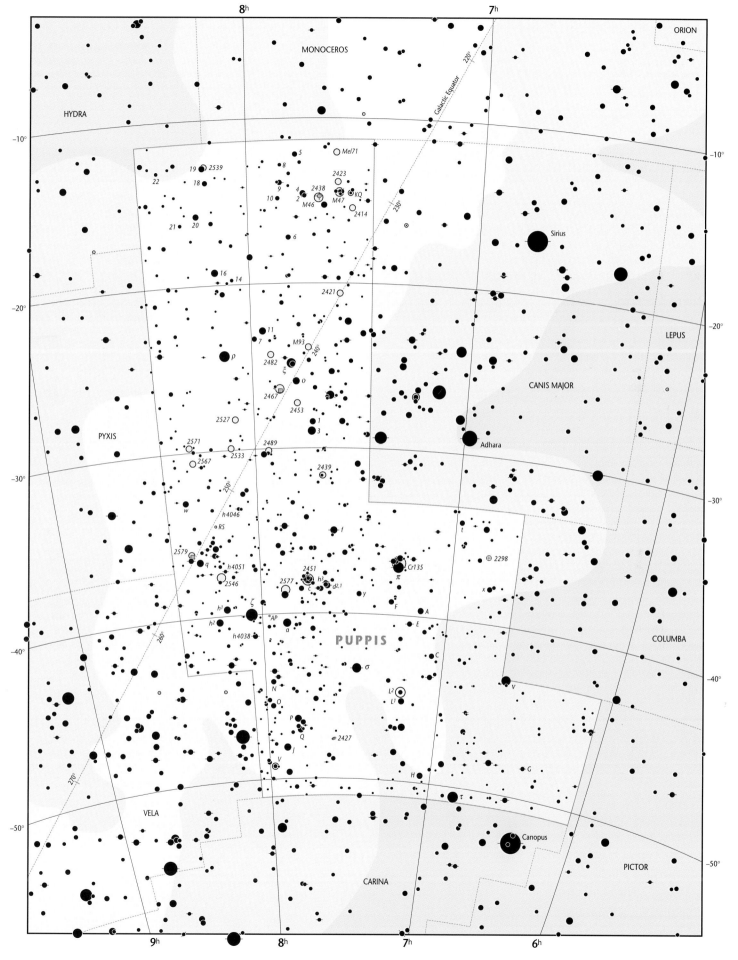

Pyxis

PYXIDIS • Pyx • THE (MAGNETIC) COMPASS

Main chart(s) 16 (10, 15)
Area: 221 sq. deg. (65th)
Culminates 00:00 local time: early February

Introduced by de La Caille, this constellation represents the magnetic compass used by mariners. It was created from part of the ancient constellation Argo Navis. The southwestern corner nearly touches the galactic equator. None of the open clusters is very notable, although NGC 2818 contains a planetary nebula. There is one reasonably bright galaxy. For variable-star observers, the object of most interest is the recurrent nova T Pyxidis.

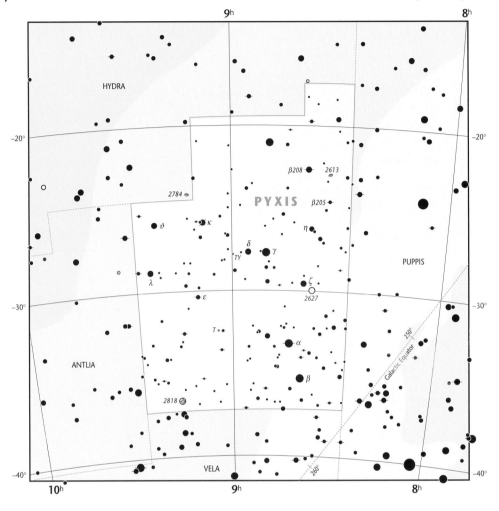

κ **Pyx** (09h08m.0, -25°52'): a long-period binary (mags. 4.6, 9.8; PA 263°, Sep. 2".1). Poorly known, the only data being for 1911.

T **Pyx** (09h04m.7, -32°23'): a recurrent nova, with five recorded outbursts: 1890, 1902, 1920, 1944, and 1966. Normally about mag. 14, but has risen as far as mag. 6.3. Requires constant monitoring.

β **205** (08h33m.1, -24°36'): a binary system (mags. 6.9, 7.0; PA 332°, Sep. 0".54; P = 136.5 yrs). A difficult pair, but currently widening, and should be resolved with 250 mm.

β **208** (08h39m.1, -22°40'): a fine binary (mags. 5.3, 6.6; PA 28°, Sep. 1".0; P = 123 yrs; spectra dwarf G6). Another pair that is currently widening, periastron being in 1980. Now resolved with 150 mm.

NGC 2613 (08h33m.4, -22°58'): edgewise spiral (Sb) galaxy, mag. 10.4. Only the central region is visible. Ideally requires at least 200 mm.

NGC 2818 (09h16m.0, -36°38'): an open cluster, mag. 8.2, d = 3200 pc (≈ 10,400 l.y.). It is slightly unusual in that it contains an associated planetary nebula on its western side. The nebula is rather faint, about mag. 13, requiring an aperture of 150 mm or more to be visible.

Reticulum

RETICULI • Ret • THE NET

Main chart(s): 14 (15, 20)
Area: 114 sq. deg. (82th)
Culminates 00:00 local time: mid-November

The original name given by de La Caille to this constellation was Reticulum Rhomdoidalis, 'The Reticle', for the grid of lines used in the eyepieces of telescopes. It is basically a single, small group of stars around α Ret, a yellow (G7) dwarf, mag. 3.3. Immediately to its west is a triangle of orange stars, γ, δ, and ι Ret.

ζ² **Ret** (03h17m.9, -63°34') and ζ¹ **Ret** (03h18m.3, -62°29') are a pair of yellow (G2) dwarf stars that form a wide double (mags. 5.2, 5.5; Sep. 5'.1). A few observers are able to resolve these with the naked eye, but for most they are a binocular double. The stars have a common proper motion, but lie at slightly different distances (39.4 and 40 l.y., respectively).

ϑ **Ret** (04ʰ17ᵐ.7, -63°15'): an apparently long-period binary system (mags. 6.1, 7.8; PA 2°, Sep. 4".0; B9 and Am spectra). The second component, a magnetic star, is suspected of being an α CVn-type variable.

NGC 1313 (03ʰ18ᵐ.3, -66°30'): a barred spiral galaxy, nominally mag. 9.4, d = 4.5 Mpc, but a challenging object with anything less than 300 mm. Most notable for a 10th mag. supernova that erupted in this system in December 1962.

NGC 1543 (04ʰ12ᵐ.8, -57°44'): a barred spiral (SB0) galaxy, mag. 10.6. A member of the Dorado Group of galaxies, as is **NGC 1574**.

NGC 1559 (04ʰ17ᵐ.6, -62°47'): a barred spiral (SBc) galaxy, mag. 10.5, just visible with 150 mm. Close to α and ϑ Ret.

NGC 1574 (04ʰ22ᵐ.0, -56°58'): a lenticular (S0) galaxy, mag. 10.5, visible with 75 mm, and a member of the Dorado Group of galaxies.

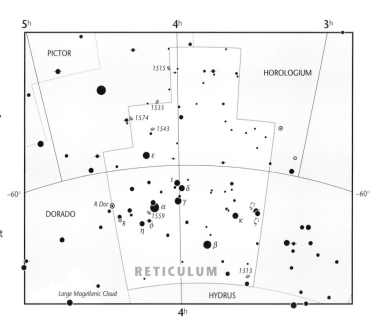

Sagitta
SAGITTAE • Sge • THE ARROW

Main chart(s): 12, 13 (6, 7)
Area: 80 sq. deg. (86th)
Culminates 22:00 local time: mid-July

This tiny constellation lies completely within the Milky Way, which hides any external galaxies. There is one globular cluster accessible to amateur-sized telescopes, and one open cluster. There are three planetary nebulae, the brightest mag. 11.6, and some interesting (and problematic) multiple systems.

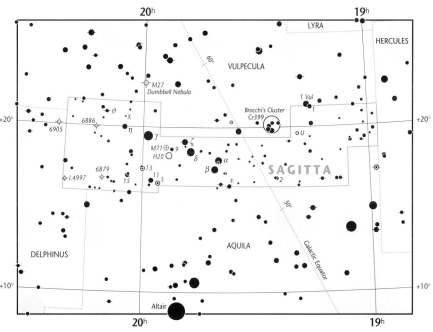

ϑ **Sge** (20ʰ09ᵐ.9, +20°55'): a probable long-period binary (mags. 6.5, 8.7; PA 329°, Sep. 11".2; F5 subgiant and G5 dwarf spectra).

13 Sge (20ʰ00ᵐ.2, +17°32'): a low-amplitude giant, irregular variable, range 5.6–5.8, M4 spectrum. The colour of this star (reported variously as orange and red) is easily detected with moderate apertures. Reputed to be a multiple system with 6 components, there is some doubt about the status of all but the principal pair (mags. 5.6, 9.9; PA 206°, Sep. 28".5).

15 Sge (20ʰ04ᵐ.1, +17°04'): another multiple system with wide components. The AB pair (mags. 5.9, 9.1; PA 276°, Sep. 190".7) is accompanied by C (mag. 6.8; PA AC 320°, Sep. 203".7). Each of these stars has a subsidiary component: P (mag. 11.6; PA AP 0°, Sep. 82".1); Q (mag. 8.9; PA BQ 230°, Sep. 181".1); and R (mag. 11.6; PA CR 185°, Sep. 95".6).

M71 (NGC 6838: 19ʰ53ᵐ.9, +18°46'): a globular cluster, mag. 8.5, visible as a hazy spot in binoculars and small apertures. Ideally requires at least 150 mm for best resolution; d = 3.9 kpc (≈ 12,720 l.y.).

NGC 6879 (20ʰ10ᵐ.5, +16°55'): a faint planetary nebula, mag. 12.5, which is difficult to locate, but forms a right-angle triangle with two stars of mag. 8, one 6' to the east, and the other 10' north. It is faintly visible with 150 mm aperture.

NGC 6886 (20ʰ12ᵐ.7, +19°59'): another, slightly brighter planetary nebula, mag. 11.4, but still a testing object. Fairly easily seen with 150 mm.

IC 4997 (20ʰ20ᵐ.2, +16°45'): the brightest of the three planetary nebulae, mag. 10.5, bluish in colour, and forming a conspicuous pair with a yellow star about 1' to the southwest. With care may be seen with just 150 mm aperture.

Sagittarius

SAGITTARII• Sgr • THE ARCHER

Main chart(s): 18, 12 (13)
Area: 867 sq. deg. (15th)
Culminates 00:00 local time: early July

Most of Sagittarius lies in the Milky Way, only a small portion on the east lying well away from the galactic plane. The galactic centre lies just within the constellation at the far southwestern corner, close to the area known as Baade's Window, around NGC 6522, at a distance of approximately 7970 pc (≈ 26,000 l.y.). It is densely populated with open and globular clusters (over 30 of each are known), and emission, reflection and dark nebulae, but only a few can be described here. Although Sagittarius contains many planetary nebulae, most are faint and difficult to detect. Only one galaxy, on the borders of the Milky Way, is described.

β¹ **Sgr** (19^{h}22^m.6, -44°48') and β² **Sgr** (19^{h}23^m.5, -44°48') form a wide, naked-eye double, with stars of mags. 4.0 and 4.3. The southern star, β¹ Sgr, is probably a long-period binary (mags. 4.0, 7.1; PA 77°, Sep. 8".3).

ζ **Sgr** (19^{h}02^m.6, -29°53'): a fine, short-period binary (mags. 3.2, 3.4; PA 273°, Sep. 0".2–0".6; P = 21.1 yrs; A3 giant and A3 dwarf spectra). Closest in 2002, and currently widening rapidly.

η **Sgr** (18^{h}17^m.6, -36°46'): a probable long-period binary (mags. 3.2, 7.8; PA 105°, Sep. 3".6). The colours of the red-orange (M3.5) primary and the white companion are readily apparent.

21 **Sgr** (18^{h}25^m.3, -20°32'): a slow binary system (mags. 4.9, 7.4; PA 287°, Sep. 2".0; K2 giant, A spectra).

M8 (NGC 6523: 18^{h}03.8^m, -24°23'), the Lagoon Nebula: a gaseous nebula that is sufficiently bright and distinct to be detectable with the naked eye. Binoculars and telescopes reveal a dark lane against the glowing background. Its distance is about 1.6 kpc (≈ 5200 l.y.).

M17 (NGC 6618: 18^{h}21^m, -16°10'), the Omega or Swan Nebula: a gaseous nebula, visible in binoculars. A telescope is required to reveal its wealth of detail, which some observers maintain rivals that of M42 in Orion.

M20 (NGC 6514: 18^{h}02.3^m, -23°03'), the Trifid Nebula: although detectable with binoculars, it requires a telescope for the detailed structure to be seen. The principal source of the radiation is an O8 star at the centre, but this is accompanied by four more stars: three visible with 150 mm, the fourth with 200 mm, and the fifth with 300 mm.

M22 (NGC 6656: 18^{h}36^m.4, -23°54'): a very bright (mag. 5) globular cluster that is actually visible to the naked eye. It appears slightly elongated in binoculars and is readily resolved into stars with 75 mm aperture. It is one of the closest globular clusters at about 3.2 kpc (≈ 10,400 l.y.).

M23 (NGC 6494: 17^{h}56^m.8, -19°01'): a rich open cluster, mag. 5.5, roughly the apparent size of the Moon. Resolved in binoculars under good conditions. Its distance is about 700 pc (≈ 2280 l.y.).

M24 (approx. 18^{h}17^m, -18°40'), the Small Sagittarius Star Cloud: a patch of the Milky Way that is extremely rich in stars, rather than a true open cluster. There is a small cluster in this area (NGC 6603) but this was not what Messier described. The visible cluster is actually part of the Galaxy's Norma Arm, and its distance is about 4.6 kpc (≈ 15,000 l.y.). The Small Sagittarius Star Cloud also contains a notable dark nebula, **Barnard 92** (approx. 18^{h}15^m.5, -18°11'), which is visible to the naked eye.

M25 (IC 4725: 18^{h}31.6^m, -19°15'): a large open cluster, detectable with the naked eye, resolved with binoculars into numerous stars, the brightest about mag. 7.0. Unusually, it contains a Cepheid variable, **U Sgr** (18^{h}31^m.9, -19°07'), range mag. 6.3–7.1, P = 6.744925 days.

M54 (NGC 6715: 18^{h}55^m.1, -30°29'): a distant globular (perhaps the most distant), d = 27.4 kpc (≈ 89,400 l.y.), mag. 7.6. Like M5 in Serpens, it shows hints of yellowish stars in the centre, and blue-tinted ones in its outer regions. It lies on the far side of our galaxy and probably once belonged to the Sagittarius Dwarf Galaxy, which is being disrupted by the Galaxy's tidal forces.

M55 (NGC 6809: 19^{h}40^m.0, -30°57'): is a moderately bright (mag. 7.0) globular cluster, visible in binoculars, that lies in a rather sparsely populated area of the constellation. Clearly resolved with even 75 mm aperture. A close globular cluster, d = 5.4 kpc (≈ 17,600 l.y.).

M69 (NGC 6637: 18^{h}31^m.4, -32°20'): a bright globular cluster, mag. 7.7, readily visible with 75 mm and clearly resolved with 150 mm. Slightly elliptical and relatively compact. Its distance is 8.6 kpc (≈ 28,000 l.y.).

M70 (18^{h}43^m.2, -32°17'): a small, bright globular cluster, mag. 7.8, visible as a hazy spot with 75 mm, and requiring 150 mm or more to reveal stars within it. Its distance is 9 kpc (≈ 29,400 l.y.).

NGC 6520 (18^{h}03^m.5, -27°54'): an open cluster, magnitude approximately 7.6 and about 4' across. There is an orange star near the centre and the surrounding field consists of numerous faint stars. A clearly visible and highly irregular dark nebula, **Barnard 86**, lies to the northwest. The dark cloud is readily visible with small apertures. The distance of the cluster and dark nebula is about 1700 pc (≈ 5545 l.y.).

NGC 6522 (18^{h}03^m.6, -30°03'): a small, but fairly bright globular cluster, mag. 9.5. It appears granular with 150 mm, but begins to be resolved with 250 mm. The cluster is notable for lying extremely close to the direction of the galactic centre. The surrounding field contains numerous stars, but is fairly free from interstellar dust.

Baade's Window: An area, 15' in diameter, centred on the globular cluster **NGC 6522**, that is relatively free from interstellar absorption, allowing a view of the region around the galactic centre to be obtained with optical telescopes. It is actually about 4° to the east of the actual galactic centre. Walter Baade was able to estimate the distances of RR Lyrae stars in this region, and thus determine the distance of the galactic centre.

NGC 6544 (18ʰ07ᵐ.3, -25°00'): a highly condensed, small globular cluster (mag. 8.1) in a fine field. Requires apertures greater than 100 mm to be resolved. It is fairly close at about 3.2 kpc (≈ 10,400 l.y.).

NGC 6818 (19ʰ44ᵐ.0, -14°09'): a bright planetary nebula (mag. 9.9), clearly visible with just 75 mm. It is large (25" across), bluish in tint, and slightly elliptical. Its distance is about 2.2 kpc (≈ 7200 l.y.).

NGC 6822 (19ʰ44ᵐ.9, -14°48'), Barnard's Galaxy: an irregular galaxy, nominally mag. 9.4, but a difficult object, only faintly seen with 200 mm aperture, although glimpsed with smaller apertures on exceptionally clear nights. A member of the Local Group, distance approximately 460 kpc (≈ 1,500,000 l.y.).

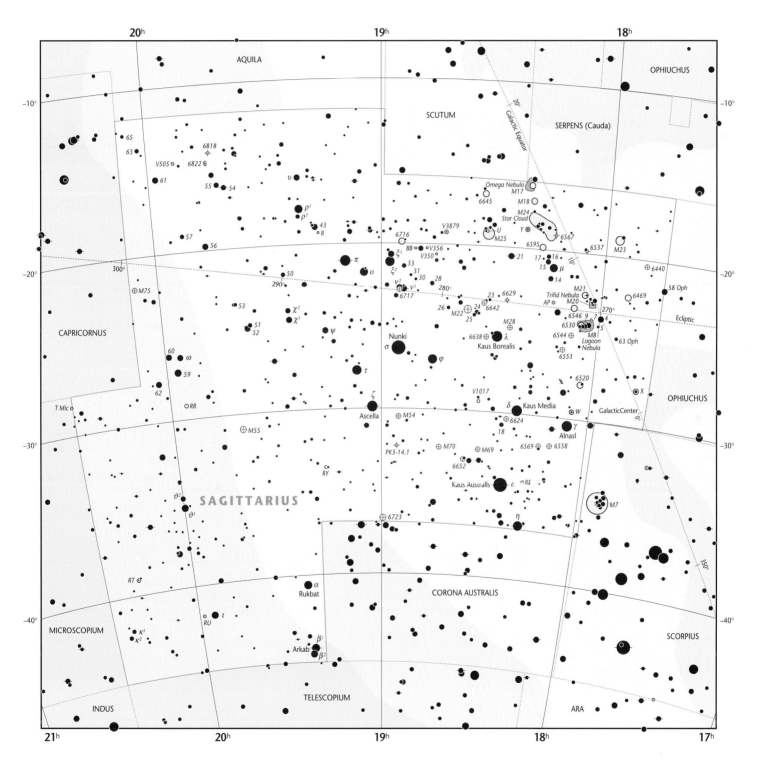

Scorpius
SCORPII • Sco • THE SCORPION

Main chart(s): 17, 18 (11, 12)
Area: 497 sq. deg. (33rd)
Culminates 00:00 local time: early June

Scorpius lies almost entirely within a densely populated area of the Milky Way and, like Sagittarius, contains numerous objects of interest. Despite being a smaller constellation, it has more open clusters than Sagittarius, with over 40 known, but slightly fewer globular clusters (20). There are many double stars, including Antares. Some twenty-odd much fainter stars in the region surrounding Antares (within an area of approximately $10° \times 7°$), have similar proper motions to that of the supergiant star. Together they form a group, known as the Antares Cluster, which is also surrounded by faint nebulosity. This group itself forms part of the much larger Scorpius-Centaurus (Sco-Cen) Association, which is the nearest concentration of hot, early-type (OB) stars to the Sun. This association lies at a distance of approximately 153 pc (≈ 500 l.y.), and stretches for about 184 pc (≈ 600 l.y.) from Scorpius, through Centaurus, to Crux. It contains some 40 OB stars, and the association as a whole has an overall mass of about 6000 solar masses.

α Sco (16ʰ29ᵐ.6, -26°26'), Antares: an orange-red (M1.5) supergiant about 600 million kilometres in diameter and some 9000 times as luminous as the Sun. It is a semiregular (SR) variable (mag. 0.9–1.8), and a striking binary system with a blue-white (B) dwarf companion (mag. 5.4; PA 276°, Sep. 2".9). The companion often appears to have a greenish tinge by contrast with the primary, the light from which also illuminates a large, nearby reflection nebula (about 75" across).

β Sco (16ʰ05ᵐ.4, -19°48'), Graffias: a quintuple system, the principal pair consisting of B0.5 and B2 dwarf stars (mags. 2.6, 4.9; PA 23°, Sep. 13".6). The third component is near the primary (mag. 6.0, PA 88°, Sep. 0".9) but now considerably closer. The primary is now known to be a spectroscopic binary, and B has proved to be an extremely close binary.

ζ¹ Sco (16ʰ54ᵐ.3, -42°22') and ζ² Sco (16ʰ54ᵐ.9) form a wide, naked-eye double. The northern star, ζ¹ Sco, is a white (B1.5) extreme supergiant (mag. 4.8) and the brightest member of NGC 6231. Its luminosity is nearly 280,000 times that of the Sun. The other star, ζ² Sco, is an orange (K4) giant of mag. 3.6.

μ¹ Sco (16ʰ52ᵐ.1, -38°03') and μ² Sco (16ʰ52ᵐ.6, -38°02') form another wide double easily seen with the naked eye. The southern star, μ¹ Sco, is a β Lyrae-type eclipsing binary, range mag. 2.9–3.2, P = 1.44626907 days. The second star, μ², slightly further north, is mag. 3.6.

ν Sco (16ʰ12ᵐ.0, -19°28'): a multiple system, the southern counterpart of ε Lyr (the Double Double), but fainter and more compact. The primary pair (mags. 4.1, 6.2; PA 3°, Sep. 1".3) is resolved with 150 mm, and the wider secondary pair (mags. 6.8, 7.5; PA 53°, Sep. 2".3) with 75 mm. The brightest star has an additional very close companion, and is also a spectroscopic binary, so the system has six components.

M4 (16ʰ23ᵐ.6, -26°31'): a large and fairly loose globular cluster, (approx. mag. 6), with a bright lane through its centre. It is visible even with the naked eye and as a fuzzy patch in binoculars, although close to Antares, which tends to cause some glare. It, and NGC 6397 in Ara, are contenders for being the closest globular cluster to us, at about 6,500 l.y.

M6 (NGC 6405: 17ʰ40ᵐ.1, -32°12'), the Butterfly Cluster: an open cluster (mag. 4.5), visible to the naked eye and resolved into individual stars in binoculars. The brightest star is the orange (K2.5) bright supergiant, semiregular variable BM Sco, range mag. 5.8–6.2, P = 850: days. The cluster is about 25' across, so requires a wide field when viewed with a telescope.

M7 (NGC 6475: 17ʰ53ᵐ.9, -34°37'): a large, bright (mag. 3.5) open cluster, readily visible to the naked eye, and best seen with low-magnification binoculars. It has about 80 members and its distance is about 600 pc (≈ 2000 l.y.).

M80 (NGC 6093: 16ʰ17ᵐ.0, -22°58'): small, compact globular cluster (about mag. 7.5), readily seen in binoculars, and just resolved with 150 mm.

NGC 6153 (16ʰ31ᵐ.5, -40°15'): a pale blue planetary nebula, mag. 10.9, in an attractive field. Easily observed with 75 mm. Its distance is about 1.8 kpc (≈ 5870 l.y.).

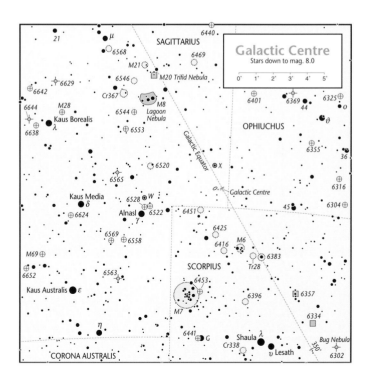

NGC 6231 (16h54m.0, -41°48'): an extremely large and bright open cluster, readily seen with the naked eye, with some stars resolved in binoculars. The cluster is more spectacular than the Double Cluster in Perseus, and contains many very hot stars with a whole range of spectral types. Blue-white, white, yellow and orange stars are visible. Its distance is about 780 l.y.

NGC 6302 (17h13m.7, -37°06'), the Bug Nebula: a bright (mag. 9.6) planetary nebula. The nebulosity is noticeably elongated and has a bright centre. Its distance is about 2 kpc (≈ 6520 l.y.).

NGC 6388 (17h36m.3, -44°44'): a compact globular cluster (mag. 6.9), readily visible with 75 mm, but which cannot be resolved easily, even with much greater apertures.

α-Scorpiids (double radiant at 16h31m, -24° & 16h04m, -24°): a meteor shower that actually appears to have several weak radiants. Active April to July, with normal limits April 20 to May 20. Maxima April 27 and May 12 for eastern and western radiants, respectively, zenithal hourly rate of about 5.

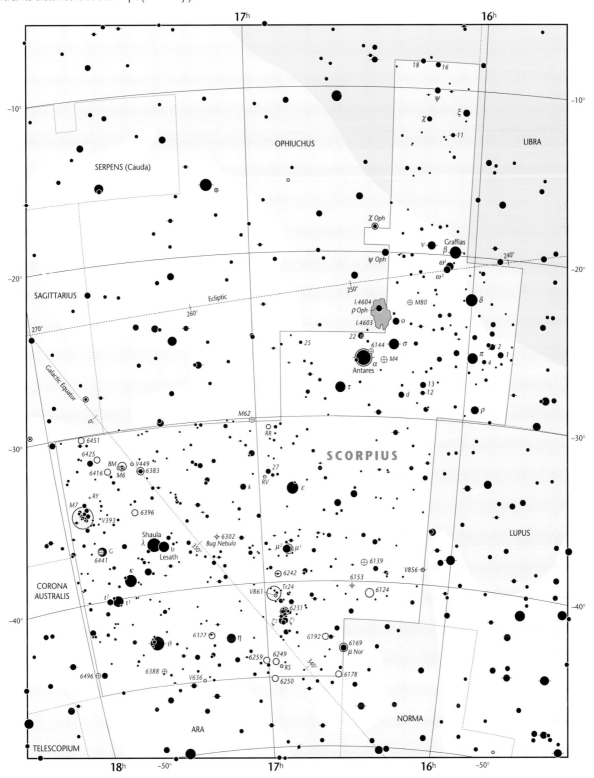

Sculptor

SCULPTORIS • Scl • THE SCULPTOR

Main chart(s): 14 (19)
Area: 475 sq. deg. (36th)
Culminates 00:00 local time: late September

This inconspicuous constellation – originally named 'The Sculptor's Workshop' by de La Caille – has no stars brighter than mag. 4.5. It does, however, contain the South Galactic Pole, where there is a clear view into extragalactic space, unimpeded by the gas, dust, and star clouds of the Galaxy, although there is one globular cluster, NGC 288. The area is therefore full of galaxies, including the late-type spirals that form the Sculptor Group, the nearest concentration beyond our own Local Group. There is also the Sculptor Dwarf Galaxy (ESO-351-G30), a dwarf spheroidal galaxy. This satellite of the Galaxy is, like the Fornax Dwarf Galaxy, of such low surface brightness that it is beyond the capabilities of most amateurs to detect it.

ε **Scl** (01ʰ45ᵐ.6, -25°03'): a binary system (mags. 5.4, 8.6; PA 23°, Sep. 4".7; F1 and K1 dwarf spectra). The system has a very long period, estimated at 1192 years.

κ¹ **Scl** (00ʰ09ᵐ.3, -27°59'): another long-period binary with yellow components (mags. 6.1, 6.2; PA 265°, Sep. 1".4; F4 and F3 giant spectra). Requires 150 mm aperture to be resolved.

NGC 55 (00ʰ14ᵐ.9, -39°11'): an edge-on, barred spiral galaxy, mag. 8.2. An aperture of 300 mm is required to show it well, but even 150 mm will show the elongated central region.

NGC 253 (00ʰ47ᵐ.6, -25°17'), the Silver Coin Galaxy: an edge-on spiral (Sc) galaxy, mag. 7.1. Readily seen as elongated even with 75 mm aperture, and a fine object with 300 mm.

NGC 288 (00ʰ52ᵐ.8, -26°35'): a poorly concentrated globular cluster, mag. 8.1, appearing as an extended, hazy spot, although individual stars may be detected even with 100 mm. Its distance is about 8.3 kpc (≈ 27,000 l.y.).

NGC 7793 (23ʰ57ᵐ.8, -32°35'): a wide-open spiral (Sd) galaxy, mag. 9.1. Difficult to detect (like M33 in Triangulum) because of its very open arms, but is visible with 150 mm, although poorly defined. Its distance is about 3.5 Mpc (≈ 11.4 million light-years).

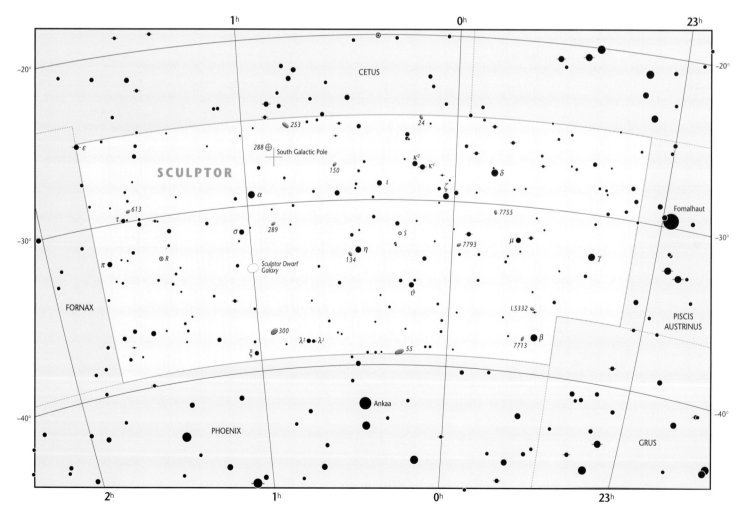

Scutum

SCUTI • Sct • THE SHIELD

Main chart(s): 12
Area: 109 sq. deg. (84th)
Culminates 00:00 local time: early July

This small constellation was introduced by Hevelius, originally under the name of Scutum Sobieski ('Sobieski's Shield') in honour of his patron, the Polish king, John Sobieski III, famous for repelling a Turkish invasion of Poland in 1683. The constellation has some of the brightest star clouds of the Milky Way, and despite being small, has 15 open clusters.

δ Sct (18ʰ42ᵐ.3, -09°03'): the prototype for a class of low-amplitude, pulsating variable stars. Its range is too small (mags. 4.6–4.8) and the changes too rapid (period 4.65 hours) for visual observations to be successful.

R Sct (18ʰ47ᵐ.5, -05°42'): an interesting variable of the RV Tauri type (alternating deep and shallow minima), with a range of mag 4.3–8.7, and a period of 146.5 days.

Σ 2373 (18ʰ45ᵐ.9, -10°30'): a slow binary (mags 7.2, 8.2; PA 338°, Sep.4".1). Yellow stars with an F2 dwarf spectrum, clearly visible with 75 mm aperture.

IC 1287 (18ʰ31ᵐ.3, -10°50'): a faint reflection nebula, difficult to observe, but illuminated by S 2325 (mags 5.8, 9.1; PA 257°, Sep. 12".3), clearly visible with 75 mm aperture.

IC 1295 (18ʰ54ᵐ.6, -08°50'): a rather faint (mag. 12.5:) planetary nebula, that may be glimpsed with 150 mm, but really requires at least 200 mm. It lies in a fine field.

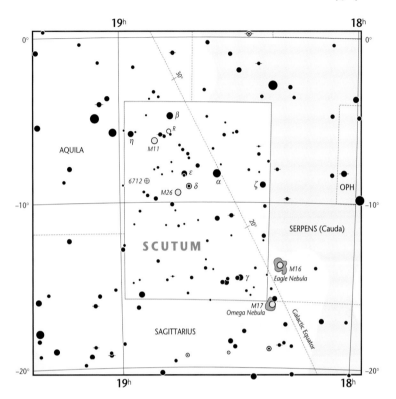

M11 (NGC 6705: 18ʰ51ᵐ.1, -06°16'), the Wild Duck Cluster: a prominent open cluster, readily seen with binoculars, and a magnificent object with larger apertures. It has hundreds of members and there is a bright, pale yellow star at one edge. The cluster's distance is about 1,720 pc (≈ 5,610 l.y.).

M26 (NGC 6694: 18ʰ45ᵐ.2, -09°24'): an open cluster, with approximately 30–40 members. It is fairly loose, so is not an easy object with small apertures. Its distance is about 1,550 pc (≈ 5,060 l.y.).

NGC 6712 (18ʰ53ᵐ.1, -08°42'): a moderately bright globular cluster (mag. 8.2), detectable with 100 mm, but still poorly resolved with 200 mm.

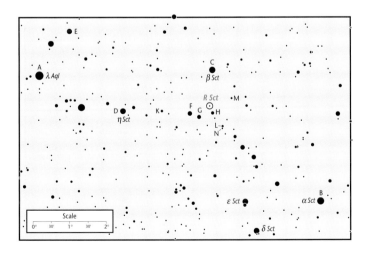

Comparisons for R Sct:					
A = λ Aql	3.41	E = 14 Aql	5.41	K	7.56
B = α Sct	4.05	F	6.23	L	8.00
C = β Sct	4.40	G	6.50	M	8.31
D = η Sct	4.99	H	7.07	N	8.62

CONSTELLATIONS

Serpens

SERPENTIS • Ser • THE SERPENT

Main chart(s): 11, 12 (5, 6)
Area (whole constellation): 637 sq. deg. (23rd)
Culminates 00:00 local time: see text

Serpens is the only constellation that is divided into two parts, Serpens Caput (the Serpent's Head) and Serpens Cauda (the Serpent's Tail), separated by Ophiuchus. Serpens Caput, lying to the west, north of Libra, culminates at 00:00 local time about mid-May. Serpens Cauda, in the east, lies within the Milky Way, and touches the galactic plane at two points. It culminates at 00:00 local time in late June. Although Serpens Cauda contains more clusters, many are affected by the strong interstellar absorption close to the galactic plane. Serpens Caput may have fewer objects but it is free from such absorption.

β **Ser** (15^h46^m, +15°25' – S. Caput): a blue-white star of mag. 3.6, which forms a wide double with an unrelated star of mag. 6.7 just to its north.

δ **Ser** ($15^h34^m.8$, +10°32' – S. Caput): a probable long-period binary (mags. 4.2, 5.2; PA 176°, Sep. 4".4; A9 subgiant and A7 dwarf spectra). It has been suggested that the period may be as long as 3168 years.

ϑ **Ser** ($18^h56^m.2$, +04°12' – S. Cauda): a triple system, with one bright pair (mags 4.5, 4.6; PA 103°, Sep. 22".3; A5 dwarf spectra). These two components are thought to be a binary pair, but have shown no change since discovery (by F.G.W. Struve) in 1830, so the period must be extremely long. It is not known whether the orange-coloured, widely separated, third component (mag. 7.9; PA BC 56°, Sep. 403.9") is actually part of the same system.

ν **Ser** ($17^h20^m.8$, -12°51' – S. Cauda): a wide double that may be resolved with binoculars (mags. 4.3, 8.3; PA 28°, Sep. 46".3).

5 Ser ($15^h19^m.2$, +01°46' – S. Caput): a probable long-period binary (mags. 5.1, 9.7; PA 36°, Sep. 11") consisting of a yellow (F8) giant and a reddish companion, visible with 100 mm.

59 Ser ($18^h27^m.2$, +00°12' – S. Cauda): a multiple system with one principal pair (mags. 5.3, 7.6; PA 320°, Sep. 3".9; G0 giant and A6 dwarf spectra). The bright component has been shown to be a spectroscopic triple system. This consists of a close binary system with a pair of A6 dwarf stars, P = 1.85 days, orbiting the G0 giant with a period of 386 days.

R Ser ($15^h50^m.7$, +15°08' – S. Caput): a long-period (M) variable, range mag. 5.2–14.4, P = 356.4 days. At maximum, it is visible for a long time in binoculars.

β **131** ($18^h13^m.6$, -15°37' – S. Cauda): a fine triple system discovered by Burnham. The principal pair (mags 7.3, 9.3; PA 278°, Sep. 3".0) may be seen with 75 mm aperture, whereas the third component (mag. 11.5; PA 295°, Sep. 8".7) requires at least 150 mm aperture.

Σ **2303** ($18^h20^m.1$, -07°59' – S. Cauda): a probable binary (mags 6.6, 9.1; PA 239°, Sep. 1".9) just visible with 75 mm aperture. The pair has shown very slow motion since discovery by Struve in 1831. The region is heavily obscured by interstellar absorption, so there are few field stars.

Σ **2375** ($18^h45^m.5$, +05°30' – S. Cauda): a long-period binary system (mags. 6.3, 6.7; PA 118°, Sep. 2".5; A1 dwarf spectra). Both components have been found to be extremely close binaries, resolvable only with very large apertures. They were discovered by W.S. Finsen in 1953, and because of their almost idential position angles and separations, with orbits highly inclined to the line of sight, he named them Tweedledum and Tweedledee.

M5 (NGC 5904: $15^h18^m.6$, +02°05' – S. Caput): a large, bright and rich globular cluster (mag. 5.8), detectable with the naked eye under good conditions, and extremely fine in a telescope. With a large enough aperture there are hints of colour, with a slightly bluish core and yellowish outer region. Thought to contain at least 500,000 stars, d = 7.5 kpc ($\approx$ 24,500 l.y.).

M16 (NGC 6611: $18^h18.6^m$, -13°44' – S. Cauda): a combined open cluster (NGC 6611), visible in binoculars, and a diffuse nebula (**IC 4703**), the Eagle Nebula, which adds a background haziness. A large telescope and good conditions are required to see detail in the gaseous nebulosity. The cluster as a whole is about 800,000 years old, but some individual stars have ages of just 50,000 years.

NGC 6535 ($18^h03^m.8$, -00°18' – S. Cauda): a faint globular cluster, mag. 10.6, only just visible with 100 mm, and 150 mm showing a hazy object with just a few individual stars. There is some absorption here, so its distance is uncertain, but is estimated at about 6.7 kpc ($\approx$ 22,000 l.y.).

NGC 6539 ($18^h04^m.8$, -07°35' – S. Cauda): a heavily obscured globular cluster, mag. 9.6, just visible with 150 mm, and not resolved with 300 mm. There is considerable absorption here as shown by the almost complete absence of field stars around the cluster. The distance is estimated as about 7 kpc ($\approx$ 23,000 l.y.).

NGC 6604 ($18^h18^m.1$, -12°14' – S. Cauda): a small open cluster, mag. 6.5, associated with nebulosity.

IC 1276 ($18^h10^m.7$, -07°12' – S. Cauda): a heavily reddened globular cluster, mag. 11.0, which is difficult to detect with 200 mm aperture even under good conditions. It is, however, over 2' in diameter, and lies about 90' west of **NGC 6539**.

IC 4756 ($18^h39^m.0$, +0527' – S. Cauda): a fine, bright, open cluster, mag. 5.4, clearly visible to the naked eye, and a large object in binoculars. Telescopically, a wide field and low magnification are required. Its brightest stars are mag. 8–9, and its distance is about 400 pc ($\approx$ 1300 l.y.).

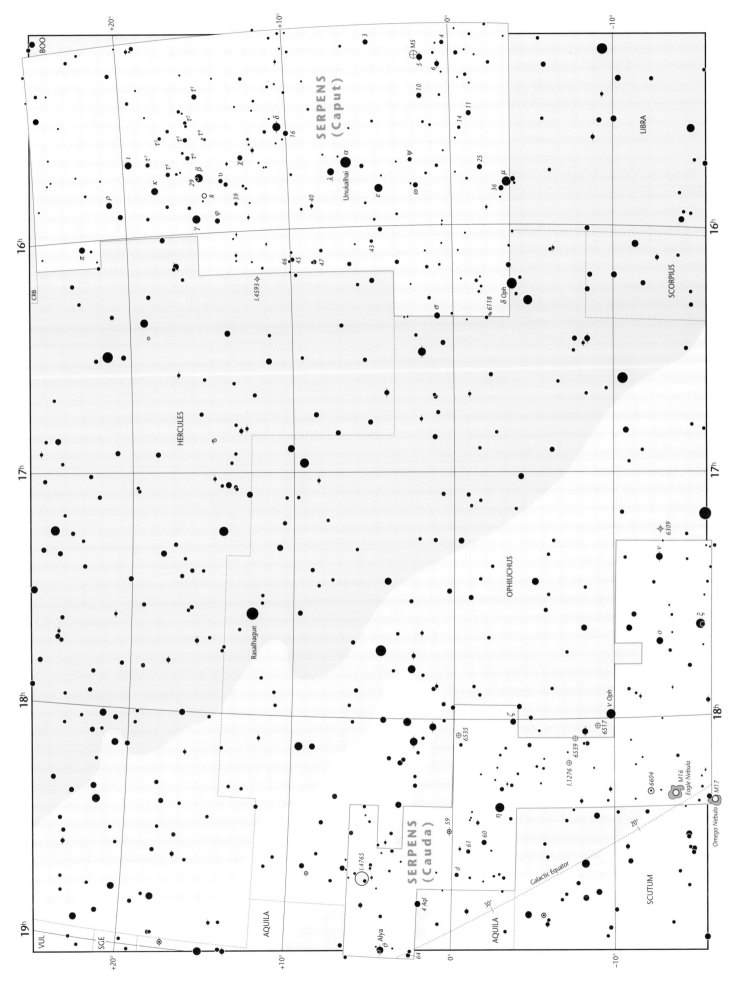

Sextans

SEXTANTIS • Sex • THE SEXTANT

Main chart: 10
Area: 314 sq. deg. (47th)
Culminates 00:00 local time: late February

Another constellation introduced by Johannes Hevelius in 1687, and which have been retained to the present day. (The others were Canes Venatici, Lacerta, Leo Minor, Lynx, Monoceros, Scutum, and Vulpecula.) Sextans represents the large, mounted sextant (with open, rather than telescopic sights) that Hevelius used for his positional measurements. It was the accuracy of his measurements with this instrument that led to the famous dispute with Hooke, in London, and to Edmond Halley actually making the trip to Danzig specifically to establish the accuracy of Hevelius' methods.

Like Canes Venatici, Leo Minor and Lynx, Sextans is a small, faint constellation. It lies well away from the Milky Way in a star-poor area, so the constellation is unremarkable, with the brightest star (α Sex) only mag. 4.5. There are a few double stars and a few observable galaxies. Even though it is not normally regarded as a zodiacal constellation, the northeastern corner is close to the ecliptic, and the Moon and planets frequently cross this area of the constellation.

γ Sex (09h52m.5, -08°06'): a binary system (mags. 5.6, 6.1; PA 56°, 0".6; P = 75.6 yrs). Rather difficult to resolve, especially as the components are beginning to close. At least 250 mm aperture is required.

35 Sex (10h43m.3, +04°45'): a probable long-period binary system (mags. 6.3, 7.4; PA 239°, Sep. 6".8; K3 and K0 giant spectra). There has been essentially no change in the relative position of the stars since F.G.W. Struve's measurements in 1832.

40 Sex (10h49m.3, -04°01'): another probable binary system (mags. 7.0, 7.7; PA 13°, Sep. 2".3; A7 spectra). Easily seen with 75 mm. Both the position angle and separation are changing slowly, but the arc covered is too short to show if the pair form a true binary system.

NGC 2967 (09h42m.1, +00°20'): a faint (Sc) galaxy, mag. 11.6. Because of the extended spiral arms, only the nuclear region is detectable. An aperture of 300 mm is required for the outer regions to become visible.

NGC 2974 (09h42m.6, +03°42'): a spiral (Sa) galaxy, mag. 10.8. It may be detected with 150 mm aperture, but really requires larger instruments. There is a star of mag. 10 at its southwestern edge.

NGC 3115 (10h05m.2, -07°43'): the Spindle Galaxy: a greatly flattened (E6) elliptical galaxy, mag. 9.2. Just detectable in binoculars under good conditions, central regions visible with 75 mm, and considerable detail with 150 mm. A larger aperture (at least 250 mm) will show a dwarf elliptical satellite galaxy (MCG-1-26-21), about 17' to the southeast.

NGC 3166 (10h13m.8, +03°26'): a barred spiral (SBa) galaxy, mag. 10.6. In the same field as NGC 3169 (10h14m.2, +03°28'): a spiral (Sb) galaxy. Both may be detected with 150 mm, and appear very similar, with only the central regions visible.

U5373 (10h00m.0, +05°20'): a faint, dwarf irregular (Irr) galaxy, mag 11.3. Designation indicates that it occurs in the Uppsala General Catalogue of Galaxies, published in 1973. Also known as the Sextans B galaxy.

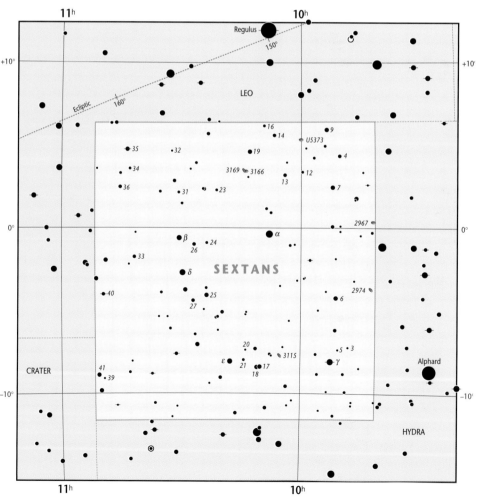

Taurus

TAURI • Tau • THE BULL

Main chart(s): 9 (2, 3, 8)
Area: 797 sq. deg. (17th)
Culminates 00:00 local time: late November

Although the eastern portion of this constellation reaches as far as the galactic plane, there are no globular clusters or notable diffuse nebulae within its borders. It does, however, have several open clusters, including the Pleiades and the Hyades, both striking groups of stars.

α **Tau** (04h36m.1, +16°31'), Aldebaran: an orange (K5) giant, which is a low-amplitude, irregular variable, range mag. 0.75–0.95. It is actually a multiple system, suspected of having 6 components. Components B, D, and F are mag. 13.6 or 13.7. Component C (mag. 11.3; PA 29°, Sep. 131".7) should be easier to detect. No magnitude is recorded for

component E, which appears not to have been observed since 1899. Contrary to appearances, α Tau does not belong to the Hyades cluster, but it a foreground star, d = 19.964 pc (65.12 l.y.).

ϑ¹ **Tau** (04h28m.8, +15°52') and ϑ² Tau (04h29m.9, +15°52') form a wide double in the Hyades, visible to the naked eye. ϑ² **Tau**, an A7 giant, is mag. 3.4, and the brightest star in the cluster. ϑ¹ **Tau** a G7 giant, is slightly fainter at mag. 3.8.

κ¹ **Tau** (04h25m.6, +22°18') and κ² Tau (04h25m.7, +22°13'): a wide pair of white stars (A7 spectra) about 5'.5 apart. Between them lies another double, possibly a binary system, known as Σ 541 (04h25m.4, +22°11').

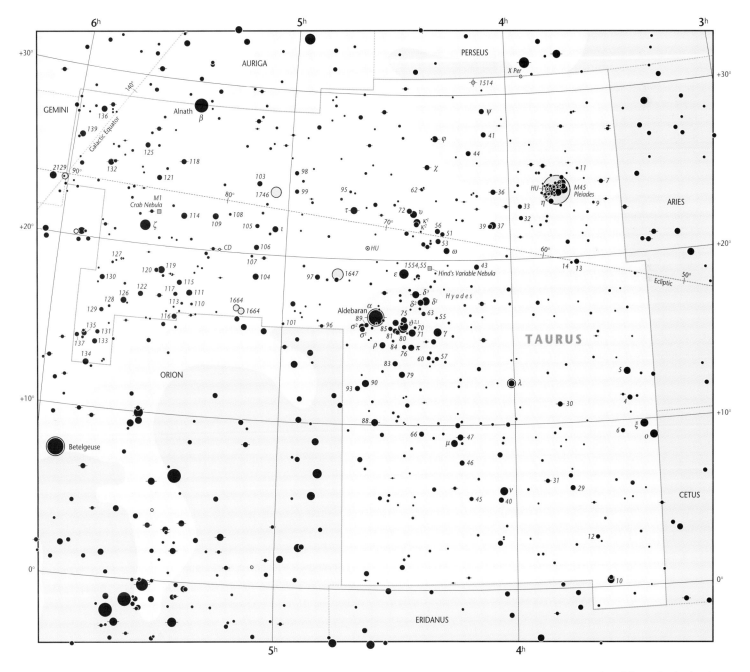

CONSTELLATIONS

Little is known about this pair (mags. 9.5, 9.8; PA 328°, Sep. 5".3), which is difficult to observe because of the glare from κ¹ and κ² Tau.

λ **Tau** (04ʰ00ᵐ.9, +12°30'): a bright, Algol-type (EA) eclipsing variable. It is easily followed with the naked eye, with a range of mag. 3.23 to 4.10, and a period of 3.952955 days (3ᵈ22ʰ52ᵐ).

Comparisons for λ Tau:

π³ Ori	3.19	ξ Tau	3.74
ε Tau	3.54	ν Tau	3.91
o Tau	3.60	5 Tau	4.09
γ Tau	3.64	μ Tau	4.30

HU Tau (04ʰ38ᵐ, +20°41') is an interesting Algol-like eclipsing binary, readily followed with binoculars. It has a range of mag. 5.45 to 6.86 and a period of 2.0563 days (2ᵈ1ʰ21ᵐ).

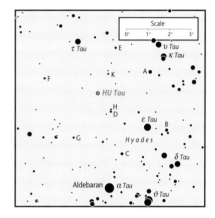

Comparisons for HU Tau:

A	5.7	D	6.6	G	7.1
B	6.0	E	6.8	H	7.2
C	6.2	F	6.9	K	7.4

47 Tau (04ʰ13ᵐ.9, +09°16'): a close binary system (mags. 4.9, 7.4; PA 351°, Sep. 1".1), requiring an aperture of about 200 mm to be resolved. The bright star has a G3 giant spectrum.

M1 (NGC 1952: 05ʰ34ᵐ.5, +22°01'), the Crab Nebula: just detectable in binoculars under good conditions, despite being rather faint (about mag. 9). The gaseous emission is the remnant of material ejected in a supernova explosion that occurred in 1054, observed by Chinese astronomers. The stellar remnant in the centre is a pulsar, a rapidly rotating neutron star (P = 33.3 milliseconds). The optical magnitude is too faint (about mag. 16) for it to be detected by most amateurs.

The V-shaped **Hyades** (approx. 04ʰ27ᵐ, +16°): the second closest open cluster (d = 150 light-years), its stars appear spread over a considerable area of sky. (The Ursa Major Moving Cluster is the closest to us.) In the Hyades (also known as Melotte 25), all the stars are moving on parallel paths. This was formerly used to determine the cluster's distance, as an important step in establishing the scale of cosmic distances.

M45 (approx. 03ʰ39ᵐ, +24°07'), the Pleiades: wonderful open cluster. Most observers find at least six stars with the naked eye, and many more

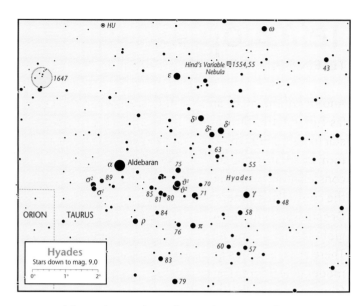

appear with binoculars. Under perfect conditions, the reflection nebulosity around Merope (NGC 1435 or Tempel's Nebula) may be glimpsed with binoculars. The total number of stars in the cluster is about 500, and the blue-white colour of the brightest stars is an indication that the stars and cluster are extremely young, with an age of about 78 million years.

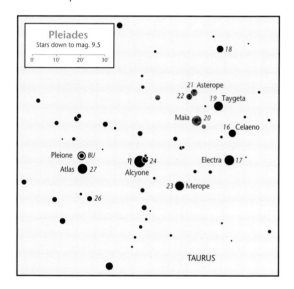

NGC 1514 (04ʰ09ᵐ.2, +30°47'): a planetary nebula with a very bright (mag. 9.4) central star. Unlike the majority of planetary nebulae, where the stellar remnant (usually a white dwarf or helium star) is invisible, in this case the star is easier to see than the surrounding nebulosity, which requires an aperture of 150–200 mm.

NGC 1647 (04ʰ46ᵐ.0, +19°04'): large open cluster, mag. 6.4, about 35' across. It has some 200 members and lies at about 550 pc (≈ 1800 l.y.).

Taurids (radiant at 03ʰ44ᵐ, +14°): a consistent meteor shower with only a moderate maximum zenithal hourly rate of 10 slow meteors, and some bright members. Active Oct. 20 to Nov. 30, maximum Nov. 3.

Telescopium

TELESCOPII • Tel • THE TELESCOPE

Main chart(s): 18 (19)
Area: 252 sq. deg. (57th)
Culminates 00:00 local time: early July

Another of the many small constellations introduced (as Tubus Astronomicus) by de La Caille. The brightest star (α Tel) is only mag. 3.5, and together with δ, ε, and ζ forms a small group in the far northwestern corner of the constellation, on the edge of the Milky Way. The rest of the constellation merely consists of a few faint stars. Despite touching the Milky Way, there is just one globular cluster and no open clusters or diffuse nebulae. There are numerous galaxies, but just one that is moderately bright. The only planetary nebula (IC 4699) is faint, sources differing as to whether it is photographic mag. 11.9 or 13.3.

ε **Tel** (18^{h}11^m.2, -45°57'): an unequal, difficult, pair (mags. 4.5, 12.9; PA 228°, Sep. 21"). The primary has a yellow, G5 giant spectrum, but the faint companion requires at least 250 mm aperture, and is believed to be a field star.

RR Tel (20^{h}04^m.2, -55°43'): a variable star of the Z And type, normally faint (around mag. 16.5) that exhibited irregular fluctuations prior to an outburst to mag. 6.5 in 1944. It subsequently displayed small-amplitude fluctuations, with a periodicity of 387 days, then 374.2 days, and finally 395 days. These changes are poorly understood and another outburst may occur at any time.

Δ **227** (19^{h}52^m.6, -54°58'): a probable long-period binary with a fine colour contrast (mags. 5.7, 6.5; PA 149°, Sep. 23"; K0 giant and A0 dwarf spectra). Discovered by J. Dunlop in early 19th century.

I 113 (18^{h}58^m.9, -48°30'): a binary system of unknown period (mags. 6.7, 10.5; PA 229°, Sep. 3".0), detectable with 75 mm, but closing slowly. The primary has a K5 giant spectrum. Discovered by R.T. A. Innes.

Hrr 8 (18^{h}30^m.4, -46°08'), Harrington 8: an asterism, just south of δ1 Tel, of 8, 9th-magnitude stars arranged in the form of a cross. It is sometimes given the fanciful name of 'X-Marks-The-Spot' Cluster.

NGC 6584 (18^{h}18^m.6, -52°13'): a fairly condensed globular cluster, mag. 9.2, readily detected with 100 mm, but resolved only with 200 mm aperture. Its distance is 13.4 kpc (≈ 43,700 l.y.).

NGC 6868 (20^{h}09^m.9, -48°23'): a moderately bright, lenticular (S0) galaxy, mag. 10.6, detectable with 100 mm. It is part of a small cluster of galaxies in the area, some of which may be visible with larger instruments.

IC 4699 (18^{h}18^m.5, -45°59'): a planetary nebula that is rather a difficult object, whichever magnitude value (11.9 or 13.3) is correct. It really requires an aperture of 300 mm, or more. There is an 11th-mag. star just over 1' to the north, and a small pair approximately 1' to the southwest. The distance is estimated as about 5000 pc (≈ 16,300 l.y.).

CONSTELLATIONS

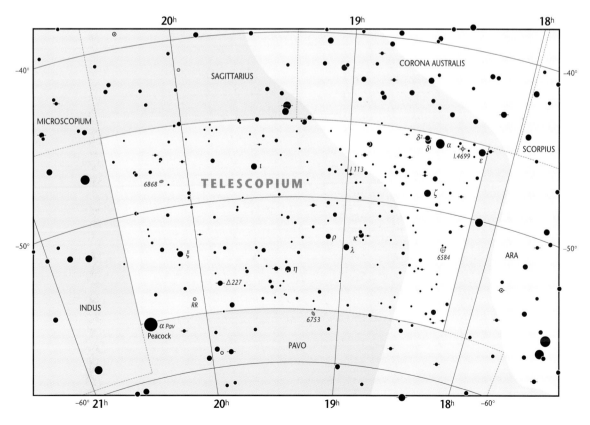

Triangulum

TRIANGULI • Tri • THE TRIANGLE

Main chart: 2
Area: 132 sq. deg. (78th)
Culminates 00:00 local time: late October

Triangulum is a small constellation lying just outside the borders of the Milky Way, but there are no clusters (of either kind), nor any nebulae. As might be expected, a few galaxies are visible, but all are faint, and of little interest when compared with the constellation's main claim to fame: M33, a prominent member of the Local Group. With adequate instrumentation, it is even possible to see clusters and nebulae in M33, although it is difficult to view the galaxy as a whole.

6 Tri (02ʰ12ᵐ.4, +30°18'), also known as ι **Tri**: a multiple system consisting of a long-period binary with yellow and blue-white stars (mags. 5.3, 6.9; PA 71°, Sep. 3".9). Each of these components is a spectroscopic binary, with periods of 14.73 and 2.24 days, respectively.

Σ 183 Tri (01ʰ55ᵐ.1, +28°48'): a triple system, where the yellow (F2) and bluish-white AB components (mags. 7.7, 8.4; PA 278°, Sep. 0".6) were too close to be resolved in 1955, but have slowly separated. The C component (mag. 8.7; PA 164°, Sep. 5".6) is relatively easy by comparison.

R Tri (02ʰ37ᵐ.0, +34°16'): a long-period (Mira) variable, with a range of over 7 magnitudes (5.4–12.6) and a period of 267 days. It is readily visible in binoculars for some weeks around maximum.

M33 (NGC 598: 01ʰ33ᵐ.9, +30°40'), the Triangulum or 'Pinwheel' Galaxy: a face-on spiral (Sc) galaxy with a low surface brightness, making it far more difficult to see than M31 in Andromeda, despite being larger than the Full Moon. It is said to be visible to people with keen eyesight under exceptionally clear conditions, when it is the most distant object visible, at approximately 2.6 million light years. It is best observed as a whole with low-magnification binoculars. Good conditions and a larger aperture (200 mm or more) are required to detect detail, excluding **NGC 604**, an emission nebula, which is relatively conspicuous.

NGC 604 (02ʰ33.9ᵐ, +30°39'): an emission nebula in M33. It is about 10' northeast of the galaxy's nucleus, and is so bright that it is often visible when the galaxy itself is invisible.

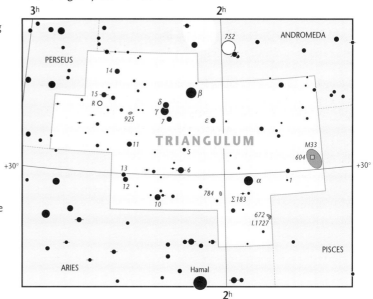

Triangulum Australe

TRIANGULI AUSTRALIS • Tra • THE SOUTHERN TRIANGLE

Main chart(s): 20 (18, 19)
Area: 110 sq. deg. (83rd)
Culminates 00:00 local time: late May

A small constellation, but brighter than its northern counterpart. There is some disagreement about whether it was first proposed by Keyser and de Houtman or by Pieter Theodor. It lies in the Milky Way and has one open cluster, one accessible planetary nebula and a few interesting double stars.

ι TrA (16ʰ28ᵐ.0, -64°03'): a visual double (mags. 5.3, 9.4; PA 12°, Sep. 13"), easily resolved with 75 mm. The brighter component has an F4 subgiant spectrum, and is a spectroscopic binary.

Rmk 20 (15ʰ47ᵐ.9, -65°27'): a binary system (mags. 6.2, 6.4; PA 147°, Sep. 1".8; A7 and A8 dwarf spectra), clearly visible with 75 mm. Discovered by C.L. Rümker, early in the 19th century.

NGC 5979 (15ʰ47ᵐ.7, -61°13'): a planetary nebula, mag. 11.5, distinguishable with 75 mm, and clearly showing a hazy disk with 100 mm.

NGC 6025 (16ʰ03ᵐ.7, -60°30'): a bright open cluster, mag. 5.1, best seen with 100 mm. Its distance is 840 pc (≈ 2740 l.y.).

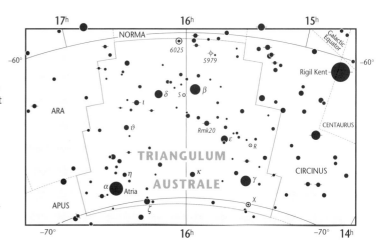

Tucana

TUCANAE • Tuc • THE TOUCAN

Main chart(s): 20 (14, 18, 19)
Area: 295 sq. deg. (48th)
Culminates 00:00 local time: mid-September

This is another of the small constellations introduced by Keyser and de Houtman. It has just a single relatively bright star, α Tuc, mag. 2.9, in the northwestern corner. Its most notable objects lie in the southeast: the Small Magellanic Cloud and 47 Tuc, a conspicuous globular cluster. There are a number of galaxies but these are faint. Because of the feeble absorption by gas and dust in our galaxy, the area was chosen for the long exposures by the Hubble Space Telescope that were used to create the Hubble Deep Field South, matching the Hubble Deep Field North (in Ursa Major) and later supplemented by the Hubble Ultra Deep Field (in Fornax, pp. 94-95).

β **Tuc** (00h31m.5, -62°58') a multiple star. Two components (β^1 and β^2) are readily visible (mags. 4.4, 4.5; PA 169°, Sep. 27".0, B9 and A2 dwarf spectra). The third component (β^3) lies about 10' southeast (mag. 5.2, A2 dwarf spectrum). Component β^1 has a close companion (mag. 13.6; PA 151°, Sep. 2".4), which appears to be stationary. Component β^2 is a close binary system (P = 44.4 yrs) and the third star, β^3, is also a close binary. Although they have identical proper motions, the distances (140, 172, and 152 l.y., respectively) of these three binaries indicate that they do not form a larger physical system.

δ **Tuc** (22h27m.3, -64°58'): a probable binary system (mags. 4.5, 8.9; PA 282°, Sep. 7".2; B9 and G0 dwarf spectra).

κ **Tuc** (01h15m.8, -68°53'): a probable binary with yellow and orange stars (mags. 5.1, 7.3; PA 336°, Sep. 5".4; F5 and K1 dwarf spectra).

Small Magellanic Cloud (SMC): one of the Milky Way's satellite galaxies, sometimes known as 'Nubecula Minor'. It is classified as irregular, and lies at a distance of approximately 61 kpc (≈ 200,000 l.y.). It appears about 3° across, and its diameter is actually about 2.7 kpc (≈ 6000 l.y.). It has less dust and more gas than the LMC, but fewer clusters and nebulae.

47 Tuc (NGC 104: 00h24m.1, -72°05'): a striking globular cluster, mag. 4.0, second only to ω Centauri. There is a dense concentration of stars towards the centre. It begins to be resolved with 75 mm aperture, and is clearly resolved with 100 mm, although appearing even more spectacular with still larger apertures. Its distance is 4.5 kpc (≈ 14,700 l.y.).

NGC 346 (in SMC: 00h59m.1, -72°11'): a bright, giant emission nebula, approximately mag. 7.0, clearly visible with binoculars.

NGC 362 (01h03m.2, -70°51'): a bright globular cluster, mag. 6.6, lying just outside the SMC. Even 75 mm shows some signs of granularity, indicating that the cluster is nearly resolved. Some stars are shown by 100 mm, and it is fully resolved with 150 mm.

NGC 376 (in SMC: 01h03m.9, -72°49'): a small, bright open cluster, mag. 10.5, readily seen with 75 mm, begins to be resolved with 100 mm, and clearly resolved with 200 mm.

NGC 419 (in SMC: 01h08m.3, -72°53'): a small, distant, and apparently spherical cluster, resembling a globular cluster, mag. 10, visible as a hazy spot in 75 mm. A double (mags. 7.2, 10.2; PA 355°, Sep. 3".9) lies about 8' to the southeast.

Hubble Deep Field South see pp. 94–95 for information.

CONSTELLATIONS

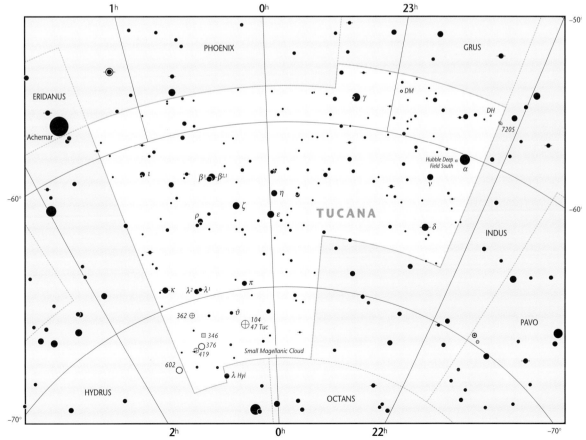

Ursa Major

URSAE MAJORIS • UMa • THE GREAT BEAR

Main chart(s): 4 (1, 5, 6)
Area: 1280 sq. deg. (3rd)
Culminates 00:00 local time: mid-March

Although the seven stars forming the asterism known as 'The Plough' or 'The Big Dipper' are known to nearly everyone living in the northern hemisphere, few realize that the constellation is so large, exceeded only by Hydra and Virgo. Because it lies well away from the galactic plane, Ursa Major contains no open clusters or diffuse nebulae. It does have many galaxies, although many of them are faint. Because of the low interstellar absorption, the Hubble Deep Field, the first of the Hubble Space Telescope's probes into the extremely distant and extremely early Universe, was made here.

The **Ursa Major Moving Cluster** is the closest cluster to the Sun, and lies at about 75 l.y., almost exactly half the distance of the next closest (the Hyades in Taurus). It includes β, γ, δ, ε, and ζ UMa. About 100 members of the group are known and they include β Aur, α CMa, α CrB, β Eri, and δ Leo. The Sun is moving through the outer region of the cluster, which is why members appear in various parts of the sky.

α UMa ($11^h03^m.7$, +61°45'), Dubhe: a close binary (mags. 1.9, 4.8; PA 223°, Sep. 0".6). The brighter component has a K0 giant spectrum. The pair were closest in 2001 and are currently separating.

ζ UMa ($13^h23^m.9$, +54°55'), Mizar (mag. 2.3), forms a famous naked-eye double with 80 UMa, Alcor (mag. 4.0), with a separation of 11'.8. They lie at different distances, however (87 and 81 l.y., respectively), so do not form a binary system. The brighter star, Mizar, is a true binary (mag. 4.0; PA 152°, Sep. 14".4), and each of those components is a spectroscopic binary, forming a quadruple system. Mizar itself was the first star to be found to be a spectroscopic binary. By coincidence, Alcor is also a spectroscopic binary. The system is relatively close to the Sun, lying at a distance of just 7.7 pc (≈ 25 l.y.).

ν UMa ($11^h18^m.5$, +33°06'): a probable binary (mags. 3.5, 9.9; PA 147°, Sep. 7".2). The brighter component has a K3 giant spectrum.

ξ UMa ($11^h18^m.2$, +31°32'): a multiple system. The principal pair of yellow stars (mags. 4.3, 4.8; PA 273°, Sep. 1".8; G0 and G5 dwarf spectra; P = 59.8 yrs), was the first binary for which the period was computed (by M. Savary in 1828). The separation is currently increasing. Both stars are spectroscopic binaries with periods of 1.83 yrs and 3.98 days, respectively, and B has been found to have an additional close companion.

47 UMa ($10^h59^m.7$, +40°25'), close to the border with Leo Minor, is mag. 5.0, and thus visible to the naked eye. The star (a G0 dwarf) is very slightly more massive and brighter than the Sun. It is the location of an extrasolar planetary system, and the first to be discovered that is somewhat similar to the Solar System. There are at least two planets, one about 2.5 Jupiter masses, orbiting at 2.09 AU from the star, and a second, about 0.75 times the mass of Jupiter, which orbits at 3.73 AU.

57 UMa ($11^h29^m.8$, +39°20'): a long-period binary system (mags 5.3, 8.3; PA 357°, Sep. 5".6; A2 and G5 dwarf spectra). Clearly visible with 75 mm aperture and exhibiting slow retrograde orbital motion.

VY UMa ($10^h45^m.4$, +67°25'): an irregular variable, range mag. 5.7–7.5. It has a carbon (C5) bright-giant spectrum and is an extremely red star – one of the reddest in the sky – and thus difficult to study.

Groombridge 1830 ($11^h53^m.0$, +37°43'): the star with the 3rd largest proper motion, after Barnard's Star (in Ophiuchus) and Kapteyn's Star (in Pictor). It is a G8 dwarf, mag. 6.4, d = 8.8 l.y.

Lalande 21185 ($11^h03^m.3$, +35°59'): the fifth closest star to the Sun, at a distance of 8.3 l.y. It is an M2 dwarf, mag. 7.5.

M81 (NGC 3031: $09^h55^m.6$, +69°03'): a spiral (Sb) galaxy, mag. 6.9, readily visible in binoculars, and appearing as elliptical with larger apertures. Its distance is about 3 Mpc (≈ 10 million l.y.).

M82 (NGC 3934: $09^h56^m.2$, +69°40'): an unusual galaxy, generally classified as peculiar (Pec), mag. 8.4. It is a 'starburst galaxy', and is actually a spiral with anomalous dust clouds and a recent burst of star formation, resulting from an encounter with M81. It is detectable in binoculars as a faint elongated object, and shows slightly more detail with larger apertures. Its distance is essentially the same as M81, about 3 Mpc (≈ 10 million l.y.).

M97 (NGC 3587: $11^h14^m.8$, +55°01'), the Owl Nebula: a planetary nebula, not visible in binoculars. Appears as bluish disk with 100 mm. A telescope of 200 mm or more is required to show some structure. Its distance is about 430 pc (≈ 1600 l.y.).

M101 ($14^h03^m.4$, +54°20'), sometimes called the Pinwheel Galaxy: a spiral (Sc) galaxy, nominally mag. 7.7, the central regions of which are detectable in binoculars. Because it is approximately face-on, its arms are not readily visible with amateur equipment, and appear as a faint elliptical halo.

M109 (NGC 3992: $11^h57^m.6$, +53°23'): a barred spiral (SBb) galaxy, mag. 9.8. The prominent central bar is relatively easy to detect with small apertures, although it requires good seeing, even with 200 mm.

NGC 4051 ($12^h03^m.2$, +44°32'): a spiral (Sc) galaxy, on the border with Canes Venatici. It is moderately bright (mag. 10.3), but because of the extended spiral arms, only the nucleus is readily detectable with instruments smaller than 200 mm.

NGC 4088 ($12^h05^m.6°$, +50°33'): a spiral (Sc) galaxy, mag. 10.5. As with NGC 4051, the outer regions become visible only with an aperture of 200 mm, or more.

Hubble Deep Field North see pp. 94–95 for information.

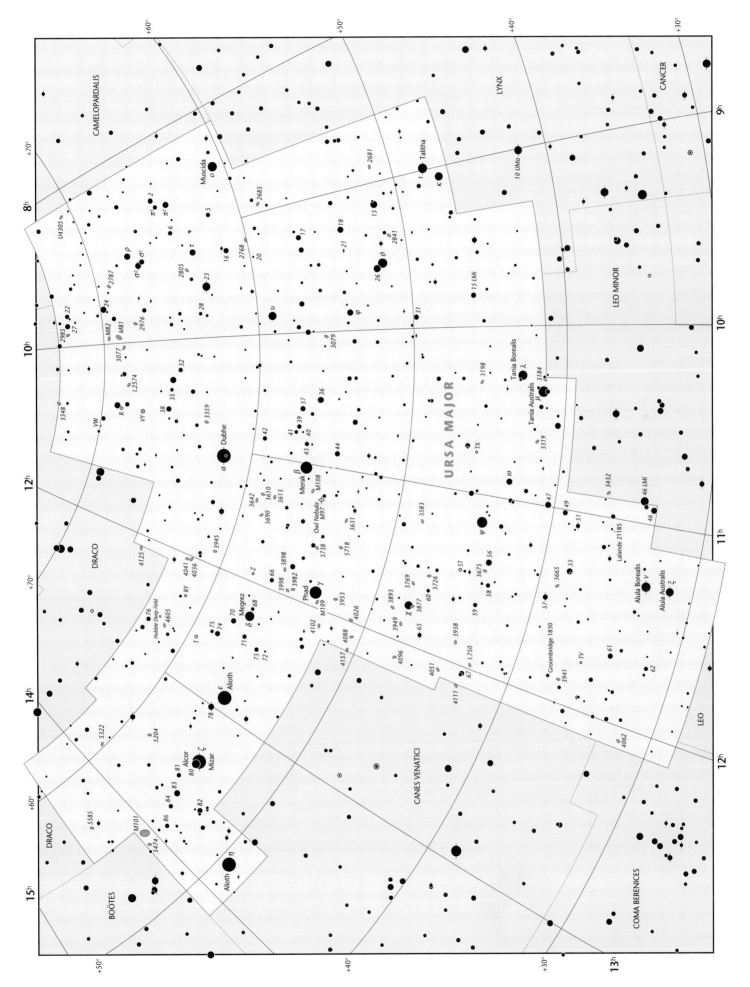

Ursa Minor

URSAE MINORIS • Umi • THE LITTLE BEAR

Main chart(s): 1 (5)
Area: 256 sq. deg. (56th)
Circumpolar: always visible

This constellation is chiefly notable, of course, for the fact that it contains the North Celestial Pole and, in particular, the bright star Polaris, (α UMi), which is slightly less than one degree from the Pole. Precession is slowly carrying Polaris even closer to the Pole, and closest approach will occur around 2100. The constellation lies outside the Milky Way and contains no clusters or diffuse nebulae. A few faint galaxies.

α **UMi** (02ʰ31ᵐ.8, +89°16'), Polaris: a variable yellow supergiant of the W Virginis type, related to the Cepheids. Its variations (range mag. 1.9–2.1) are not observable visually. In recent decades its range has decreased, and it is believed to be reaching the end of the evolutionary stage at which it displays variability. It is also a double star, and the second component (mag. 9.0; PA 218°, Sep. 18".4) is clearly visible with small apertures. The primary is also a spectroscopic binary, P = 29.6 yrs.

γ **UMi** (15ʰ20ᵐ.7, +71°49'), Pherkad: a white (A3) giant, mag. 3.0, which forms a wide visual double with 11 UMi (sometimes known as Pherkad Minor), an orange (K4) giant, mag. 5.0.

5 **UMi** (14ʰ27ᵐ.2, +75°42'): a multiple star. The AB pair (mags. 4.3, 13.3; PA 127°, Sep. 13".3) requires a large aperture for the B component to be detected. The third (C) component (mag. 9.8; PA AC 131°, Sep. 58".8) is more readily visible.

> **Ursids** (radiant at 14ʰ28ᵐ, +78°): a little-known meteor shower, warranting observation. Active Dec. 17–25, maximum Dec. 22, maximum zenithal hourly rate of 10. Has produced outbursts in 1945, 1982 and 1986.

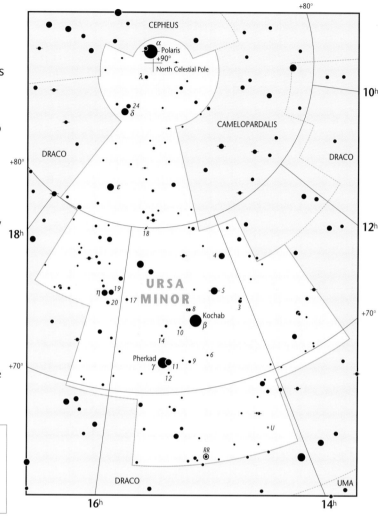

Vela

VELORUM • Vel • THE SNAILS

Main chart(s): 16 (15, 17, 20)
Area: 500 sq. deg. (32nd)
Culminates 00:00 local time: mid-February

Vela lies almost completely in the Milky Way, and contains numerous open clusters (over 40) and many diffuse nebulae. One notable object is the gigantic Gum nebula, a complex series of patches of nebulosity, which spreads over an area of approximately 30° × 40°, including portions of Antlia, Carina, Puppis, and Pyxis (see Puppis). The Vela supernova remnant lies at its centre, and the Vela pulsar, the second to be identified optically (after the Crab pulsar in Taurus).

The stars δ Vel, κ Vel, ε Car, and ι Car form the 'False Cross', sometimes taken for the Southern Cross (Crux),

especially by northerners new to southern skies. A few faint galaxies appear in the northeastern corner.

γ **Vel** (08ʰ09ᵐ.5, -47°20'), Regor: a multiple star. The primary component is the brightest and nearest example of a Wolf-Rayet star, which is an extremely luminous, late stage in the evolution of an O-type star. It is mag. 1.9, has a temperature over 50,000 K, and has a supergiant WC8 + O9 spectrum. It forms a wide, but probable, binary with component B (mag. 4.2; PA 220°, Sep. 41".2; B2 giant spectrum). Further components are C (mag. 8.3; PA AC 151°, Sep. 62".3), D (mag. 9.1; PA AD 141°, Sep. 93".5), and E (mag. 12.5; PA DE 146°, Sep. 1".8).

μ **Vel** (10ʰ46ᵐ.8, -49°25'): a binary system (mags. 2.7, 6.3; PA 46°, Sep. 2".0; G5 giant and F8 dwarf), P = 116 yrs. The separation is currently increasing, but at least 150 mm is required for it to be resolved.

β **Vel** (08ʰ40ᵐ.6, -46°39'): an F3 extreme supergiant, apparent mag. 3.8, at approximately 950 pc (≈ 3100 l.y.). This implies that its absolute magnitude (M) is -6.1, and luminosity is 180,000 times that of the Sun.

Vela Supernova Remnant (approx. 08ʰ30ᵐ, -44°30'): largest supernova remnant (SNR) that is visible to the naked eye, especially if a nebular filter is used to accentuate the contrast. It is approximately 5° across.

IC 2391 (08ʰ40ᵐ.2, -53°04'): a very bright open cluster including o Vel (mag. 3.6), d = 152 pc (≈ 500 l.y.). The cluster is mag. 2.5:, contains about 30 stars and is about 1° across.

IC 2395 (08ʰ41ᵐ.1, -53°04'): a bright open cluster (mag. 4.6), best observed with small apertures (75–100 mm).

NGC 2547 (08ʰ10ᵐ.7, -49°16'): a large, bright open cluster (integrated mag. 4.7), some 17' across, requiring a wide field. Its distance is about 400 pc (≈ 1300 l.y.).

NGC 2626 (08ʰ35ᵐ.6, -40°40'): an unusually bright reflection nebula, illuminated by a star of mag. 10. It is readily seen with 150 mm.

NGC 3201 (10ʰ17ᵐ.6, -46°25'): a fairly loose globular cluster, mag. 6.8, and slightly irregular in outline. Well resolved with 100 mm. Its distance is about 5.2 kpc (≈ 17,000 l.y.).

NGC 3132 (10ʰ07ᵐ.7, -40°26'), the Eight-Burst Nebula: a planetary nebula, mag. 9.2, and relatively easy to detect. The star visible in the centre, mag. 12.1, is not the star exciting the nebula, which is a faint (mag. 16), blue-white star, 1".6 from the apparent central star.

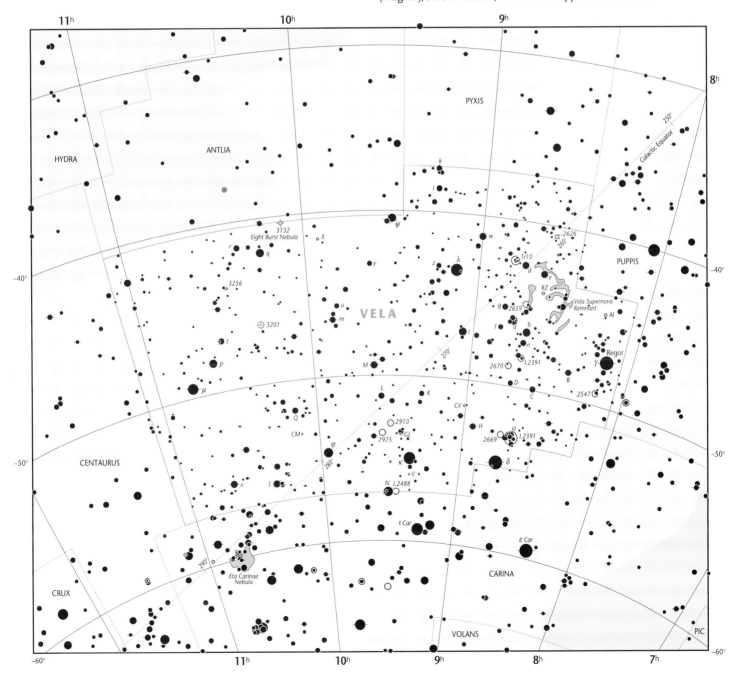

Virgo
VIRGINIS • Vir • THE VIRGIN

Main chart(s): 11 (10)
Area: 1294 sq. deg. (2nd)
Culminates 00:00 local time: mid-April

Although Virgo is the second largest constellation (after Hydra) it contains few bright stars, few variables and double stars. Being well away from the Milky Way, it has no open clusters or diffuse nebulae. There is one globular cluster, but all the planetary nebulae are very faint. To compensate for this, Virgo contains a remarkable number of galaxies, being the location of the Virgo Cluster. This forms the heart of the Local Supercluster, a gigantic system, probably consisting of some 10,000 galaxies. (Our own Local Group of 30-odd galaxies lies at its edge.) The Cluster is centred on four massive elliptical galaxies: M49, M60, M86, and M87, and lies at a distance of approximately 17 Mpc ($\approx$ 55 million l.y.).

In the northwestern part of the constellation the Cluster extends into Coma Berenices, hence the fact that it is sometimes known as the Virgo-Coma Cluster. (It should not, however, be confused with the Coma Cluster, which is a separate, more distant group of galaxies.) Unfortunately, most of these galaxies are faint and there are so many that only the most prominent are described here. Many more are shown on the charts and listed earlier in this book.

α **Vir** (13h25m, -11°10'): a blue-white, first-magnitude star (mag. 0.98), which actually consists of an extremely close binary, where both stars are tidally distorted by their mutual gravitational attraction. This produces a slight variation in brightness as the pair rotates, which is detectable only with sensitive electronic methods.

γ **Vir** (12h46m.7, -01°27'), Porrima: a binary system with two yellow stars (mags. 3.5, 3.5; PA 267°, Sep. 1".8; both F0 spectra). There is some disagreement about the period, with values of 171.4 yrs and 168.7 yrs being quoted. Using the latter, closest approach (0".26) occurs in 2005, when the stars will be difficult to separate.

ϑ **Vir** (13h09m.9, -05°32'): a probable binary (mags. 4.4, 9.4; PA 343°, Sep. 6".9). The primary has an A1 subgiant spectrum, and is actually a very close binary. The secondary has an Am (magnetic) spectrum.

17 Vir (12h22m.5, +05°18'): another probable binary (mags. 6.6, 9.4; PA 337°, Sep. 20".0; F8 and K5 dwarf spectra).

70 Vir (13h28m, +13°46'), lying close to the northern border with Coma Berenices, is an apparently unremarkable, 5th-magnitude star, slightly cooler and smaller than the Sun, but also brighter. It has one of the first extrasolar planetary systems to be discovered. The planet is very large, about 6.8 Jupiter masses, with an extremely eccentric orbit, averaging about 0.5 AU from the star. Its orbital period is 116.6 days.

M49 (NGC 4472: 12h29m.8, +08°00'): a conspicuous elliptical (E4) galaxy, mag. 8.4. It is a massive galaxy, and is the brightest in the Virgo Cluster.

M58 (NGC 4579: 12h37m.7, +11°49'): a spiral (Sb) galaxy, mag. 9.8. The nucleus is readily visible with just 75 mm, looking like a faint star. Larger apertures show the spiral arms as a hazy elliptical area.

M60 (NGC 4649: 12h43m.7, +11°33'): a bright, elliptical (E1) galaxy, mag. 8.8, readily detected as an almost perfectly circular patch with 75 mm. Like M49, it is one of the massive galaxies at the centre of the Virgo Cluster. About 7'.5 to the northwest is NGC 4647 (12h43m.5, +11°35'), a much fainter spiral (Sc) galaxy, requiring at least 100 mm to be detected.

M61 (NGC 4303: 12h21m.9, +04°28'): a large spiral (Sc) galaxy, mag. 9.7. It is visible, but faint, with 75 mm. Larger apertures show it to be almost circular, with a dense nucleus.

M84 (NGC 4374: 12h25m.1, +12°53'): a large elliptical (E1) galaxy, mag. 9.3. The small, bright centre is readily seen with 75 mm, but the faint outer regions require a much larger aperture.

M86 (NGC 4406: 12h26m.4, +12°57'): another large elliptical (E3) galaxy, mag. 9.2, slightly larger but otherwise similar to M84, and also readily seen with 75 mm.

M87 (NGC 4486: 12h30m.8, +12°24'): a giant elliptical (E1) galaxy, mag. 8.6, easily seen even with small apertures. This large, massive galaxy lies close to the heart of the Virgo Cluster, and photographs reveal that it is surrounded by a halo of hundreds of globular clusters. It is also an active galaxy, with a pair of jets (only one readily visible on photographs), and a strong radio source, known as Virgo A.

M90 (NGC 4569: 12h36m.8, +13°10'): a large spiral (Sb) galaxy, mag. 9.5. Like M58 and M84, the bright nucleus is readily seen with a small aperture (75 mm), but the outer arms require a large instrument. Even then, they generally appear just as a diffuse elliptical shape.

M104 (NGC 4594: 12h40m.0, -11°37'), the Sombrero Galaxy: a spiral (Sb) galaxy, mag. 8.5. It gains its popular name from its appearance with an aperture of 150 mm or more, when it exhibits a dense dark lane of dust in its galactic plane. It lies far to the south, on the border with Corvus, and is probably easiest found from that constellation. Its elongated shape is just detectable with binoculars.

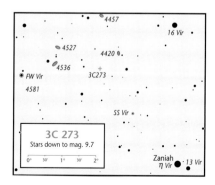

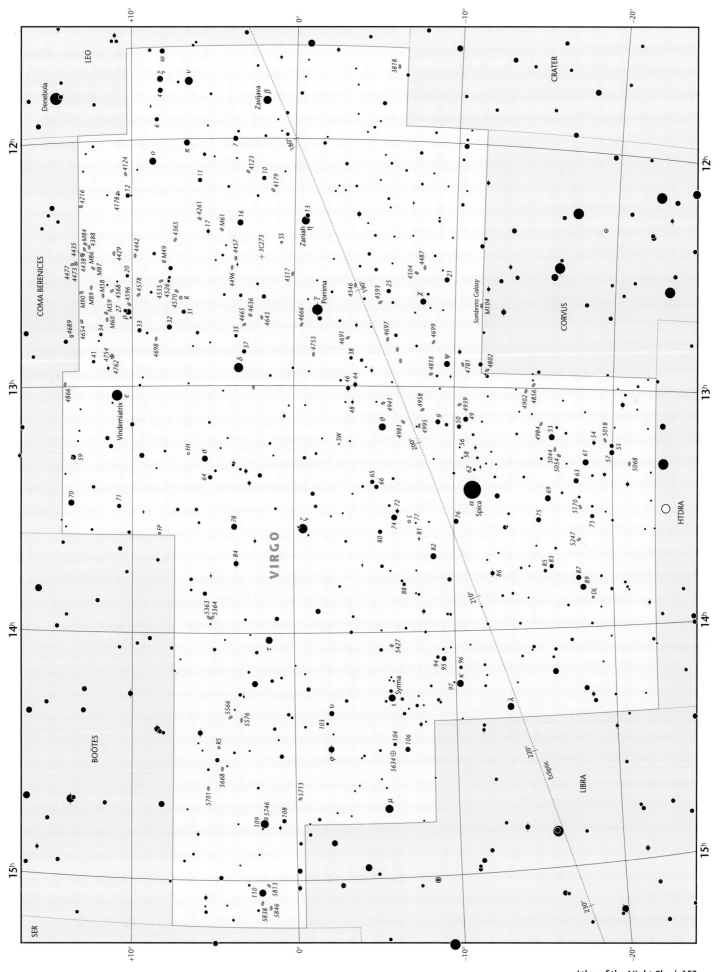

NGC 5634 (14ʰ29ᵐ.6, -05°59'): a moderately bright, distant, globular cluster, mag. 9.6). It is just visible with 75 mm aperture, but requires 200 mm to be fully resolved. Its distance is about 22 kpc (≈ 72,000 l.y.).

3C 273 (1226+023: 12ʰ29ᵐ.1, +02°03'): the brightest quasar, mag. 12.7 and the first to be discovered. It is a powerful radio source and was located through a lunar occultation by the Parkes radio telescope in Australia. It is the easiest to detect with amateur-sized telescopes, requiring about 150 mm to reveal it as a starlike object. Its distance is about 600 Mpc (almost 200 million light-years).

Virginids (double radiant at 14ʰ04ᵐ, -09° and 13ʰ36ᵐ, -11°): a meteor shower active March–April, maximum April 10. The meteors have slow, long paths, and a low zenithal hourly rate of about 5.

Volans
VOLANTIS • Vol • THE FLYING FISH

Main chart(s): 20 (15, 16)
Area: 141 sq. deg. (76th)
Culminates 00:00 local time: mid-January

A small constellation (originally called Piscis Volans) lying between Centaurus and the Large Magellanic Cloud. Although half lies in the outer portion of the Milky Way, there are no open or globular clusters, nor any diffuse nebulae. There are several faint galaxies, but only one is reasonably bright. The three doubles given may all be binaries with extremely long periods.

γ **Vol** (07ʰ08ᵐ.8, -70°30'): a possible binary (mags. 4.0, 5.9; PA 300°, Sep. 13".6; G8 giant and F5 dwarf spectra). There has been no orbital change since the pair's original discovery in 1835, but they have identical proper motions, so may be an extremely long-period binary.

ε **Vol** (08ʰ07ᵐ.9, -68°37'): another possible extremely long-period binary (mags. 4.4, 7.4; PA 23°, Sep. 5".4; white B5 giant and B9.5 dwarf spectra). As with γ and ζ Vol, this pair was discovered in 1835 by John Herschel, but there appears to have been no orbital motion, yet the stars have identical proper motions.

ζ **Vol** (07ʰ41ᵐ.8, -72°36'): also a possible long-period binary (mags. 4.0, 9.8; PA 116°, Sep. 16".7). The primary has an orange (K0) giant spectrum, and the secondary is white.

NGC 2442 (07ʰ36ᵐ.4, -69°32'): a large, spiral (SB) galaxy, mag. 11.2, visible in 100 mm as just a faint elliptical haze. A larger aperture (300 mm) reveals the central nucleus and the asymmetrical extensions at each end that are the main arms, one much larger and more prominent than the other.

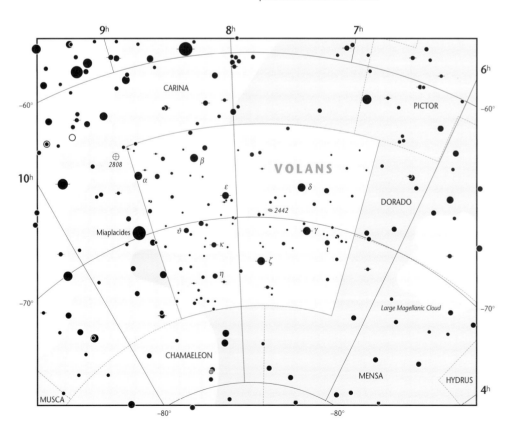

Vulpecula

VULPECULAE • Vul • THE FOX

Main chart(s): 6, 7 (12, 13)
Area: 268 sq. deg. (55th)
Culminates 00:00 local time: late July

Another of the small constellations introduced by Hevelius, who originally named it Vuplecula et Anser (the 'Fox and Goose'). Like Sagitta to the south, although Vulpecula lies squarely across the galactic plane, it is relatively small and contains just a few objects of interest. Because of the considerable absorption so close to the galactic equator, no galaxies are detectable with amateur-sized telescopes.

2 Vul (19h17m.7, +23°02'): a triple system. In the principal pair (mags 5.5:, 9.2; PA 131°, Sep. 1".8), the primary is a B0.5 subgiant of the β Cephei type, with small-amplitude variations of less than 0.1 mag. The third component is much fainter (mag. 11.0; PA 119°, Sep. 51"). The three stars have identical proper motions, indicating that they are a true multiple system.

16 Vul (20h02m.0, +24°56'): a probable true binary system (mags 5.8, 6.2; PA 120°, Sep. 0".9; F7 spectra). Although close, the pair is resolved with apertures of 150 mm or more.

Σ 2653 (20h13m.7, +24°14'): a binary system (mags. 6.6, 9.5; PA 272°, 2".6), clearly visible with 75 mm aperture. The primary has a magnetic A spectrum.

M27 (NGC 6853: 19h59m.6, +22°43'), the Dumbbell Nebula: a relatively bright (mag. 7.6), bluish planetary nebula. Its non-circular shape is detectable with binoculars, but about 200 mm is required for the dumbbell appearance to be clearly visible. The planetary is relatively close: its distance is about 320 pc (≈ 1050 l.y.).

NGC 6882 (20h11m.7, +26°33') and **NGC 6885** (20h12m.0, +26°29'): a pair of open clusters that may be viewed together with a wide field. Clearly seen with 100 mm, but considerably improved with a larger aperture. NGC 6885 is about twice as large as NGC 6882. Their distance is approximately 1000 pc (≈ 3260 l.y.).

NGC 6940 (20h34m.6, +28°18'): a large open cluster, mag. 6.3, unresolved in binoculars, appearing like a nebulous patch. It is best seen with 150 mm and a wide field, when it is resolved into individual stars, including an orange giant. The cluster's distance is about 800 pc (≈ 2600 l.y.).

Cr 399 (Collinder 399: 19h25m.4, +20°11'): Brocchi's cluster (also known as 'the Coathanger'), readily visible in binoculars. It is a loose cluster of stars, six of which form the 'bar' of the 'coathanger' with another four forming the 'hook'.

CONSTELLATIONS

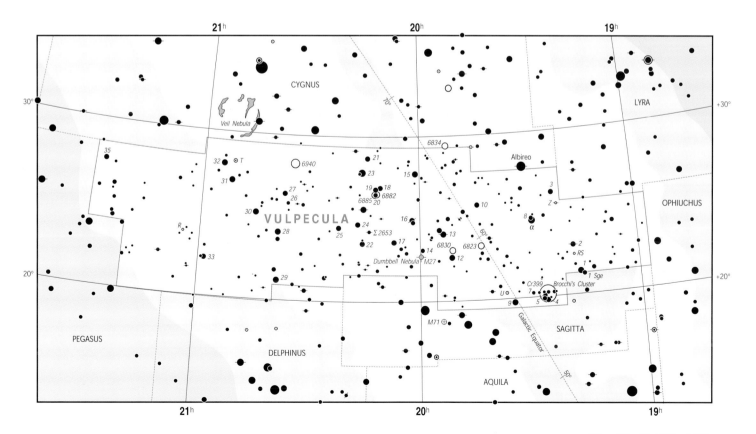

Observing the Moon

The phases of the Moon are very familiar to everyone. They are normally reckoned from New Moon, when the Moon is between the Sun and the Earth, and is invisible (except at eclipses). The illuminated portion increases (waxes) until First Quarter (a 'half moon') and Full Moon, and then decreases (wanes) again towards Last Quarter and the next New Moon. The phases immediately before and after Full Moon, when more than half of the disk is illuminated are known as 'gibbous'.

The boundary between the illuminated and dark portions of the Moon is known as the terminator, and this sweeps across the Moon from east to west during the course of a month, giving rise to the familiar changes in phase. The complete cycle of phases, from New Moon through First Quarter, Full, Last Quarter, and back to New Moon again is known as a lunation (with an average length of 29.53059 days). During the crescent phases, before and after New Moon, the dark area of the surface is often weakly illuminated by earthshine, sunlight reflected from the Earth. This is unusually strong when the Earth has extensive cloud cover. Some lunar features (particularly Aristarchus) are often easily visible under this reflected light.

Anyone who takes more than a casual interest in the Moon soon realizes that, despite its daily and monthly motion across the sky, it always turns one face towards the Earth, and the other side is permanently invisible. The Moon's period of rotation on its axis is exactly the same as its period of revolution around the Earth. It shares this property, known technically as synchronous rotation, with nearly all the natural satellites of the planets. (Saturn's satellite Hyperion may be the only exception.) Tidal forces, acting on the uneven distribution of mass within the Moon have caused one face (the near side) to permanently face the Earth, and the other (the far side) to be permanently averted. We are, however, able to see slightly more than 50 per cent of the surface, thanks to the effects known as libration.

Libration

The Moon's orbit is an ellipse, and it is sometimes travelling faster in orbit, and sometimes slower, than its average speed. The rotation rate remains constant, so the Moon's position is sometimes 'ahead of' and sometimes 'behind' the rotation. The disk appears to rock backwards and forwards, and this libration in longitude (east–west) may be as much as 7°53' in each direction. Similarly, because the Moon's orbit is inclined to the Earth's orbital plane (the ecliptic), it is sometimes above and sometimes below the Earth. The disk appears to nod up and down, and this libration in latitude (north–south) may be as much as 6°51' in each direction. Small effects arise from the observer's position on Earth, and whether the Moon is viewed at rising or setting, that also contribute to apparent changes in the Moon's orientation.

These effects may combine or partially cancel one another, but the overall result is that theoretically about 59 per cent of the Moon's surface is visible from Earth, although the extreme boundaries of the libration zone on the lunar surface appear extremely rarely, and even then with great foreshortening. The full libration cycle is very complex and only repeats over very many years, so the actual numerical values for libration at any given date are not listed here. The information may be found in specialized astronomical handbooks and almanacs.

Features in the libration zone are often difficult to identify, so this atlas includes four charts (pp. 192–195), drawn using a special method of projection to show the features under exaggerated libration, greater than any that occurs naturally. Three zones are marked by different tints. Moving from the centre of the lunar disk towards the limb, the zones are: always visible (neutral tint); frequently invisible (pink tint); and rarely visible (blue tint). Naturally, even features in the always visible region are often more clearly revealed when there is a favourable libration.

Visibility of features

Because the Moon has no atmosphere to diffuse the light, illumination of the surface is one of extreme contrast. In general, features are either brightly illuminated or in deep shadow. Surface detail is easiest to see under grazing illumination, which occurs around sunrise and sunset for any particular feature, when it is close to the terminator. In general, features are visible on the same days in each lunation, although the fluctuations caused by libration mean that some months may be more favourable than others. For features in the libration zone, the necessity of having both a favourable libration and suitable lighting means that very long periods of time (many years) may elapse before a particular feature is again clearly visible.

The position of features on the Moon may be specified in terms of a system of selenographic coordinates (Fig. L1). The reference points for the coordinate grid are the Moon's rotational axis (o), running through the North (N) and South (S) Poles, and the lunar equator (r), perpendicular to the rotational axis. The prime meridian (m) runs through the apparent centre of the Moon's disk at a time when the libration in both latitude and longitude is zero.

In a manner similar to the use of latitude and longitude on the Earth, selenographic latitude (β) is measured in degrees, north (+) or south (-) of the lunar equator. Selenographic longitude (λ) is measured in degrees, east (+) or west (-) of the prime meridian. Frequently, however, as in this atlas, positive and negative signs are not used. Instead, selenographic latitude is expressed in degrees N or S of the equator, and selenographic longitude in degrees E or W of the prime meridian.

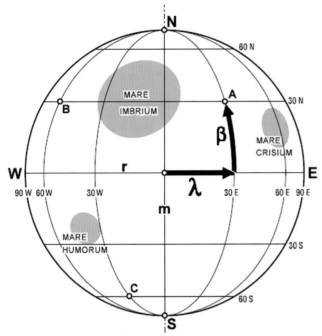

Fig. L1 Selenographic coordinates

Note that when viewing the Moon with the naked eye, binoculars, or a non-inverting telescope, north (N) is at the top, towards Mare Imbrium, and south (S) is at the bottom, towards Mare Humorum. (This assumes that the observer is in the Earth's northern hemisphere.) East (E) is on the right, towards Mare Crisium, and west (W) is on the left, towards Mare Imbrium. As on Earth, the Sun rises in the east and sets in the west. This follows the International Astronomical Union's recommendation regarding lunar coordinates in 1961. Books published before 1961 use the earlier convention, where lunar directions were similar to those used for positions on the sky, i.e., with east to the left, and west to the right (for northern-hemisphere observers). This change led to just one anomaly on the Moon. Mare Orientale ('Eastern Sea') is now on the western limb.

Lunar features

Even the most casual glance shows that the surface of the Moon is divided into two major forms: light-coloured, rugged terrain, known technically as terrae (Latin for 'lands'), but more commonly called the highlands; and dark, low-lying areas known as maria (Latin for 'seas'). Even though we know that the Moon is essentially waterless – if we exclude the controversial evidence for ice within certain polar craters – terms such as mare, and others associated with water, have been retained in many lunar names. The names of different types of feature on the Moon are given in Table L1, along with the translation of the Latin terms. (The actual naming of features on the Moon is described in the sections of text that accompany Maps 1, 4, 13, and 16.)

Lunar features

Catena	chain of craters
Dorsum	mare ridge
Dorsa	network or group of mare ridges
Lacus	lake
Mare (maria)	seas
Mons	mountain, hill
Montes	mountain range or group of mountains
Oceanus	ocean
Palus	marsh
Promontorium	promontory, cape
Rima	rille, fissure, cleft
Rimae	network or group of rilles
Rupes	scarp
Sinus	bay
Terra	land mass, continent
Terrae	highlands
Vallis (valles)	valleys

Table L1

The highlands

The highlands represent the oldest lunar terrain. During the final phases of the Moon's formation, the whole surface was subjected to such intense bombardment by meteoroids, that the surface was molten. This eventually cooled and formed the lunar crust, mainly found today in the lunar highlands. Subsequent impacts covered the surface with craters of all sizes. Some very large impacts created a number of extremely large basins, which are discussed in more detail later. The highland regions today are essentially saturated with craters: any impacts would destroy as many craters as they created.

The maria

Some of the large impact basins were deep enough for their centres, or even the whole basins, to be filled with molten material (lava) from the Moon's interior. Because the Moon's crust is thinner on the near side than on the far side, more of the basins on the near side were flooded, often with a series of different lava flows. It is these dark, basaltic lava flows that have produced the maria, and these are now known to be significantly younger than the surrounding highlands.

The maria may be roughly divided into circular and non-circular types. Circular maria are those that clearly fill either the centre or the whole of individual impact basins, as with Mare Crisium and Mare Serenitatis, respectively. Non-circular maria, such as Mare Frigoris and Mare Fecunditatis, are of less certain origin. They may simply be low-lying regions flooded by overflows of lava from neighbouring impact basins.

Because they arose after the early severe bombardment, the maria contain few craters, and these are generally small, with a few exceptions, such as Kepler (Map 5) and Copernicus (Map 6). Many maria contain ridges, sometimes known as wrinkle ridges, many of which are thought to be compression features produced when the lava flows were in the final stages of cooling. Individual ridges are named 'Dorsum', and networks of ridges use the plural form 'Dorsa'. Isolated hills, some with summit craters, found in some mare areas, are the most obviously volcanic features on the Moon. The Marius Hills area in Oceanus Procellarum (Map 5) shows many fine examples of this sort. Both ridges and hills are particularly noticeable under grazing illumination.

Craters and basins

Craters are, of course, the dominant type of feature on the Moon. They range in size from the enormous basins, hundreds or even thousands of kilometres across, to microscopic pits in surface rocks. On the near side there are about 300,000 craters larger than 1 km, including 234 craters with diameters that exceed 100 km. These craters may be broadly divided into three groups: simple craters, complex craters, and basins. Simple craters have smooth walls, level floors, and a depth-to-diameter ratio of about 1:5. They are generally circular in outline.

At a diameter of about 16 km in mare areas and 21 km in the highlands, there is a fairly abrupt transition from simple craters to complex ones. The overall form of complex craters tends to be circular, but individual sections of the rims may appear scalloped or irregular. The inner walls display terraces, where large blocks of material have slipped downwards along approximately concentric faults. The floors are often highly uneven, and there is frequently a central peak or peaks. There may also be fracturing of the floors and walls. The smaller complex craters have similar depth-to-diameter ratios as simple craters (about 1:5), but the largest may have ratios that are as low as 1:40, indicating a very shallow depression.

At diameters of about 300 km, other structural changes become evident, most notably the formation of concentric mountainous rings (with craterlike rims and arcuate ridges). These large impact features as known as basins, 'ringed basins' or 'multi-ringed basins'. The definition of the term 'basin' is somewhat fuzzy, mainly because the transition from complex craters to basins is not sharply defined – some features smaller than 300 km also contain rings or ring-like patterns. The nature and importance of lunar basins was recognized by geologists in the 1960s. By utilizing spacecraft imagery and laser altimetry, and by measuring gravity anomalies, etc., increasing numbers of basins have been discovered. These are shown on the near-side and far-side maps (pp. 196–197). Details of the basins are shown on p. 222.

Although high-velocity impacts vaporize much of the target rocks, some of the surface layers may be overturned, forming raised rims to craters. Material may also be thrown from the crater. This ejecta may, in turn, create secondary impact craters when it hits the surface, but it may also come to rest as a distinct deposit, which generally displays an obvious structure radiating from the centre of impact. This is particularly noticeable with craters in mare areas, but ejecta from some of the major impacts, such as the event that created the Imbrium basin, may be traced over large areas of the Moon.

Ray craters

Certain craters such as Copernicus (Map 6), Kepler (Map 5), Proclus (Map 8) and Tycho (Map 14) are the centres of conspicuous ray systems. One of Tycho's rays is exceptionally long, and may be traced right across Mare Serenitatis (Map 7) and towards the northeastern limb. It is now accepted that these ray craters are relatively young, and that the rays consist of small crater pits and powdered material from secondary impacts which has yet to be darkened by solar radiation. In general, ray systems are best observed under high illumination, and therefore appear most conspicuous around Full Moon.

Rilles (rimae)

Rilles are narrow, steep-sided valleys with roughly parallel walls. They are of three types: linear (or straight) rilles, arcuate rilles, and sinuous rilles. Linear rilles are fractures cutting across the surface. They often take the form, known to geologists as a 'graben', where a long block of surface has dropped between two parallel, sloping faults. Rima Ariadaeus (Map 7) and the fractures inside Hevelius (Map 5) are examples of this sort. Older works sometimes use the word 'cleft' rather than rima or rille.

Arcuate rilles are similar to linear rilles, but are curved, often running more or less parallel to the outer rim of a mare region or large complex crater. The rilles of Rimae Hippalus on the southeastern side of Mare Humorum (Map 10) are of this general type. Again, they are caused by surface fractures.

Sinuous rilles have a completely different origin and wind across the surface in a manner reminiscent of rivers or, more significantly, lava tubes. Vallis Schröteri (Map 5) and Rima Hadley (Map 7) are two examples. Sinuous rilles are lava channels, and generally start at a crater or depression. Unlike rivers, they become narrower and shallower the farther away from their source and may show sudden changes of direction. Some sinuous rilles are believed to be lava tubes, whose roofs have collapsed.

Scarps (rupes)

The term rupes is applied to any feature where a fault appears to break the surface, but it does not have a strict geological definition. The most famous example is Rupes Recta (the Straight Wall) in Mare Nubium (Map 10), but many other rupes appear around the edges of mare areas, for example, Rupes Liebig on the western edge of Mare Humorum (Map 9). An interesting comparison may be made between Rupes Cauchy and Rima Cauchy in eastern Mare Tranquillitatis (Map 8). The former is a single fault, but the latter has a distinct graben-like structure.

The lunar maps

All the maps of the Moon in this atlas are oriented the same way: with north at the top. This corresponds to the naked-eye or binocular view as seen by an observer in the Earth's northern hemisphere, and also to the way in which lunar and planetary maps obtained from space-probe imagery (and the images themselves) are normally presented. The main maps are drawn to a scale of 1:4.7 million and the lunar disk is divided into 16 sections as shown on the key chart. In addition, to assist observers whose telescopes introduce an odd number of reflections, a set of maps shows the Moon to a slightly smaller scale (1:7 million), but left–right reversed. If your telescope gives an inverted image, you may wish to turn the maps upside down, although some observers find (once they have a little experience) that this is unnecessary.

Shown here are the four orientations that may arise with various optical configurations:

A: Upright (North up) – naked eye, binoculars, telescope with terrestrial eyepiece

B: Upside down (South up) – Newtonian, Cassegrain, refractor without star diagonal

C: Upright, left/right reversed – refractor or catadioptric telescope (Schmidt-Cassegrain, Maksutov) with star diagonal

D: Upside down and left/right reversed – very rare and rather theoretical (e.g., telescope with star diagonal and terrestrial eyepiece)

The libration maps (pp. 192–195) and general near and far side maps (pp. 196–197) are shown in just a single orientation: A, upright (North up).

Although, as explained on p. 156, the position of features on the Moon may be described using the coordinates β (selenographic latitude) and λ (selenographic longitude), for simplicity, standard compass directions are shown on the grid, and used in the descriptions. Meridians and parallels of latitude are marked in red at 10° intervals, and in blue for the intermediate 5° meridians and parallels. The maps of the libration zones (pp. 192–195) are marked at 10° intervals only. Each map has a generous overlap with adjoining sections, the numbers of which are shown in the overlap zone or, in the case of the libration maps, on the inner boundary.

The brief descriptions given with each map are not intended to be exhaustive, but should be taken as a guide to the location and significance of some of the most interesting features visible on that portion of the Moon. No attempt has been made to describe features in the order in which they may become visible during a lunation. Instead they are grouped by location or general geological similarities.

For all the craters mentioned, and some of the other features, the latitude and longitude are given in parentheses after the feature's name. For craters, the diameters and depths (where reliably known) are also included.

A full index of all the lunar features named on the various maps is given on pp. 218–220. Translations of the general Latin terms for the various features are given in Table L1 (p. 157), and those for specific features are shown alongside the individual maps, together with a list of the days in the lunation (i.e., the age of the Moon in days after New Moon) when the feature is best observed. Usually this will be at sunrise and sunset, but bright features may have an extended period of visibility around Full Moon.

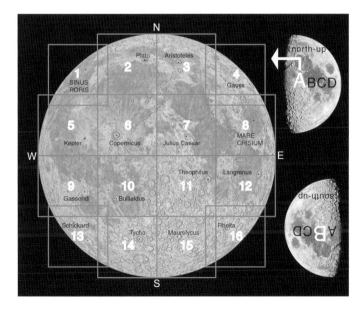

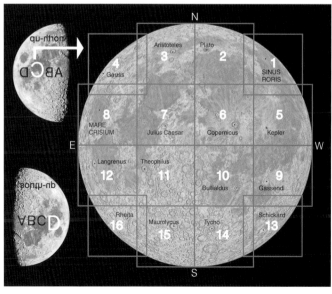

1 | Sinus Roris

This is a comparatively featureless area of the Moon, consisting of the lava plains at the northern edge of Oceanus Procellarum and Sinus Roris, which links Oceanus Procellarum with the western end of Mare Frigoris.

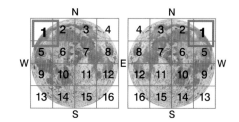

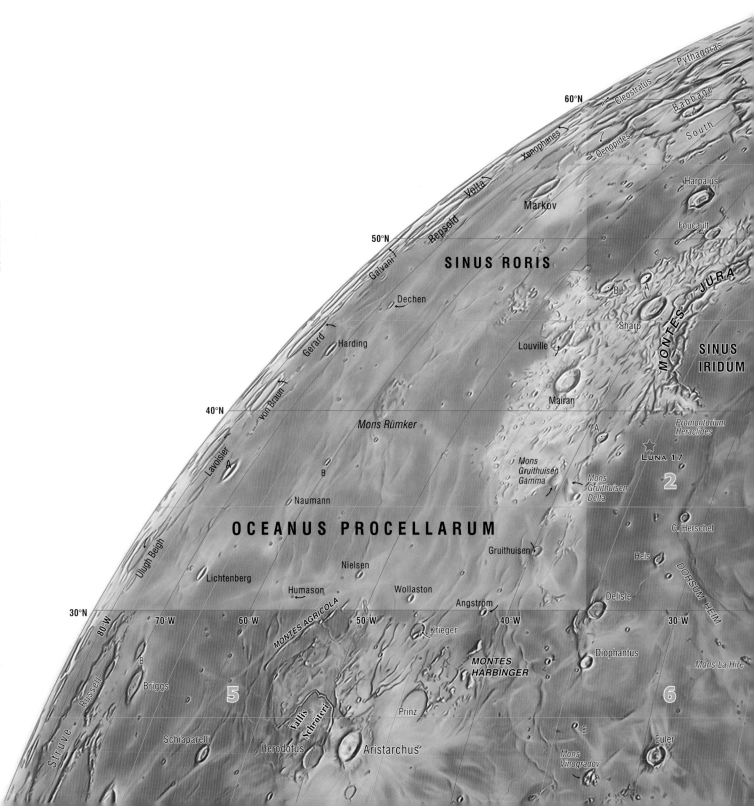

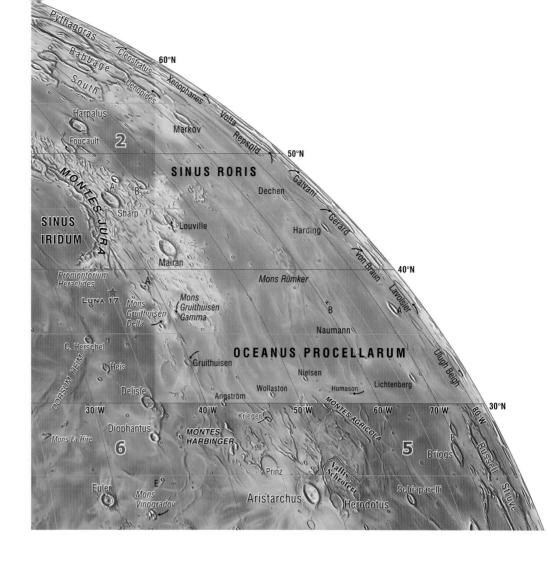

Apart from the craters along the limb, the only highland region is the relatively low terrain west of the Montes Jura, around Sinus Iridum, with the sharp-rimmed crater Mairan (41.6°N, 43.4°W, 40 km), and the degraded crater Louville (44.0°N, 46.0°W, 36 km). On the other side of Sinus Roris is Markov (53.4°N, 62.7°W, 40 km), another crater with a sharp rim.

In the libration zone, and best seen shortly before Full Moon, are a number of fairly large craters. Starting in the north, we have: Xenophanes (57.5°N, 82.0°W, 125 km); Volta (53.9°N, 84.4°W, 123 km); Repsold (51.3°N, 78.6°W, 109 km), a partially eroded crater; Galvani (49.6°N, 84.6°W, 80 km); Gerard (44.5°N, 80.0°W, 90 km), a low, degraded crater; von Braun (41.1°N, 78.0°W, 60 km); Lavoisier (38.2°N, 81.2°W, 70 km); and Ulugh Beigh (32.7°N, 81.9°W, 54 km), an eroded, flooded crater.

There are three notable mountainous areas. The most striking, and effectively unique on the Moon, is Mons Rümker (41°N, 58°W). This is an elevated region, some 70 km across, which appears to consist of a large number of individual volcanic domes.

Name	Translation
Oceanus Procellarum	Ocean of Storms
Sinus Roris	Bay of Dew

Feature	Age of Moon (days)
Mons Rümker	12, 26
Sinus Iridum	10, 24
Sinus Roris	11, 25

Some remain distinct, but others have coalesced to create an undulating plateau above the surrounding mare.

To the east, south of Mairan, lie Mons Gruithuisen Gamma, and Mons Gruithuisen Delta. The first is a large, slightly elongated, smooth dome-shaped massif with a summit crater about 2 km in diameter. The second is less regular in outline, but similar in altitude. Both are about 20 km across. Gruithuisen itself (32.9°N, 39.7°W, 15 km, 1860 m), is a small, but relatively deep crater farther south.

2 | Plato

Mare Imbrium dominates this region. It is 1250 km across, with an area of about 830,000 sq km, slightly more than Hudson Bay in Canada. The Imbrium impact basin is the second youngest (after Mare Orientale), and also the second largest (after the South Pole–Aitken Basin).

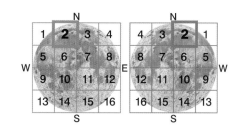

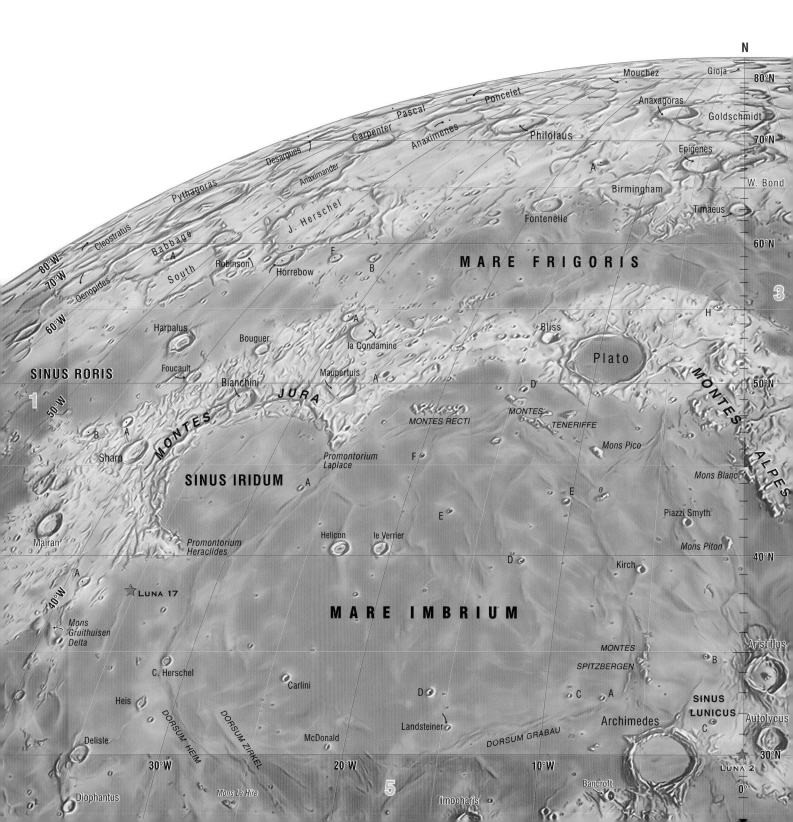

N

Gioja
Mouchez
80°N
Anaxagoras
Poncelet
Goldschmidt
Pascal
Philolaus
70°N
Carpenter
Anaximenes
Desargues
Epigenes
Anaximander
A
Birmingham
Timaeus
Pythagoras
W. Bond
J. Herschel
Fontenelle
60°N
Cleostratus
Babbage
A
MARE FRIGORIS
80°W
South
F
Robinson
70°W
Horrebow
B
Oenopides
Bliss
H
60°W
Harpalus
A
Plato
Bouguer
la Condamine
MONTES
Foucault
Maupertuis
A
D
50°N
SINUS RORIS
Bianchini
JURA
MONTES
MONTES
1
50°W
MONTES RECTI
TENERIFFE
ALPES
Sharp
Mons Pico
B
A
MONTES
Promontorium
Laplace
F
Mons Blanc
SINUS IRIDUM
A
E
B
Piazzi Smyth
E
Mons Piton
Promontorium
Heraclides
Helicon
le Verrier
E
Mairan
D
40°N
40°W
Kirch
A
☆ LUNA 17
Aristillus
Mons
Gruithuisen
MARE IMBRIUM
Delta
MONTES
B
SPITZBERGEN
C. Herschel
Carlini
C
A
SINUS
Heis
D
LUNICUS
Archimedes
C
Delisle
Landsteiner
DORSUM HEIM
DORSUM GRABAU
Autolycus
DORSUM ZIRKEL
McDonald
30°N
30°W
20°W
10°W
0°
☆ LUNA 2
Diophantus
Mons La Hire
Bancroft
5
Timocharis

3

As in Mare Orientale (Map 9), the Imbrium impact created a series of concentric mountainous rings. Portions are well-preserved as the Montes Alpes and Caucasus, and the Montes Carpatus and Apenninus in the south. The innermost rings were eroded or submerged by the lava that flooded the central basin, although remnants persist in Montes Recti, Teneriffe, and Spitzbergen, as well as in isolated peaks such as Mons Pico and Mons Piton. The location of the various mare ridges (Dorsum Grabau, Zirkel, and Heim) may have been influenced by the topography of the underlying surface. The Montes Archimedes (Map 6) represent a relatively high, post-impact surface not submerged by the lava flows.

Both Plato (51.6°N, 9.4°W, 109 km), a conspicuous crater with a dark, flat floor, and Sinus Iridum (260 km in diameter) were created by later impacts, but flooded at about the same time as the main Imbrium basin. The Montes Jura are probably remnants of the original wall of Sinus Iridum.

A narrow highland strip separates Mare Imbrium from Mare Frigoris. Within this highland area there are well-defined craters, such as Sharp (45.7°N, 40.2°W, 39 km), Bianchini (48.7°N, 34.3°W, 38 km), on the edge of Sinus Iridum, and La Condamine (53.4°N, 28.2°W, 37 km), as well as the greatly degraded crater Maupertuis (49.6°N, 27.3°W, 45 km).

Mare Frigoris runs right across the northern region of the Moon, from Sinus Roris and the ray crater Harpalus (52.6°N, 43.4°W, 39 km) in the west, to Lacus Mortis and Hercules (Map 3) in the east. It is one of the non-circular mare areas, not associated with one specific impact, but where lavas have flooded a series of adjoining low-lying areas of the surface. Its area is approximately 435,000 sq km, slightly less than Earth's Red Sea.

Among the rugged terrain at the northern and northwestern limbs are craters in various degrees of preservation. Some, such as Anaxagoras (73.4°N, 10.1°W, 50 km), a bright ray crater, are relatively fresh, whereas the large craters of J. Herschel (62.0°N, 42.0°W, 165 km) and South (58.0°N, 50.8°W, 104 km) are heavily degraded. Goldschmidt (73.2°N, 3.6°W, 113 km), Birmingham (65.1°N, 10.5°W, 92 km) and Babbage (59.7°N, 57.1°W, 143 km) are rather better preserved.

One complex crater is prominent towards the northwestern limb. This is Pythagoras (63.5°N, 63.0°W, 142 km), with terraced inner walls and a conspicuous central peak. Running up towards the north polar region are a number of well-defined craters, notably Anaximander (66.9°N, 51.3°W, 67 km), Carpenter (69.4°N, 50.9°W, 59 km), Anaximenes (72.5°N, 44.5°W, 80 km), and Philolaus (72.1°N, 32.4°W, 70 km), the last with interior terracing and central peaks.

Name	Translation
Lacus Mortis	Lake of Death
Mare Frigoris	Sea of Cold
Mare Imbrium	Sea of Showers
Sinus Iridum	Bay of Rainbows
Sinus Lunicus	Lunik Bay
Sinus Roris	Bay of Dew

Feature	Age of Moon (days)
Anaxagoras	13, 17
Anaximenes	11, 25
Archimedes	8, 22
Hercules	5, 18
Mons Pico	8, 22
Mons Piton	8, 22
Montes Alpes	8, 21
Montes Caucasus	6, 20
Philolaus	9, 23
Plato	9, 22
Pythagoras	12, 26

3 | Aristoteles

Contrasting mare areas feature in this region of the Moon, in particular the eastern end of Mare Frigoris and the northern edge of circular Mare Serenitatis. The two are linked by the lava-flooded areas of Lacus Mortis and Lacus Somniorum.

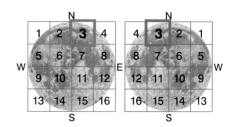

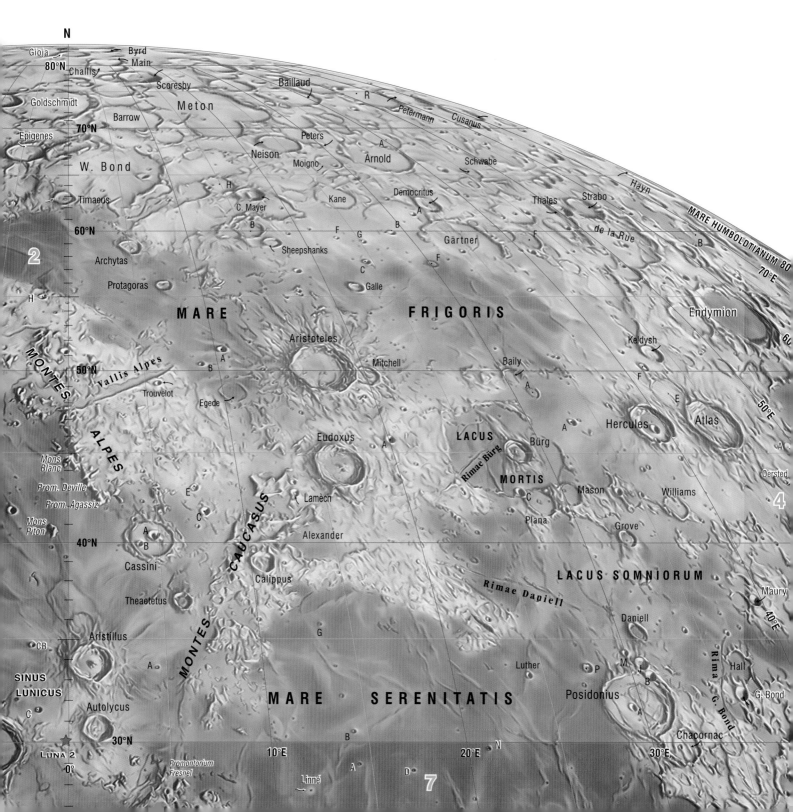

N

Gioja
Byrd
80°N
Challis
Main
Scoresby
Baillaud
R
Meton
Petermann
Cusanus
Goldschmidt
Barrow
Peters
A
Arnold
70°N
Epigenes
Neison
Schwabe
Hayn
Moigno
W. Bond
Democritus
Thales
Strabo
Timaeus
H
Kane
A
MARE HUMBOLDTIANUM
80
C. Mayer
de la Rue
60°N
B
F
G
B
Gärtner
70°E
Sheepshanks
F
Archytas
C
Endymion
Protagoras
Galle
60
2
H
MARE   FRIGORIS
Keldysh
Aristoteles
MONTES
Mitchell
Baily
A
50°N
Vallis Alpes
A
B
F
50°E
Trouvelot
Hercules
Atlas
Egede
LACUS
A
E
ALPES
Eudoxus
A
Bürg
Mons
Blanc
MORTIS
Oersted
Prom. Deville
Lamech
Rimae Bürg
C
Mason
Williams
Prom. Agassiz
E
Mons
Piton
CAUCASUS
C
Plana
Grove
40°N
A
Alexander
B
Cassini
Calippus
LACUS   SOMNIORUM
Theaetetus
Rimae Daniell
Maury
G
Aristillus
Daniell
40°E
CB
A
Rima G. Bond
SINUS
MONTES
Luther
P
M
Hall
LUNICUS
Posidonius
B
G. Bond
C
Autolycus
MARE   SERENITATIS
A
Chacornac
30°N
B
N
LUNA 2
0°
10°E
20°E
30°E
Promontorium
Fresnel
A
D
7
Linné

Mare Frigoris is generally taken to extend as far as Hercules (46.7°N, 39.1°E, 69 km), the floor of which has dark patches and a smaller, central crater. To the east of Hercules lies Atlas (46.7°N, 44.4°E, 87 km), with terracing and a fractured floor.

North of Mare Frigoris lies the large crater W. Bond (65.3°N, 3.7°E, 156 km), with a rather irregular outer rim. Even more irregular is Meton (73.8°N, 19.2°E, 130 km). Between the two craters lies Barrow (71.3°N, 7.7°E, 92 km), its southeastern wall broken by two embayments. Farther east, Gärtner (59.1°N, 34.6°E, 115 km) has lost the original wall between it and Mare Frigoris, but retains its light floor. The rim of De la Rue (59.1°N, 53.0°E, 134 km) has been partly destroyed by later cratering, including Strabo (61.9°N, 54.3°E, 55 km) to the north. Thales (61.8°N, 50.3°E, 31 km) is very bright around Full Moon. On the edge of this map lies Endymion (53.6°N, 56.5°E, 123 km), with a dark, smooth floor.

The Montes Alpes on the edge of Mare Imbrium are broken by Vallis Alpes, which is 180 km long, and has a cleft running along its floor. Between the end of Montes Alpes and Montes Caucasus on the northwestern edge of Mare Serenetatis lies Cassini (40.2°N, 4.6°E, 56 km, 1240 m) with a flooded floor and two prominent inner craters, the larger of which, Cassini A, is 17 km across.

The conspicuous crater Aristoteles (50.2°N, 17.4°E, 87 km) exhibits inner terracing, central peaks and a clearly defined, radially structured, outer ejecta blanket. To its south lies the smaller crater Eudoxus (11.3°N, 16.3°E, 67 km), again with complex interior terraces. To the southwest is the ray crater Aristillus (33.9°N, 1.2°E, 55 km, 3650 m) with triple central peaks rising to 900 m above the floor.

Between Eudoxus and Hercules lies the complex area of Lacus Mortis (45°N, 27°E), which appears to be a large, badly degraded, flooded crater, some 150 km across. Its floor is broken by faults, ridges and the Rimae Bürg, while the conspicuous crater Bürg (45.0°N, 28.2°E, 39 km) lies in the centre.

South of Lacus Mortis is Lacus Somniorum, an irregular area of mare lavas with a wide opening onto Mare Serenitatis, guarded on the southeast by the distinctive crater Posidonius (31.8°N, 29.9°E, 95 km, 2300 m), with a fractured floor, inner ridges, and an inner crater (Posidonius A). The conspicuous cleft of Rima G. Bond lies to the east, bordering the breached crater Hall (33.7°N, 37.0°E, 35 km, 1140 m), and G. Bond itself (32.4°N, 36.2°E, 20 km, 2780 m).

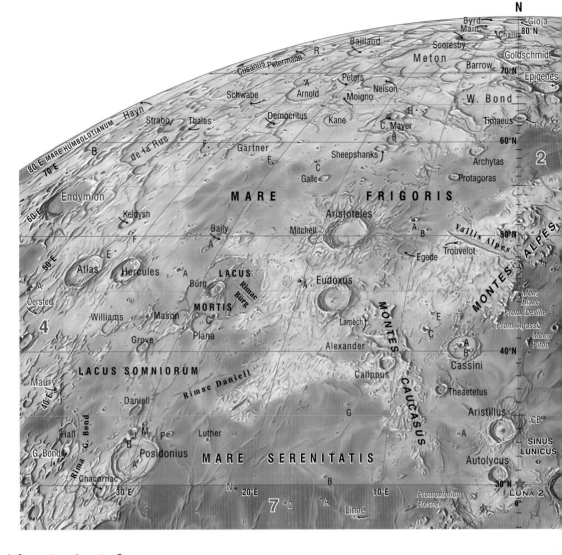

Name	Translation
Lacus Mortis	Lake of Death
Lacus Somniorum	Lake of Dreams
Mare Frigoris	Sea of Cold
Mare Humboldtianum	Humboldt Sea
Mare Imbrium	Sea of Showers
Mare Serenitatis	Sea of Serenity
Sinus Lunicus	Lunik Bay
Vallis Alpes	Alpine Valley

Feature	Age of Moon (days)
Aristillus	8, 21
Aristoteles	6, 20
Atlas	5, 18
Autolycus	7, 21
Barrow	7, 21
Bürg	5, 19
Cassini	7, 21
Endymion	4, 18
Eudoxus	6, 20
Hercules	5, 18
Lacus Somniorum	4, 18
Meton	6, 20
Montes Alpes	8, 21
Posidonius	5, 20
Sinus Iridum	10, 24
Thales	13–17
Vallis Alpes	8, 22

4 | Gauss

This is a highland region, broken only by small areas of mare-type lavas in Lacus Somniorum, Lacus Temporis, Lacus Spei, as well as the rather larger area found, albeit on the limb, in Mare Humboldtianum.

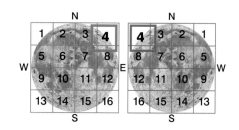

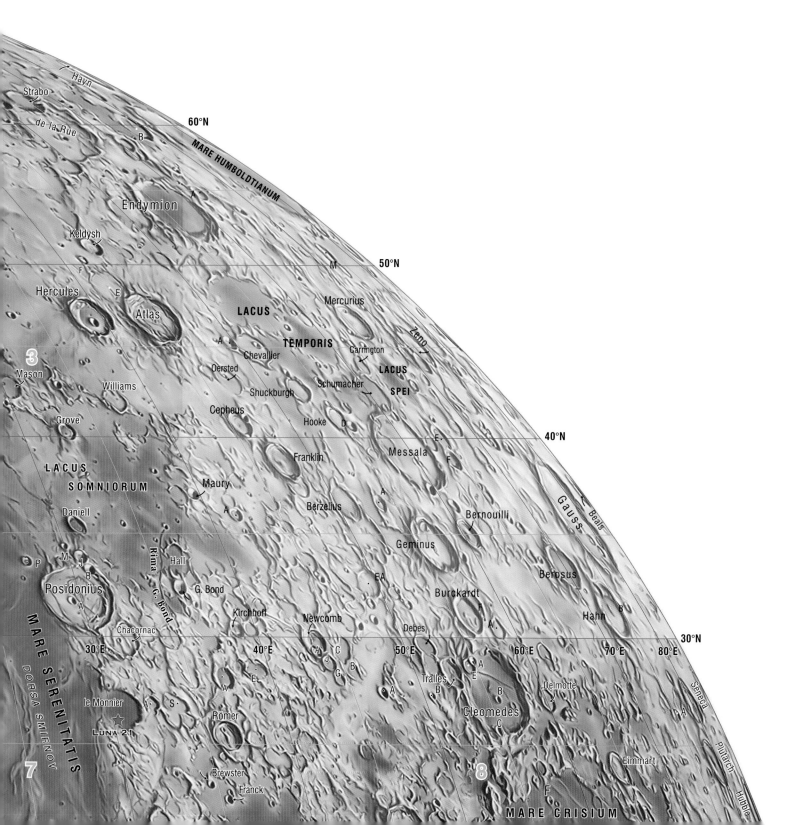

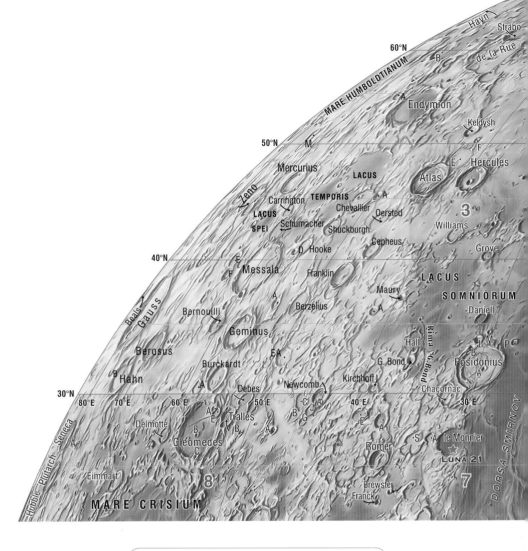
In the southwest lies a small patch of mare lavas forming the easternmost extension of Lacus Somniorum. Farther north and east lie the very irregular, pale, low-lying patches forming Lacus Temporis (46°N, 57°E) with, yet farther east, the small but noticeably darker area known as Lacus Spei (43°N, 65°E, 80 km). On the limb, and best seen when there is a favourable libration, is the much larger Mare Humboldtianum (Map L1, p. 193). This is, in fact, the lava-flooded centre of a larger basin, the outer wall of which runs from Strabo, east of de la Rue and Endymion (all Map 3), and northeast of Mercurius (44.6°N, 66.2°E, 67 km) before crossing the limb. It encloses craters such as Endymion B, Mercurius M, and the smaller crater (Mercurius E) immediately south of the latter.

The largest crater in this sector is Gauss (35.7°N, 79.0°E, 177 km), with a number of interior craters. Gauss lies just within the libration zone, so is sometimes completely invisible, except for its western wall. The craters Zeno (45.2°N, 72.9°E, 65 km) and Hahn (31.3°N, 73.6°E, 84 km) lie just outside the libration zone, as does Berosus (33.5°N, 69.9°E, 74 km), a flooded crater northwest of Hahn.

Name	Translation
Lacus Temporis	Lake of Time
Lacus Somniorum	Lake of Dreams
Lacus Spei	Lake of Hope
Mare Crisium	Sea of Crises
Mare Humboldtianum	Humboldt Sea
Mare Serenitatis	Sea of Serenity

Feature	Age of Moon (days)
Endymion	4, 18
Franklin	4, 18
Geminus	3, 17
Lacus Somniorum	4, 18

Three prominent features lie south of Lacus Temporis: the large crater Messala (39.2°N, 60.5°E, 125 km), and the craters Geminus (34.5°N, 56.7°E, 85 km) and Burckhardt (31.1°N, 56.5°E, 56 km). West of Lacus Temporis are Chevallier (44.9°N, 51.2°E, 52 km) a partially destroyed flooded crater, Shuckburgh (42.6°N, 52.8°E, 38 km), and Hooke (41.2°N, 54.9°E, 36 km). Still farther west, and slightly to the south are the prominent craters Cepheus (40.8°N, 45.8°E, 39 km) and Franklin (38.8°N, 47.7°E, 56 km), both with small central peaks.

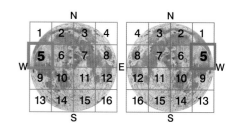

Although the mare basalts in Oceanus Procellarum cover most of this region, some of the most interesting lunar features are to be found here, including some that are unique.

LUNAR MAPS

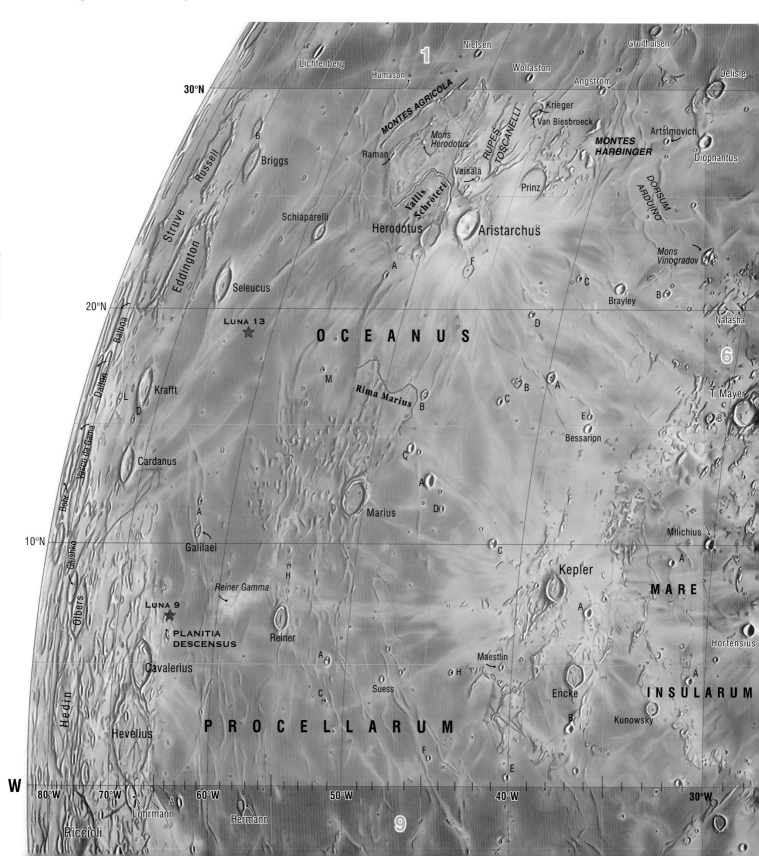

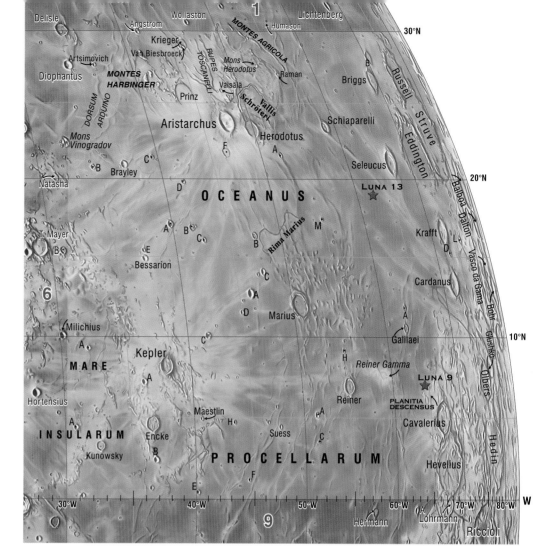

In the north there is an approximately rectangular area of highland terrain, which is crossed by Vallis Schröteri, the largest sinuous rille. It starts at a small (6 km) crater, 25 km north of the flooded crater Herodotus (23.2°N, 49.7°W, 34 km). Widening to about
10 km across, it creates the feature known as the 'Cobra Head', but gradually narrows to about 0.5 km as it meanders north and northwest, before finally turning southwest. Its total length is approximately 160 km, with an initial depth of about 1000 m.

East of Herodotus is Aristarchus (23.7°N, 47.4°W, 40 km, 3000 m). This crater and its rays are the brightest feature on the Moon, often detectable when illuminated by earthshine, or during a lunar eclipse. North of Aristarchus lies the scarp of Rupes Toscanelli and the clefts of Rimae Aristarchus. To the east is the flooded and partially destroyed crater Prinz (25.5°N, 44.1°W, 46 km), whose remaining wall rises to about 1100 m. The boundary of the Mare Imbrium basin lies east of this area, marked by Montes Harbinger as well as Dorsum Arduino and other ridges.

South of Herodotus and Aristarchus is another sinuous rille, Rima Marius, about 250 km long, and 2 km wide where it begins near the crater Marius C. Between the rille and the flooded crater Marius (11.9°N, 50.8°W, 41 km), and also west and southwest of the crater, lies a broad area, commonly known as the Marius Hills, with a wide range of volcanic features, including domes, cones with summit craters, peaks, and ridges.

Kepler (8.1°N, 38.0°W, 31 km, 2570 m) is a conspicuous crater with an uneven floor and a large ray system. To the west lies Reiner (7.0°N, 54.9°W, 29 km) and beyond that, Reiner Gamma, the only example on the nearside of a feature known as a swirl. This is a flat area covered in a bright deposit of uncertain origin, once thought to be ejecta from Cavalerius (5.1°N, 66.8°W, 57 km). Both the floor and ramparts of the adjacent complex crater,

Name	Translation
Mare Insularum	Sea of Islands
Oceanus Procellarum	Ocean of Storms
Planitia Descensus	Descent Plain

Feature	Age of Moon (days)
Aristarchus	11, 25
Herodotus	11, 25
Hevelius	13, 27
Kepler	11, 25
Reiner Gamma	13, 26
Vallis Schröteri	11, 25

Hevelius (2.2°N, 67.6°W, 115 km) have been affected by extensive regional fracturing, as has the larger, partially destroyed crater Hedin (2.9°N, 76.5°W, 150 km). To the north, Olbers (7.4°N, 75.9°W, 74 km) is another ray crater.

On the western limb Vasco da Gama (13.6°N, 83.9°W, 83 km) and Bohr (12.4°N, 86.6°W, 71 km) lie in the libration zone, as do Dalton (17.1°N, 84.3°W, 60 km) and the flooded crater Balboa (19.1°N, 83.2°W, 69 km). To the northeast lie three large degraded craters: Struve (22.4°N, 77.1°W, 164 km), the floor of which runs into Russell (26.5°N, 75.4°W, 103 km), and to the east, Eddington (21.3°N, 72.2°W, 118 km), where the eastern and southern walls have been largely destroyed.

The main features in this area are the bright, ray crater Copernicus and the
southern portion of Mare Imbrium, bordered on the east by Montes
Apenninus, the highest mountain range on the Moon, and the less distinct
Montes Carpatus on the west.

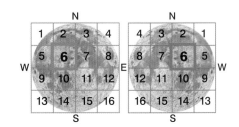

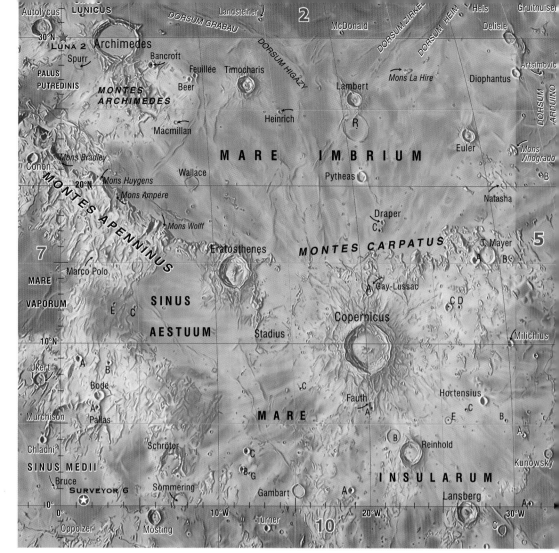

Copernicus (9.7°N, 20.1°W, 93 km, 3800 m) has a rim that rises about 900 m above the surrounding plains. The terracing on the inner walls created by slumping is clearly visible as are the central peaks, the highest of which is about 1200 m above the crater floor. Being a relatively young crater, the radial structure of the ejecta from Copernicus, including the ray system, is readily apparent.

Within Mare Imbrium is Timocharis (26.7°N, 13.1°W, 33 km), east of which lies the isolated patch of highland material of Montes Archimedes. The southern border of Mare Imbrium is formed by the Montes Apenninus and Carpatus. The Montes Apenninus reach heights of 5000 m in places, and have (for the Moon) a relatively steep escarpment on their northern flank, sloping down towards the centre of Mare Imbrium at an average gradient of 25–30°. On the southern side, the slope towards Mare Vaporum is much more gradual. Here, the radial nature of the Imbrium ejecta is clearly visible. The Montes Carpatus, by contrast, are more subdued, varying between 1000 and 2000 m in height.

Eratosthenes (14.5°N, 11.3°W, 58 km, 3570 m), near the end of the Montes Apenninus, is an extremely conspicuous crater when close to the terminator. It is nearly as deep as Copernicus and shows similar internal terraces and prominent central peaks. Reinhold (3.3°N, 22.8°W, 42 km), southwest of Copernicus, has terraces but no central peak.

East of Copernicus and southwest of Eratosthenes is the famous ghost crater Stadius (10.5°N, 13.7°W, 69 km), where mare lavas have flooded most of the crater itself. The course of the rim (including various crater pits) may be distinguished at sunrise and sunset, but essentially disappears under vertical illumination. One portion of the wall, in the northeast (towards Eratosthenes) remains to a height of 650 m. Wallace (20.3°N, 8.7°W, 26 km) and Lambert R, in Mare Imbrium, are similarly flooded craters. A crater chain runs northwest from the western side of Stadius.

There are various domes in this region, most notably the fine group northeast of Hortensius (6.5°W, 28.0°W, 14.0 km, 2860 m), most of which have crater pits, as does the dome west of Milichius (10.0°N, 30.2°W, 12 km, 2510 m). A large dome lies southwest of Gambart C. Grazing illumination reveals dark areas of lava flows northeast of this area towards Sinus Aestuum, as well as various wrinkle ridges (dorsa), particularly in Mare Imbrium. The heavily degraded craters of Pallas (5.5°N, 1.6°W, 46 km), and Schröter (2.6°N, 7.0°W, 35 km) lie northwest and west, respectively, of Sinus Medii.

Name	Translation
Mare Imbrium	Sea of Showers
Mare Insularum	Sea of Islands
Mare Vaporum	Sea of Vapours
Palus Putredinis	Marsh of Decay
Sinus Aestuum	Bay of Billows
Sinus Lunicus	Lunik Bay
Sinus Medii	Central Bay

Feature	Age of Moon (days)
Copernicus	9, 22
Eratosthenes	8, 22
Montes Apenninus	8, 22
Montes Carpatus	9, 23
Pallas	8, 22
Reinhold	9, 23
Timocharis	8, 22

Mare material covers large parts of this region. Mare Serenitatis is a circular mare, filling most of its impact basin, whereas Mare Tranquillitatis is an irregular mare, not associated with a basin.

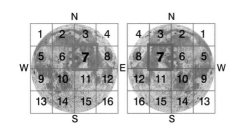

SINUS LUNICUS
Autolycus
LUNA 2
Spurr
PALUS PUTREDINIS
APOLLO 15
Mons Hadley Delta
Aratus
Mons Bradley
Conon
Galen
MONTES
APENNINUS
Promontorium Fresnel
Santos-Dumont
Mons Hadley
Linné
Banting

MARE
SERENITATIS

Posidonius
Chacornac
DORSA SMIRNOV
Sarabhai
Very
le Monnier
LUNA 21
Brewster
DORSA ALDROVANDI
Littrow
Clerke
Abetti
APOLLO17
Mons Vitruvius
Römer
G. Bond

Bessel
Deseilligni
DORSUM AZARA
DORSUM VON COTTA
DORSUM BUCKLAND
DORSA LISTER
DORSA
Mons Argaeus
Brackett
Bobillier
Sulpicius Gallus
LACUS ODII
LACUS FELICITATIS
SINUS FIDEI
Bowen
Yangel
LACUS DOLORIS
MONTES HAEMUS
LACUS GAUDII
Daubrée
LACUS HIEMALIS
LACUS LENITATIS
Menelaus
Tacquet
Promontorium Archerusia
Auwers
Al-Bakri
Fabbroni
Dawes
Beketov
Plinius
Vitruvius
Gardner
Jansen
Cajal
DORSA BARLOW

Marco Polo
MARE VAPORUM
Manilius
SINUS HONORIS
Ross
Maclear
MARE
Carrel

Boscovich
Julius Caesar
Sosigenes
TRANQUILLITATIS
Arago

Rima Hyginus
Rima Hyginus
Silberschlag
Rima Ariadaeus
Ariadaeus
Lamont
Sinas

Ukert
Bode
Pallas
Murchison
Chladni
Triesnecker
Rimae Triesnecker
Dembowski
Agrippa
Whewell
Tempel
de Morgan
Cayley
Godin
d'Arrest
Dionysius
Manners
Ritter
Sabine
Schmidt
Aldrin
Collins
Armstrong
SURVEYOR 5
RANGER 8
APOLLO 11
STATIO TRANQUILLITATIS
Maskelyne

SINUS MEDII
Bruce
Blagg
Rhaeticus
SURVEYOR 6
Oppolzer
Seeliger
Theon Senior
Lade
Moltke
Delambre

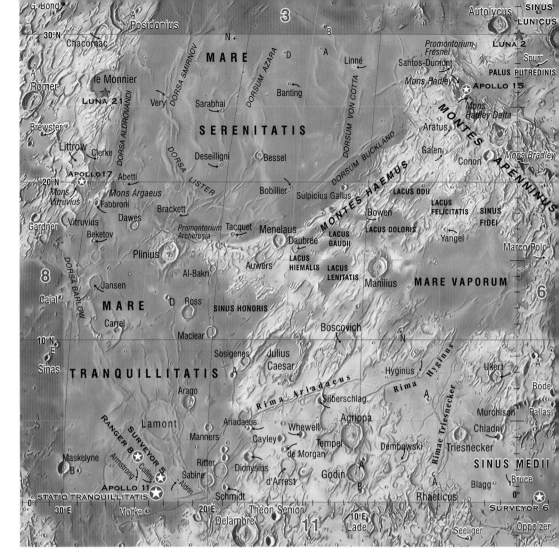

Mare Vaporum and Sinus Medii are reasonably well defined, but there are also several other areas of mare-type material, notably Palus Putredinis in the north, near Rima Hadley, the landing site of Apollo 15 (26.08°N, 3.66°E). In addition, there is the series of smaller areas running from Lacus Felicitatis in the north to Lacus Hiemalis between Mare Vaporum and Mare Serenitatis, as well as Sinus Fidei and Sinus Honoris.

The dorsae within Mare Serenitatis run roughly parallel to the edge, but it is noticeable how other ridges (including Montes Haemus on the edge of Mare Serenitatis) lie radially to Mare Imbrium, not Mare Serenitatis. They are part of the ejecta blanket from the Imbrium impact.

Within Mare Serenitatis lies the tiny crater Linné (27.7°N, 11.8°E, 2.0 km), which became famous (or infamous) when Schmidt announced, in 1866, that it had disappeared. In fact, no changes had occurred to it or the surrounding mare. At roughly the same latitude on the eastern side lies the breached crater le Monnier (26.6°N, 30.6°E, 60 km), where the lunar rover, Luna 21 landed. Due south of le Monnier is the Taurus-Littrow region, with Littrow (21.5°N, 31.4°E, 30 km) a degraded crater that has lost its southern wall, near the Apollo 17 landing site (20.17°N, 30.77°E).

On either side of the breach between the rims of Mare Serenitatis and Mare Tranquillitatis are two distinctive craters: flat-floored Vitruvius (17.6°N, 31.3°E, 29 km) and Plinius (15.4°N, 23.7°E, 43 km) with its central peak. Farther west lie two other complex craters: Menelaus (16.3°N, 16.0°E, 26 km) and Manilius (14.5°N, 9.1°E, 38 km). The degraded craters Boscovich (9.8°N, 11.1°E, 46 km) and Julius Caesar (9.0°N, 15.4°E, 90 km) are farther south.

Some of the Moon's major rilles lie in this area: Rimae Triesnecker, an extensive network east of Triesnecker (4.2°N, 3.6°E, 26 km), Rima Hyginus, broken by tiny Hyginus (7.8°N, 6.3°E, 9 km), and Rima Ariadaeus, running west from Ariadaeus (4.6°N, 17.3°E, 11 km), a breached crater on the edge of Mare Tranquillitatis.

Towards the centre of Mare Tranquillitatis are low ridges outlining the submerged crater Lamont (4.4°N, 23.7°E, 106 km), only visible under grazing illumination. South of here is the Apollo 11 landing site, Statio Tranquillitatis or Tranquillity Base (0.8°N, 23.46°E). West, near the edge of the mare, lie the twin craters of Sabine (1.4°N, 20.1°E, 30 km), and Ritter (2.0°N, 19.2°E, 29 km).

Name	Translation
Lacus Doloris	Lake of Sorrow
Lacus Felicitatis	Lake of Happiness
Lacus Gaudii	Lake of Joy
Lacus Hiemalis	Lake of Winter
Lacus Lenitatis	Lake of Softness
Lacus Odii	Lake of Hatred
Mare Serenitatis	Sea of Serenity
Mare Tranquillitatis	Sea of Tranquility
Mare Vaporum	Sea of Vapours
Palus Putredinis	Marsh of Decay
Sinus Fidei	Bay of Trust
Sinus Honoris	Bay of Honour
Sinus Lunicus	Lunik Bay
Sinus Medii	Central Bay

Feature	Age of Moon (days)
Agrippa	7, 21
Julius Caesar	6, 20
Manilius	7, 21
Montes Haemus	6, 20
Palus Putredinus	8, 21
Plinius	6, 20
Rima Ariadaeus	6, 20
Sinus Medii	7, 21

Within the highland region still farther west lie the subdued, flat-floored crater d'Arrest (2.3°N, 14.7°W, 30 km), Tempel (3.9°N, 11.9°E, 45 km), and two craters with central peaks: Agrippa (4.1°N, 10.5°E, 44 km) and Godin (1.8°N, 10.2°E, 34 km).

8 | Mare Crisium

This region includes the northeastern portion of Mare Tranquillitatis, the northern section of Mare Fecunditatis, a similar irregular mare, and one of the Moon's most prominent features, Mare Crisium.

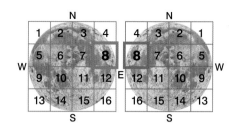

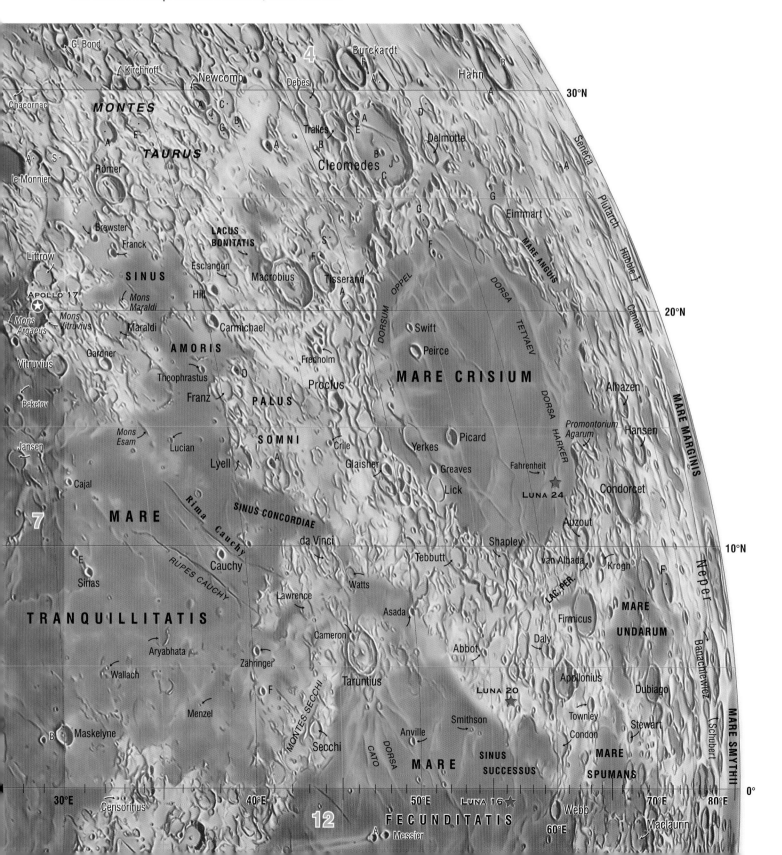

Mare Crisium is an approximately elliptical mare, with its major axis running east–west, and an area of about 176,000 sq. km (slightly more than twice the size of Lake Superior in North America). It lies in the centre of the much larger Crisium impact basin, which includes the crater Cleomedes, Mare Undarum, Mare Spumans, and most of Palus Somni.

Apart from these areas, mare-type material also occur in Lacus Bonitatis, in the tiny Mare Anguis on the eastern edge of Mare Crisium, and in larger, more significant amounts in Mare Marginis and Mare Smythii, both of which lie in the libration zone on the eastern limb. The prominent, complex crater Neper (8.5°N, 84.6°E, 137 km), with a dark floor and central peaks, lies between the two maria.

Cleomedes (27.7°N, 56.0°E, 125 km) is a complex crater, with a central peak, a rifted floor, and small inner craters. To its west, and on the western edge of the Montes Taurus, is Römer (25.4°N, 36.4°E, 39 km), a prominent crater with interior terraces and a central peak. On the edge of Sinus Amoris is Maraldi (19.4°N, 34.9°E, 39 km), with a flooded floor, and south of that, two unnamed, heavily degraded rings, Maraldi E and, farther out into Mare Tranquillitatis, Maraldi B, with only remnants of the latter's wall still visible.

Between Sinus Amoris and Mare Crisium are the prominent, complex crater Macrobius (21.3°N, 46.0°E, 64 km), and the smaller Tisserand (21.4°N, 48.2°E, 36 km). South of Macrobius, east of Palus Somni, lies the bright ray crater Proclus (16.1°N, 46.8°E, 28 km), whose rays are readily visible on both mare and highland material in the vicinity.

Southwest of Palus Somni, towards Mare Tranquillitatis is Sinus Concordiae, and the wide rille Rima Cauchy, which is some 210 km long and extends southeast towards the flooded crater, Lawrence (7.4°N, 43.2°E, 24 km). Cauchy itself (9.6°N, 38.6°E, 12 km) is bright at Full Moon. Further into the mare is Rupes Cauchy, a scarp that turns into a rille and which is about 150 km long.

Southeast of Mare Crisium is the dark-floored, flooded crater Condorcet (12.1°N. 69.6°E, 74 km), and to the south is the similar crater Firmicus (7.3°N, 63.4°E, 56 km), near which lies a tiny patch of mare-type material, known as Lacus Perseverantiae (marked 'Lac. Per.' on the map). A similar flooded crater is Dubiago (4.4°N, 70.0°E, 51 km), and both Mare Undarum and Mare Spumans resemble a series of lava-flooded craters, as does Sinus Successus at the edge of Mare Serenitatis.

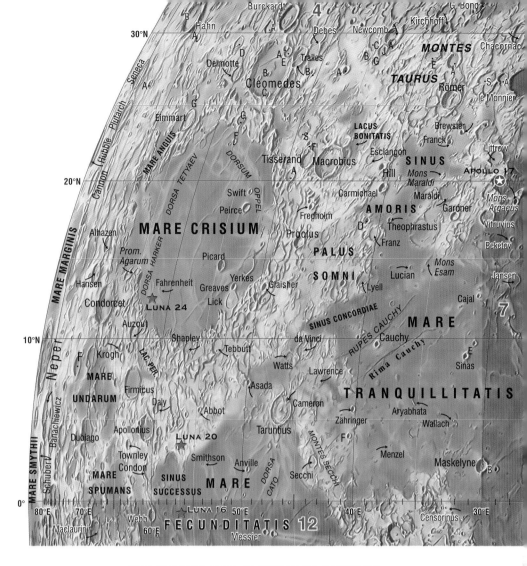

Name	Translation
Lacus Bonitatis	Lake of Goodness
Lacus Perseverantiae	Lake of Perseverance
Mare Anguis	Serpent Sea
Mare Crisium	Sea of Crises
Mare Fecunditatis	Sea of Fertility
Mare Marginis	Marginal Sea
Mare Smythii	Smyth Sea
Mare Spumans	Foaming Sea
Mare Tranquillitatis	Sea of Tranquillity
Mare Undarum	Sea of Waves
Palus Somni	Marsh of Dreams
Sinus Amoris	Bay of Love
Sinus Concordiae	Bay of Harmony
Sinus Successus	Bay of Success

Feature	Age of Moon (days)
Cleomedes	3, 16
Macrobius	4, 18
Proclus	4, 18
Taruntius	4, 18

On the edge of Mare Fecunditatis lies Taruntius (5.6°N, 46.5°E, 56 km) with a pronounced central peak and an inner wall, concentric with the outer rim. To the southwest lies a low range of mountains, the Montes Secchi, which separate Mare Tranquillitatis from Mare Fecunditatis.

9 | Gassendi

There are few notable features in the southwestern portion of Oceanus Procellarum and inside Mare Humorum, but the highland region to the west has many interesting formations and offers a glimpse of the Mare Orientale.

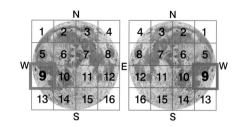

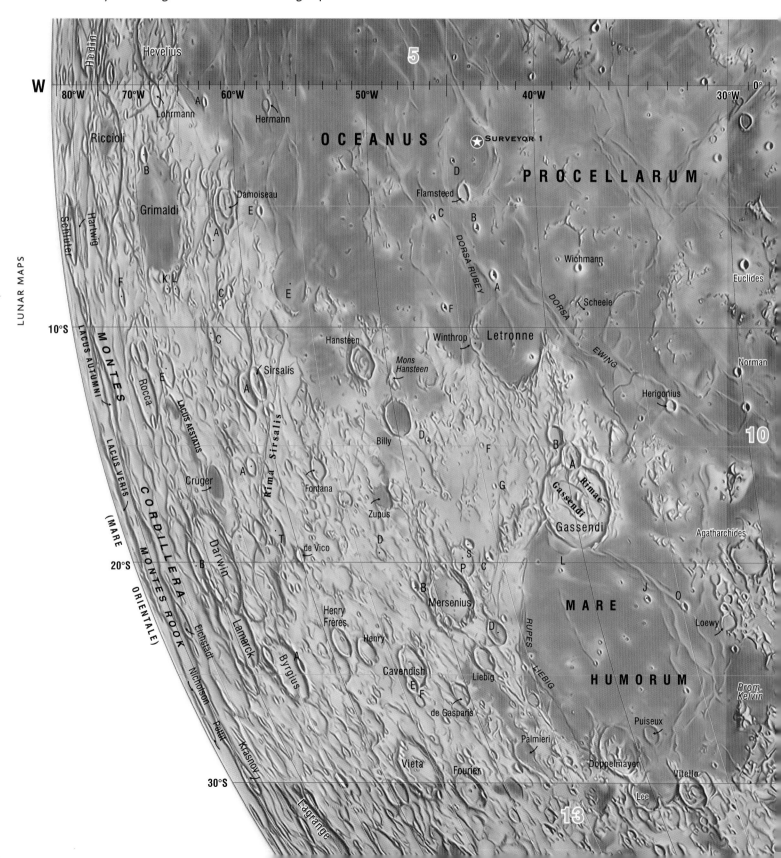

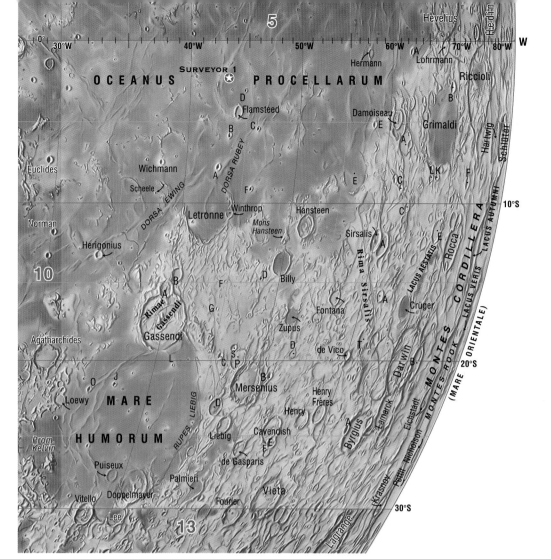

On the edge of Oceanus Procellarum is the breached and flooded crater Letronne (10.8°S, 42.5°W, 116 km), and just outside the mare are several striking features. In the northwest, there is Riccioli (3.3°S, 74.6°W, 139 km), a complex crater with extensive fracturing of its floor, named after the astronomer who introduced the system of lunar nomenclature still used today. Grimaldi (5.5°S, 68.3°W, 172 km), to the southeast, is a conspicuous, dark-flooded crater with heavily degraded outer walls. In the libration zone to the west is Schlüter (5.9°S, 83.3°W, 89 km) a complex crater with internal terraces.

On the limb to the south lies Mare Orientale, fully visible only on images obtained by space-probes. It is the youngest lunar impact basin, and one that clearly shows the structure of such basins. As is often the case, the central region is flooded by lava, but in Mare Orientale the outer mountain rings have been preserved. These are Montes Rook, the innermost ring, and Montes Cordillera. Parts of the latter lie just outside the libration zone and are therefore generally visible beyond the large, degraded crater Darwin (20.2°S, 69.5°W, 120 km). Mare-type material has flooded portions of the low-lying areas between Mare Orientale's mountain rings and these form Lacus Autumni and Lacus Veris. Outside the basin, north of Darwin, similar processes have formed Lacus Aestatis and the dark floor of Crüger (16.7°S, 66.8°W, 45 km). Billy (13.8°S, 50.1°W, 45 km) is a similar crater farther east.

Mare Humorum is another circular mare filling the centre of its basin. Ridges occur on its eastern side and on the west is a distinct scarp, Rupes Liebig. In the south is the greatly degraded crater Doppelmayer (28.5°S, 41.4°W, 63 km), with a prominent central peak, but only traces of its northern rim. To the north of Mare Humorum lies the very prominent, complex crater Gassendi (17.6°S, 40.1°W, 101 km, 1860 m), with a highly fractured floor (Rimae Gassendi) and various central peaks and hills. Its northern rim is broken by Gassendi A, which is 33 km across.

Southwest of Gassendi lies Mersenius (21.5°S, 49.2°W, 84 km), which has an unusual floor that appears to be flooded, yet is

Name	Translation
Lacus Aestatis	Lake of Summer
Lacus Autumni	Lake of Autumn
Lacus Veris	Lake of Spring
Mare Humorum	Sea of Humours
Mare Orientale	Eastern Sea
Oceanus Procellarum	Ocean of Storms

Feature	Age of Moon (days)
Billy	12, 26
Byrgius A	14–23
Gassendi	11, 25
Grimaldi	13, 27
Letronne	11, 25

actually convex. South of Mersenius is an unnamed patch of mare-type material running down towards dark Palmieri (28.6°S, 47.7°W, 40 km). To the west, Vieta (29.2°S, 56.3°W, 87 km) is prominent, and between it and Mersenius lies Cavendish (24.5°S, 53.7°W, 56 km), with its rim broken by Cavendish E. Beyond the similarly sized craters of Henry (24.0°S, 56.8°W, 41 km) and Henry Frères (23.5°S, 58.9°W, 42 km) lies Byrgius (24.7°S, 65.3°W, 87 km) on the eastern wall of which Byrgius A is the centre of a ray system. The heavily eroded crater Lamarck (22.9°S, 69.8°W, 100 km) lies between Byrgius and Darwin.

10 | Bullialdus

At the far southeastern edge of Oceanus Procellarum, Montes Riphaeus separate it from Mare Cognitum, which itself runs into Mare Nubium. A chain of conspicuous craters runs down the eastern edge of the region.

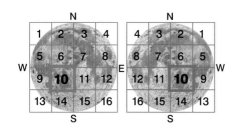

MARE INSULARUM

SINUS MEDII

Gambart

6

Sömmering

SURVEYOR 6

Bruce

30°W

20°W

10°W

0°

0°

Lansberg

C

B

Turner

F

Mösting

Oppolzer

Réaumur

SURVEYOR 3

APOLLO 12

APOLLO 14

Mösting A

Flammarion

Spörer

A

Lalande

C

Gyldén

MONTES

Fra Mauro

C

Herschel

C

A

Euclides

RIPHAEUS

MARE

Parry

Ammonius

Bonpland

C

Kuiper

T

Ptolemaeus

Tolansky

Palisa

10°S

RANGER 7

Y

Norman

C

COGNITUM

E

Guericke

Kundt

Davy

C

RANGER 9

Herigonius

C

Mons Moro

A

9

C

Darney

C

Alphonsus

11

Lassell

B

E

A

Opelt

Alpetragius

Lubiniezky

Promontorium Taenarium

Agatharchides

Gould

MARE

Arzachel

A

Bullialdus

20°S

Loewy

A

A

Nicollet

A

Thebit

E

B

Wolf

Birt

RUPES RECTA

D

König

la Caille

MARE

Hippalus

NUBIUM

G

HUMORUM

Lippershey

B

Prom. Kelvin

Kies

Purbach

RUPES KELVIN

Rima Hippalus

A

Campanus

A

B

B

Regiomontanus

Vitello

Mercator

Hesiodus

Pitatus

30°S

Dunthorne

Rima Hesiodus

A

Deslandres

Walther

PALUS

EPIDEMIARUM

14

Hell

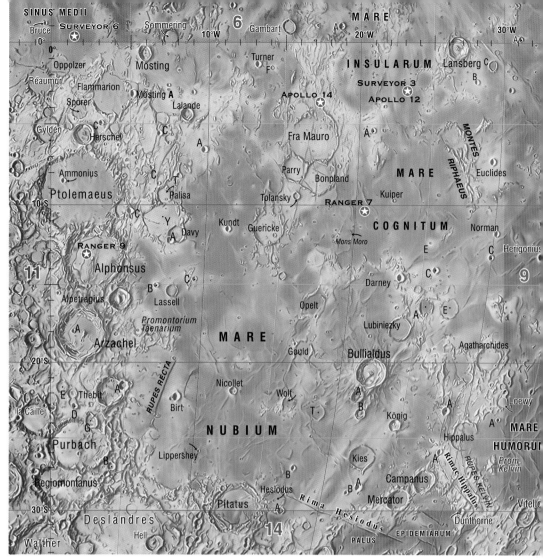

In the north, on the edge of Mare Insularum, is Landsberg (0.3°S, 26.6°W, 38 km), with its prominent central peak. To the east lie a series of degraded craters: Fra Mauro (6.1°S, 17.0°W, 101 km), with a fractured floor, and close to the Apollo 14 landing site (3.67°S, 17.47°W); Bonpland (8.3°S, 17.4°W, 60 km); and Guericke (11.5°S, 14.1°W, 63 km). Among them, Parry (7.9°S, 15.8°W, 47 km) is better preserved.

South of Mare Cognitum lies the flooded crater Lubiniezky (17.8°S, 23.8°W, 43 km), its wall breached on the side towards Bullialdus (20.7°S, 22.2°W, 60 km), a crater with prominent inner terracing and a central peak. The crater's ejecta show a well-developed radial structure. To the west are two more flooded craters: Agatharchides (19.8°S, 30.9°W, 48 km) and, on the edge of Mare Humorum, Hippalus (24.8°S, 30.2°W, 57 km), whose mare wall has been breached. It is crossed by the conspicuous rilles of Rimae Hipplaus, which are about 250 km long. To the south is Rupes Kelvin, a scarp along the edge of Mare Humorum.

At the southern edge of Mare Nubium are: the twin craters of Campanus (28.0°S, 27.8°W, 48 km) and Mercator (29.3°S, 26.1°W, 46 km), the latter with a flooded floor; Kies (6.4°S, 84.0°E, 63 km), flooded with a low rim; badly degraded Hesiodus (29.4°S, 16.3°W, 42 km); and the prominent, complex crater Pitatus (29.9°S, 13.5°W, 106 km), with a flooded, rifted floor.

Eastern Mare Nubium has one of the Moon's famous features, Rupes Recta, the 'Straight Wall' (22°S, 7°W), a fault about 110 km long, 25 km wide, and perhaps as high as 450 m in places. Although it appears prominent under grazing illumination, it is relatively gentle, averaging about 7–10°, although possibly as much as 25° at certain points. Beyond it, running up the edge of the mare, we come to the heavily cratered southern highlands. In the south is the irregular crater Regiomontanus (28.3°S, 1.0°W, 108 km), its northern wall destroyed by Purbach (25.5°S, 2.3°W, 115 km). Farther north is Thebit (22.0°S, 4.0°W, 56 km), notable for the perfectly formed crater of Thebit A on its northwestern wall.

Still farther north are Arzachel (18.2°S, 1.9°W, 96 km), a complex crater with concentric terracing and a central peak, and Alpetragius (16.0°S, 4.5°W, 39 km), with a giant central peak. Alphonsus (13.7°S, 3.2°W, 108 km) is a complex crater with notable dark patches on its fractured floor, thought to have arisen from lava fountains. It lies next to Ptolemaeus (9.3°S, 1.9°W, 164 km), a flat-floored crater, conspicuous by its very size. To the north are Herschel (5.7°S, 2.1°W, 40 km), with prominent inner terraces, and Flammarion (3.4°S, 3.7°W, 74 km), on whose wall lies the bright ray crater Mösting A (3°12'43.2"S, 5°12'39.6"W, 13 km), which is used as the reference point for the system of lunar coordinates.

Name	Translation
Mare Cognitum	Known Sea
Mare Humorum	Sea of Humours
Mare Insularum	Sea of Islands
Mare Nubium	Sea of Clouds
Palus Epidemiarum	Marsh of Epidemics
Sinus Medii	Central Bay

Feature	Age of Moon (days)
Alphonsus	8, 22
Arzachel	8, 22
Birt	8, 22
Bullialdus	9, 23
Campanus	10, 24
Fra Mauro	9, 23
Landsberg	10, 24
Mercator	10, 24
Montes Riphaeus	10, 24
Pitatus	8, 22
Ptolemaeus	8, 22
Purbach	8, 22
Rupes Recta	8, 23
Thebit	8, 22

Heavily cratered terrain in the central highlands covers most of this area, with the exception of Sinus Asperitatis, on the southern edge of Mare Tranquillitatis, and the western side of Mare Nectaris.

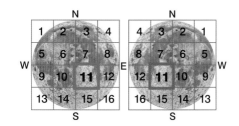

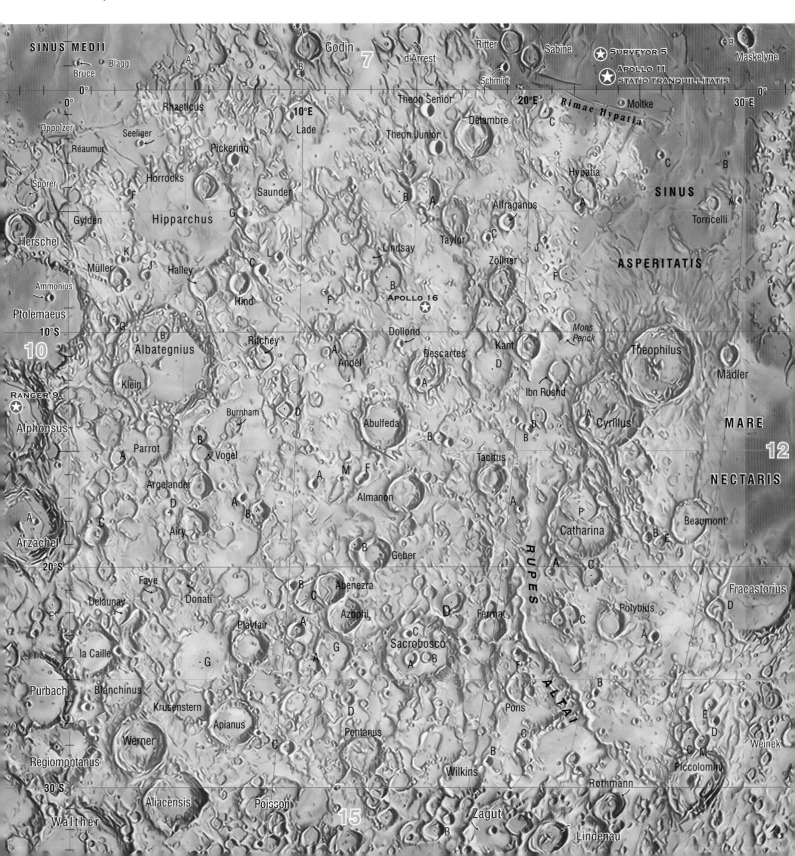

In the northwest, the irregular crater Rhaeticus (0.0°N, 4.9°E, 45 km), with a badly eroded wall, and degraded Réaumur (2.4°S, 0.7°E, 52 km), lie on the edge of Sinus Medii. To the southeast are the irregular remnants of Hipparchus (5.1°S, 5.2°E, 138 km), enclosing the prominent, deep crater Horrocks (4.0°S, 5.9°E, 30 km, 2980 m). Halley (8.0°S, 5.7°E, 36 km) lies immediately to the south. Albategnius (11.7°S, 4.3°E, 114 km) is the largest crater in this region, with a central peak and the crater Klein (12.0°S, 2.6°E, 44 km) occupying a large part of its floor.

In the southwest there are three large craters: la Caille (23.8°S, 1.1°E, 67 km), with a flooded floor; Blanchinus (25.4°S, 2.5°E, 61 km); and Werner (28.0°S, 3.3°E, 70 km), with prominent terracing and a central peak. To their east lie a large, unnamed and degraded crater, Playfair G, Playfair itself (23.5°S, 8.4°E, 47 km), Krusenstern (26.2°S, 5.9°E, 47 km), and Apianus (26.9°S, 7.9°E, 63 km). Farther east we find Pontanus (28.4°S, 14.4°E, 57 km), with an irregular floor, and, working northwards, Sacrobosco (23.7°S, 16.7°E, 98 km), notable for the three distinct craters, A, B, and C, on its floor.

Northwest of Sacrobosco lie three craters of similar sizes: Azophi (22.1°S, 12.7°E, 47 km), Abenezra (21.0°S, 11.9°E, 42 km), distinctly angular in outline, and Geber (19.4°S, 13.9°E, 44 km). The larger craters of Almanon (16.8°S, 15.2°E, 49 km) and Abulfeda (13.8°S, 13.9°E, 65 km, 3110 m) are to the north. The Apollo 16 landing site (9.00°S, 15.51°E) was on the relatively flat area north of Descartes (11.7°S, 15.7°E, 48 km), and southwest of Taylor (5.3°S, 16.7°E), an almost elliptical crater, 42 km long by 34 km wide. To the north is Delambre (1.9°S, 17.5°E, 51 km), with a prominent central massif.

On the edge of Mare Tranquillitatis are the rilles of Rimae Hypatia, some 180 km long. To the south, Hypatia itself (4.3°S, 22.6°E) is a very irregular crater, about 40 km long and 28 km wide. Immediately to the south of Sinus Asperitatis lies a prominent trio of craters: Theophilus (11.4°S, 26.4°E, 110 km), which has prominent central peaks rising to 1400 m; Cyrillus (13.2°S, 24.0°E, 98 km), which has a greatly degraded outer wall; and Catharina (18.1°S, 23.4°E, 104 km), where the northern wall has been destroyed by the impact that created Catharina P.

Southwest of Catharina, and running down towards Piccolomini (29.7°S, 32.2°E, 87 km), a crater with an extremely prominent central peak, is Rupes Altai (the Altai Scarp). This fault, about 480 km long, is part of the outer edge of the Nectaris basin and slopes down towards the interior. To its east lie Polybius (22.4°S, 25.6°E, 41 km) and, on the edge of Mare Nectaris, Beaumont (18.0°S, 28.8°E, 53 km) and the breached crater Fracastorius (21.5°S, 33.2°E, 112 km).

Name	Translation
Mare Nectaris	Sea of Nectar
Sinus Asperitatis	Bay of Asperity
Sinus Medii	Central Bay

Feature	Age of Moon (days)
Abulfeda	6, 20
Albategnius	7, 22
Catharina	6, 20
Cyrillus	5, 19
Delambre	6, 20
Fracastorius	6, 20
Hipparchus	7, 21
Mädler	5, 19
Piccolomini	5, 18
Theophilus	5, 19
Werner	7, 21

12 | Langrenus

This region includes significant amounts of both mare and highland terrain. Mare Fecunditatis has a total area of about 325,000 sq km, slightly less than the combined areas of the Earth's Aegean and Adriatic Seas.

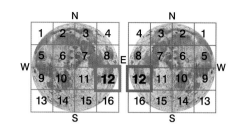

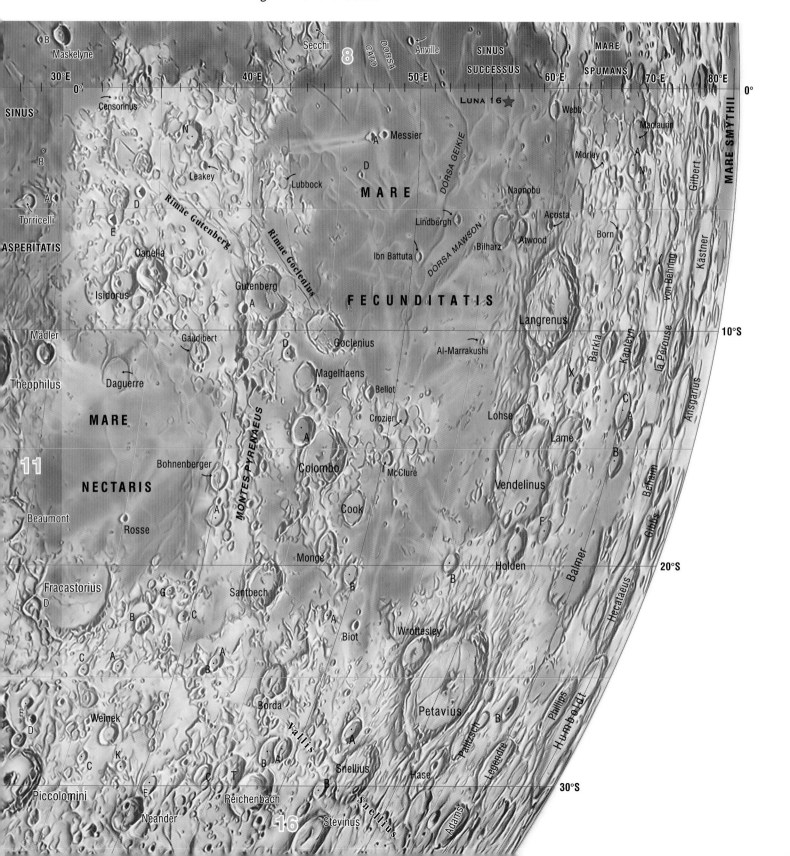

B
Maskelyne
30°E
0°
Censorinus
SINUS
B
N
Leakey
A
Torricelli
ASPERITATIS
D
E
Capella
Isidorus
Mädler
Gaudibert
Theophilus
Daguerre
MARE
Bohnenberger
11
NECTARIS
Beaumont
Rosse
Fracastorius
D
G
B
C
B
C
A
B
A
C
A
B
E
Weinek
D
K
C
Piccolomini
Neander
16

Secchi
8
DORSA
CATO
Anville
SINUS
SUCCESSUS
40°E
50°E
60°E
Messier
A
D
MARE
Lubbock
Rimae Gutenberg
Rimae Goclenius
DORSA GEIKIE
Lindbergh
Gutenberg
A
Ibn Battuta
DORSA MAWSON
FECUNDITATIS
D
Goclenius
Al-Marrakushi
Magelhaens
A
Bellot
MONTES PYRENAEUS
Crozier
Colombo
McClure
Cook
Monge
B
B
Santbech
A
Biot
Wrottesley
Vallis
Borda
A
B A
Snellius
Snellius
Hase
Reichenbach
Stevinus

MARE
SPUMANS
70°E
80°E
0°
Webb
Maclaurin
Morley
A
N
Naonobu
Acosta
Atwood
Born
Bilharz
Langrenus
X
Barkla
Kapteyn
la Pérouse
C
Lohse
A
Lamé
B
Vendelinus
Behaim
F
Balmer
Holden
20°S
Petavius
B
Palitzsch
Phillips
Legendre
Humboldt
Adams
30°S

Gilbert
von Behring
Kästner
MARE SMYTHII
10°S
Ansgarius
Hecataeus
Gibbs

Mare Fecunditatis is not associated with a particular impact basin, unlike Mare Nectaris, whose basin actually extends as far as the complex craters Gutenberg (8.6°S, 41.2°E, 74 km), breached on the east by Gutenberg E, and Goclenius (10.0°S, 45.0°E, 72 km). Both craters exhibit rifted floors. To the northeast lie the rilles of Rimae Goclenius, which are 240 km long. Other conspicuous rilles, the Rimae Gutenberg, run northwest nearly as far as Sinus Asperitatis. North of Mare Nectaris are Capella (7.5°S, 35.0°E, 49 km), through which runs a crater chain (Vallis Capella), and Isidorus (8.0°S, 33.5°E, 42 km), with a prominent inner crater, Isidorus A.

The Montes Pyrenaeus run south from Gutenberg, bordered on the west by Mare Nectaris and the crater Bohnenberger (16.2°S, 40.0°E, 33 km), while south of Goclenius lie Magelhaens (11.9°S, 44.1°E, 40 km), Colombo A, and Colombo itself (15.1°S, 45.8°E, 76 km). Dark-floored Cook (17.5°S, 48.9°E, 46 km) lies on the edge of southern Mare Fecunditatis. An unnamed area of mare-type material lies to the southwest, near Santbech (20.9°S, 44.0°E, 64 km).

Within Mare Fecunditatitis lie the small craters Messier (1.9°S, 47.6°E) and Messier A. Messier is elliptical, 11 km long by 9 km wide, and Messier A is a double crater and the source of a pair of bright rays that run towards the west. East and south of here are prominent mare ridges: Dorsa Geikie and Dorsa Mawson. East of the mare is the conspicuous, complex crater Langrenus (8.9°S, 61.1°E, 127 km), with terraced walls, a hilly floor, and a central massif. To the north lies the southern portion of Mare Spumans and, on the limb, Mare Smythii (both Map 8).

South of Mare Smythii lies a succession of large craters on the edge of the libration zone: Gilbert (3.2°S, 76.0°E, 112 km); Kästner (6.8°S, 78.5°E, 108 km); la Pérouse (10.7°S, 76.3°E, 77 km); and Ansgarius (12.7°S, 79.7°E, 94 km). South of Langrenus is the large crater Vendelinus (16.4°S, 61.6°E, 131 km), its northeastern wall broken by Lamé (14.7°S, 64.5°E, 84 km). To the southeast is Balmer (20.3°S, 69.8°E, 138 km), the remnants of a large crater without a northern wall. Towards the limb lies Hecateus (21.8°S, 79.4°E, 167 km) and, to its south, the large, complex crater Humboldt (27.0°S, 80.9°E, 189 km), with central mountains and both radial and concentric fractures.

The conspicuous crater Petavius (25.1°S, 60.4°E, 188 km) has a complex central massif, a rifted floor, and dark patches similar to

those in Alphonsus (Map 10). To the northwest is Wrottesley (23.9°S, 56.8°E, 57 km), with a prominent central peak, and to the east lies Palitzsch, a valley-like formation, 110 km long. Legendre (28.9°S, 70.2°E, 78 km) lies towards the limb, and Snellius (29.3°S, 55.7°E, 82 km) to the southwest. Vallis Snellius is a long (592 km), connected series of depressions, apparently radial to Mare Nectaris, and possibly connected with its formation. It is the longest such feature on the nearside.

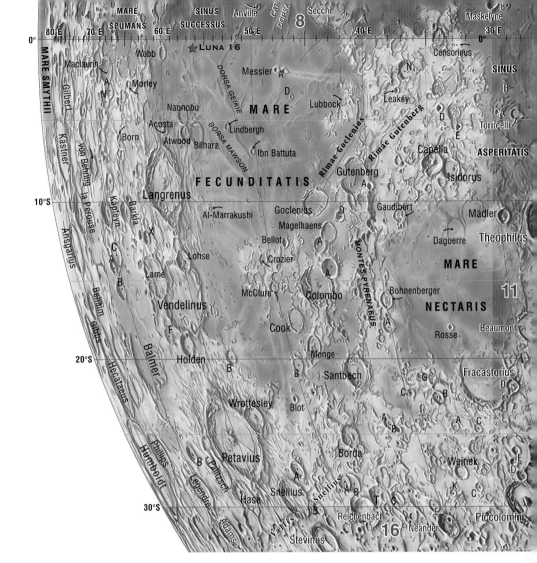

Name	Translation
Mare Fecunditatis	Sea of Fertility
Mare Nectaris	Sea of Nectar
Mare Smythii	Smyth Sea
Mare Spumans	Foaming Sea
Sinus Asperitatis	Bay of Asperity
Sinus Successus	Bay of Success

Feature	Age of Moon (days)
Goclenius	4, 18
Gutenberg	5, 19
Langrenus	2, 16
Petavius	3, 17
Snellius	3, 17
Vendelinus	2, 16

13 | Schickard

Southwest of Mare Humorum is a rather featureless area of highland material, broken only by Lacus Excellentiae. Towards the limb, however, are several interesting features, including Wargentin, a crater filled to the brim with lava.

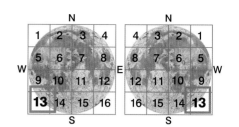

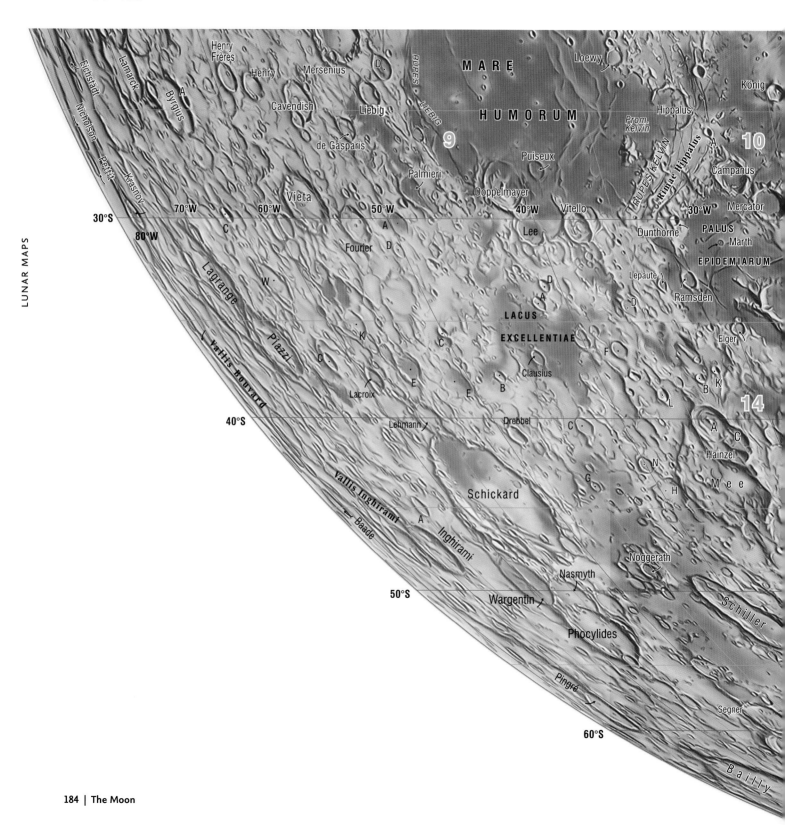

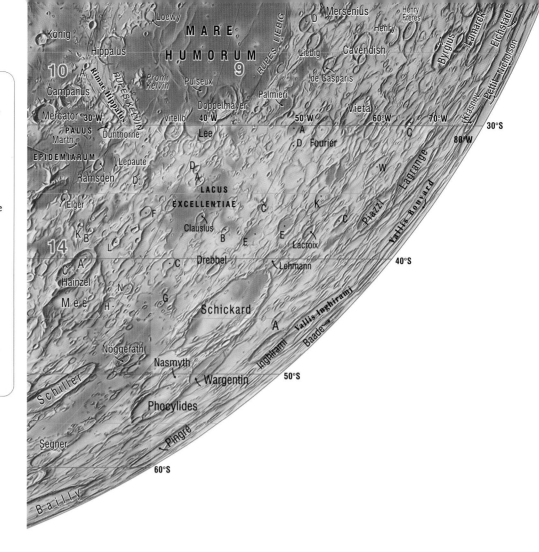

On the southern edge of Mare Humorum lie Vitello (30.4°S, 37.5°W, 42 km) and the breached crater Lee (30.7°S, 40.7°W, 41 km). To the west, beyond the relatively featureless terrain and towards the limb, are the degraded craters Lagrange (32.3°S, 72.8°W, 225 km) and Piazzi (36.6°S, 67.9°W, 134 km). Close to the limb, and only clearly visible under favourable libration conditions, are two valley systems: Vallis Bouvard, about 280 km long, and Vallis Inghirami, about 140 km long. Inghirami (47.5°S, 68.8°W, 91 km) is a fairly prominent crater with irregular inner hills.

The most conspicuous feature is Schickard (44.3°S, 55.3°W, 206 km), a large crater, noted for its partially flooded (and thus mottled) floor. To the southwest is Wargentin (49.6°S, 60.2°W, 84 km), which is completely filled to the top of its wall with lava, the surface of which exhibits mare-type wrinkle ridges. Alongside it lies Nasmyth (50.5°S, 56.2°W, 76 km), whose southern wall has been destroyed by the subsequent impact that created Phocylides (52.7°S, 57.0°W, 121 km). Towards the limb, only visible with favourable libration, lies Pingré (58.7°S, 73.7°W, 88 km).

Name	Translation
Lacus Excellentiae	Lake of Excellence
Mare Humorum	Sea of Humours
Palus Epidemiarum	Marsh of Epidemics

Feature	Age of Moon (days)
Schickard	12, 26

14 | Tycho

The heavily cratered southern highlands occupy most of this region, notable for Tycho, the centre of the longest ray system on the Moon, the highly distinctive crater Clavius, and Baily, one of the largest craters, also regarded as a small basin. Only in the northwest is there any mare-type material.

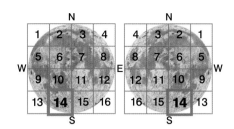

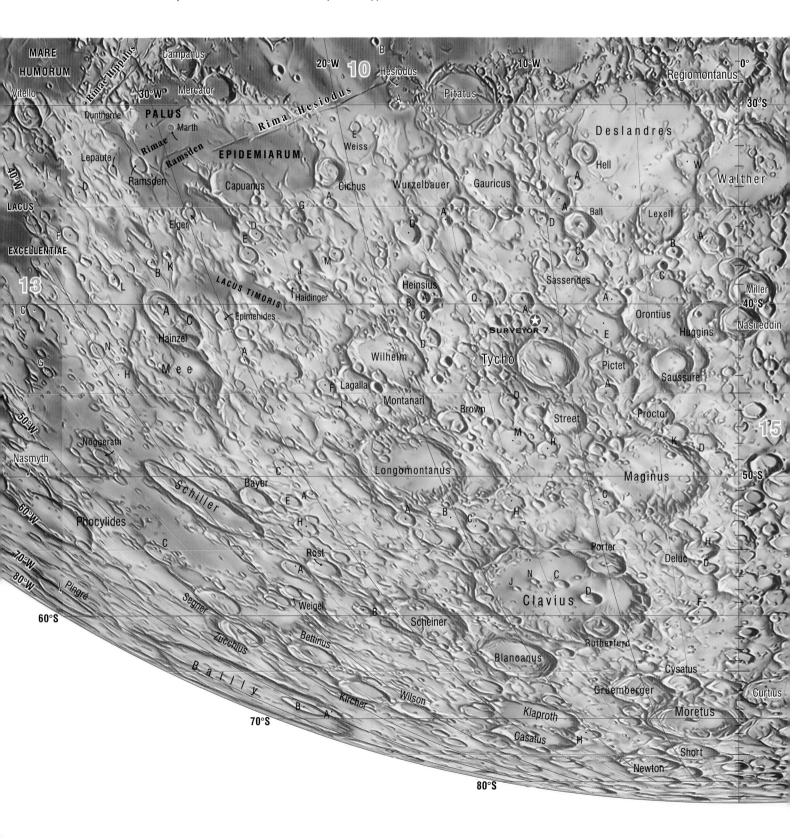

MARE HUMORUM

Campanus
Rimae Hippalus
20°W   10   Hesiodus   10°W   0°
Vitello   30°W   Mercator   Pitatus   Regiomontanus   30°S
Dunthorne   PALUS   B   Deslandres
Lepaute   Rimae   Marth   Weiss   Hell   W
Ramsden   Rima Hesiodus   EPIDEMIARUM   A   Walther
40°W   D   Capuanus   Cichus   Wurzelbauer   Gauricus   Ball   Lexell
LACUS   Elger   G   A   D   B   A
EXCELLENTIAE   D   C   C   Sasserides   C
13   K   E   Heinsius   A   Orontius   Miller   40°S
C   B   L   M   B   A   Q   A   Huggins   Nasireddin
A   C   Haidinger   C   SURVEYOR 7   E   Pictet   Saussure
N   Hainzel   Epimenides   Wilhelm   D   Tycho   A
G   H   A   F   Lagalla   Brown   Street   Proctor
Mee   J   Montanari   M   H   K   D   15
50°W   C   H   Maginus   50°S
Nöggerath   Longomontanus   C
Nasmyth   Bayer   E   A   B   H
Schiller   H   A   B   C   Porter   H
60°W   Rost   Deluc   D
Phocylides   C   A   J   N   C   F
70°W   Segner   Weigel   B   Clavius   D
80°W   Pingré   Scheiner   Rutherfurd
60°S   Zucchius   Bettinus   Blancanus   Cysatus
B   Kircher   Wilson   Gruemberger   Moretus
70°S   A   Klaproth   Curtius
Casatus   H   Short
50°W   Newton
80°S

Palus Epidemiarum contains Rimae Ramsden, a series of intersecting rilles, and Rima Hesiodus, about 300 km long, running towards Mare Nubium. Nearby is the flooded crater Capuanus (34.1°S, 26.7°W, 59 km). To the south lie three overlapping craters, Hainzel (41.3°S, 33.5°W, 70 km), Hainzel A to the northwest, and Hainzel C. Immediately to the south is the heavily eroded crater Mee (43.7°S, 35.3°W, 126 km).

Farther south lies Schiller (51.9°S, 39.0°W), which is about 180 km long by 70 km wide. Beyond Segner (58.9°S, 48.3°W, 67 km) and Zucchius (61.4°S, 50.3°W, 64 km), lies Bailly (66.5°S, 69.1°W, 287 km), the largest crater on the Moon, filling its own impact basin. Farther onto the visible disk lie three similar-sized craters: Bettinus (63.4°S, 44.8°W, 71 km), Kircher (67.1°S, 45.3°W, 72 km), with a flooded floor, and Wilson (69.2°S, 42.4°W, 69 km), a degraded crater. Closer to the South Pole are the flooded craters Casatus (72.8°S, 29.5°W, 108 km) and Klaproth (69.8°S, 26.0°W, 119 km) and, to the southeast, Newton (76.7°S, 16.9°W, 78 km). Clustered to the north and east are Short (74.6°S, 7.3°W, 70 km), Moretus (70.6°S, 5.8°W, 111 km), with a prominent central peak, Gruemberger (66.9°S, 10.0°W, 93 km), and Cysatus (66.2°S, 6.1°W, 48 km).

North of this area lie Blancanus (63.8°S, 21.4°W, 117 km), Scheiner (60.5°S, 27.5°W, 110 km), and Clavius (58.8°S, 14.1°W, 245 km), a famous, prominent crater, notable for Rutherfurd (60.9°S, 12.1°W, 48 km) just inside its wall, for the curving chain of craters on its floor, and for Porter (56.1°S, 10.1°W, 51 km), superimposed on the northern rim. Northwest of Clavius is the prominent crater Longomontanus (49.6°S, 21.8°W, 157 km), and north of that, Montanari (45.8°S, 20.6°W, 76 km), its western rim broken by subsidiary craters, Wilhelm (43.4°S, 20.4°W, 106 km), and badly eroded Lagalla (44.6°S, 22.5°W, 85 km).

North of Heinsius (39.5°S, 17.7°W, 64 km), and its prominent subsidiary craters Heinsius A, B, and C, and south of Pitatus on the edge of Mare Nubium, lie the irregular and greatly degraded craters of Wurzelbauer (33.9S, 15.9°W, 88 km) and Gauricus (33.8°S, 12.6°W, 79 km). East of Wilhelm is Tycho (43.4°S, 11.1°W, 102 km, 4850 m), a very prominent crater with a pronounced central peak, notable for a dark halo around the crater, and as the source of the most extensive ray system.

In the north, the outer rim of Deslandres (33.1°S, 4.8°W, 256 km) has been partially destroyed by several impacts, including Hell (32.4°S, 7.8°W, 33 km), Ball (35.9°S, 8.4°W, 41 km), and Lexell (35.8°S, 4.2°W, 62 km). Between here and Tycho lies Sasserides (39.1°S, 9.3°W, 90 km), also badly degraded. Farther east lies Orontius (40.6°S, 4.6°W, 105 km), its eastern wall broken by Huggins (41.1°S, 1.4°W, 65 km), in turn breached by Nasireddin (41.0°S, 0.2°E, 52 km). To the south, Sassure (43.4°S, 3.8°W, 54 km) has largely obliterated a similar-sized earlier crater. Finally, south of Saussure, lie Proctor (46.4°S, 5.1°W, 52 km) and Maginus (50.5°S, 6.3°W, 194 km), the south wall of which is considerably degraded.

Name	Translation
Lacus Excellentiae	Lake of Excellence
Mare Humorum	Sea of Humours
Mare Nubium	Sea of Clouds
Palus Epidemiarum	Marsh of Epidemics

Feature	Age of Moon (days)
Blancanus	9, 23
Clavius	8, 22
Deslandres	8, 22
Longomontanus	8, 22
Maginus	8, 22
Moretus	8, 22
Orontius	8, 22
Palus Epidemiarum	10, 24
Saussure	8, 22
Scheiner	9, 22
Schiller	11, 25
Tycho	8, 13, 24
Wilhelm	9, 23

15 | Maurolycus

The southern highlands in this region are extremely primitive terrain. They preserve the traces of the early extreme bombardment, shortly after the crust solidified. They are completely saturated with craters and are devoid of any mare material.

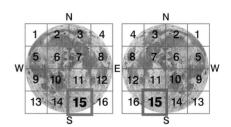

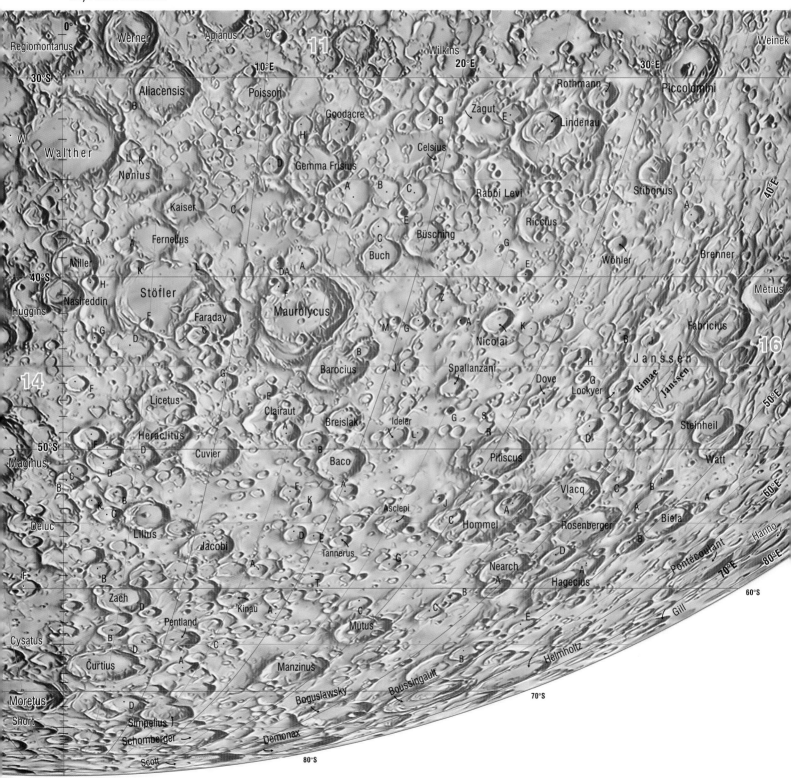

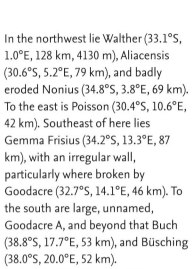

In the northwest lie Walther (33.1°S, 1.0°E, 128 km, 4130 m), Aliacensis (30.6°S, 5.2°E, 79 km), and badly eroded Nonius (34.8°S, 3.8°E, 69 km). To the east is Poisson (30.4°S, 10.6°E, 42 km). Southeast of here lies Gemma Frisius (34.2°S, 13.3°E, 87 km), with an irregular wall, particularly where broken by Goodacre (32.7°S, 14.1°E, 46 km). To the south are large, unnamed, Goodacre A, and beyond that Buch (38.8°S, 17.7°E, 53 km), and Büsching (38.0°S, 20.0°E, 52 km).

South of Walther are Miller (39.3°S, 0.8°E, 61 km) and Nasireddin (41.0°S, 0.2°E, 52 km). East of here lie Fernelius (38.1°S, 4.9°E, 65 km), Stöfler (41.1°S, 6.0°E, 126 km), its southeastern wall broken by Faraday, the complex crater Maurolycus (42.0°S, 14.0°E, 114 km), and Barocius (44.9°S, 16.8°E, 82 km). South of Stöfler and Maurolycus are: Licetus (47.1°S, 6.7°E, 74 km); Heraclitus (49.2°S, 6.2°E, 90 km), a badly degraded crater; Cuvier (50.3°S, 9.9°E, 75 km), with a flooded floor; and Clairaut (47.7°S, 13.°9E, 75 km), whose southern wall is broken by two subsidiary craters.

South of Heraclitus are Lilius (54.5°S, 6.2°E, 61 km), with a prominent central peak; Zach (60.9°S, 5.3°E, 70 km), and Curtius (67.2°S, 4.4°E, 95 km). Schomberger (76.7°S, 24.9°E, 85 km) is just outside the libration zone, but Scott (82.1°S, 48.5°E, 103 km), Demonax (77.9°S, 60.8°E, 128 km) and Helmholtz (68.1°S 64.1°E, 94 km) are within it. Farther east, Boguslawsky (72.9°S, 43.2°E, 97 km), with a flooded floor, is always visible, as is Boussingault (70.2°S, 54.6°E, 142 km), which has a large interior secondary crater (Boussingault A), giving the feature the appearance of a double wall. Farther onto the disk are Manzinus (67.7°S, 26.8°E, 98 km), with a flooded floor, and Mutus (63.6°S, 30.1°E, 77 km).

There is a cluster of craters near Hommel (54.7°S, 33.8°E, 126 km), whose wall is broken by subsidiary craters. To the north is the prominent crater Pitiscus (50.4S, 30.9E, 82 km); east, Vlacq (53.3°S, 38.8°E, 89 km), Rosenberger (55.4°S, 43.1°E, 95 km), and Biela (54.9°S, 51.3°E, 76 km); and to the south, Nearch (58.5°S, 39.1°E, 75 km) and Hagecius (59.8°S, 46.6°E, 76 km). East of Hagecius lies Pontécoulant (58.7°S, 66.0°E, 91 km).

Feature	Age of Moon (days)
Aliacensis	7, 21
Fabricius	4, 18
Hommel	5, 19
Janssen	4, 24
Manzinus	5, 19
Maurolycus	6, 20
Pitiscus	5, 19
Rabbi Levi	6, 20
Stöfler	7, 21
Vlacq	5, 19
Walther	7, 21
Zagut	6, 20

In the east lies the large feature Janssen (45.4°S, 40.3°E, 199 km), with clefts on the floor, central peaks, subsidiary craters, and a wall broken by Fabricius (42.9°S, 42.0°E, 78 km), itself a complex crater. To the south lie the prominent craters Steinheil (48.6°S, 46.5°E, 67 km) and Watt (49.5°S, 48.6°E, 66 km). Northwest of Janssen is a conspicuous cluster of craters, including: Zagut (32.0°S, 22.1°E, 84 km), with a central crater (Zagut A), and its eastern wall interrupted by Zagut E; Lindenau (32.3°S, 24.9°E, 53 km) in the northwestern sector of a large, degraded, unnamed crater; Rabbi Levi (34.7°S, 23.6°E, 81 km), with subsidiary craters on its floor; and Riccius (36.9°S, 26.5°E, 71 km), the eastern half of which is heavily degraded.

16 | Rheita

This area is largely highland terrain, pock-marked with craters, but reveals part of Mare Australe on the limb. It has two of the Moon's conspicuous crater-chains.

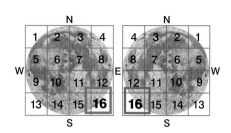

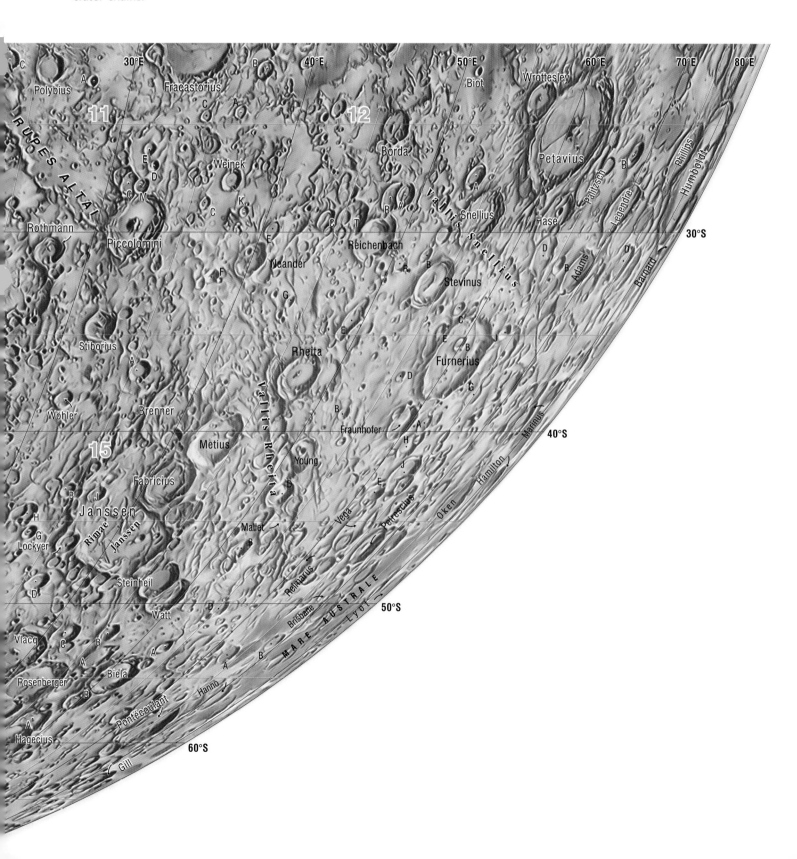

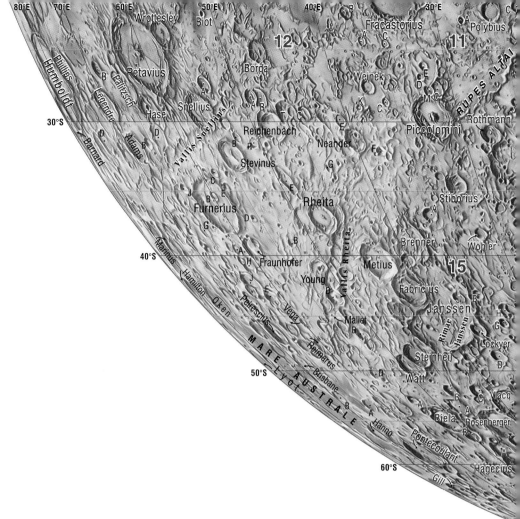

The chain of craters forming Vallis Rheita has many similarities with Vallis Snellius, described earlier (Map 12). It is about 450 km long and (like Vallis Snellius) lies radially to Mare Nectaris, and may be related to the latter's formation. It is most prominent between Rheita (37.1°S, 47.2°E, 70 km) and Reimarus (47.7°S, 60.3°E, 48 km).

Northwest of Rheita lies Neander (31.3°S, 39.9°E, 50 km), with central peaks; to the southwest is Metius (40.3°S, 43.3°E, 87 km). In the northeast, and running approximately parallel to Vallis Snellius, lie Reichenbach (30.3°S, 48.0°E, 71 km), Stevinus (32.5°S, 54.2°E, 74 km), with a prominent central peak, and the very conspicuous crater Furnerius (36.0°S, 60.6°E, 135 km), with a rifted floor and a prominent inner crater (Furnerius B). East of Stevinus lie Adams (31.9°S, 68.2°E, 66 km), and on the very limb, Barnard (29.5°S, 85.6°E, 105 km).

Towards the limb, beyond Brisbane (49.1°S, 68.5°E, 44 km) and Peirescius (46.5°S, 67.6°E, 61 km), lies Mare Australe, which extends north from near Hanno (56.3°S, 71.2°E, 56 km), behind Oken (43.7°S, 75.9°E, 71 km) to as far as Marinus (39.4°S, 76.5°E, 58 km), (all three of which lie within the libration zone). The mare encompasses the large, flooded crater Lyot (49.8°S, 84.5°E, 132 km).

Name	Translation
Mare Australe	Southern Sea

Feature	Age of Moon (days)
Furnerius	2, 16
Metius	4, 18
Rheita	4, 18
Stevinus	5–9

Libration

NE (L1) & NW (L2) Sectors

The area around the Moon's North Pole is covered by both of these libration charts. In the NW sector, the craters normally near the limb, such as Galvani, Repsold, Volta, and Xenophanes (Map 1) are more fully revealed, as are Pythagoras, Carpenter, Anaximenes, Philolaus, Anaxagoras and Goldschmidt (all Map 2). More importantly, features such as Brianchon (75.0°N, 86.2°W, 134 km) and, near the North Pole, Peary (88.6°N, 33.0°E, 73 km) and Byrd

(85.3°N, 9.8°E, 93 km) are more clearly visible, and McLaughlin (47.1°N, 92.9°W, 79 km), Smoluchowski (60.3°N, 96.8°W, 83 km), the large crater Rozhdestvenskiy (85.2°N, 155.4°W, 177 km), Plaskett (82.1°N, 174.3°E, 109 km) and Nansen (82.1°N, 174.3°E, 109 km) may sometimes be seen.

In the northwest, craters such as Röntgen (33.0°N, 91.4°W, 126 km) and Nernst (35.3°N, 94.8°W, 116 km) are occasionally visible. These two craters and Laue (28.0°N, 96.7°W, 87 km) actually break into the nearer wall of the very large, degraded crater Lorentz (32.6°N, 95.3°W, 312 km), which may be glimpsed at rare intervals.

Farther south, the large crater

Colour key

Neutral tint	always visible
Pink tint	frequently invisible
Blue tint	rarely visible

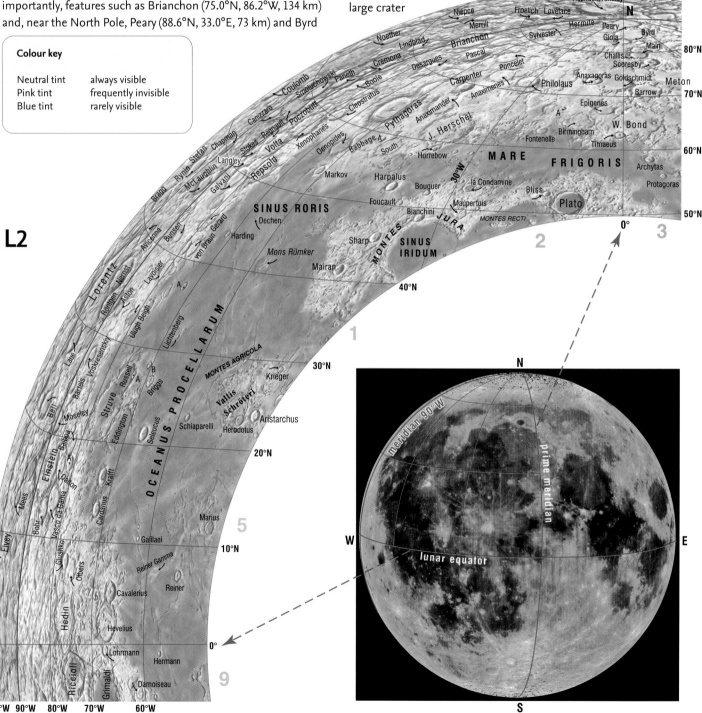

Einstein and its central crater are more clearly seen with favourable libration, as are the neighbouring craters of Balboa, Dalton, Vasco da Gama, and Bohr (all Map 5). There are few very distinct features in the area beyond them, but occasionally Elvey (8.8°N, 100.5°W, 74 km), Mees (13.6°N, 96.1°W, 50 km), and Bell (21.8°N, 96.4°W, 86 km) become visible.

In the NE sector, the large crater Schwarzschild (70.1°N, 121.2°E, 212 km) may come into view. It also becomes possible to pick out more clearly Petermann (74.2°N, 66.3°E, 73 km), Cusanus (72.0°N, 70.8°E, 63 km), and Hayn (64.7°N,

85.2°E, 87 km), with its large central peak. The whole area around, and including, Mare Humboldtianum (Map 4) and its basin becomes clearer to understand. Belkovich (61.1°N, 90.2°E, 214 km) and even farther east, Compton (55.3°N, 103.8°E, 162 km) are revealed.

Farther south, the interior of Gauss (Map 4) and Riemann (38.9°N, 86.8°E, 163 km) appear with less foreshortening. Significant craters that become partially visible include the giant feature Harkhebi (39.6°N 98.3°E 237 km). It may be possible to make out some details of Fabry (42.9°N, 100.7°E, 184 km), lying within Harkhebi, and even some of Maxwell (30.2°N, 98.9°E, 107 km) and Lomonosov (27.3°N, 98.0°E, 92 km). Other major craters that appear include Vestine (33.9°N, 93.9°E, 96 km) and Joliot (25.8°N, 93.1°E, 164 km).

Near the lunar equator, Mare Marginis, Neper, and Mare Smythii (all Map 8) are more clearly seen. On rare occasions it may be possible to observe Biruni (17.9°N, 92.5°E, 77 km), Dreyer (10.0°N, 96.9°E, 61 km), and Babcock 2°N, 93.9°E, 99 km).

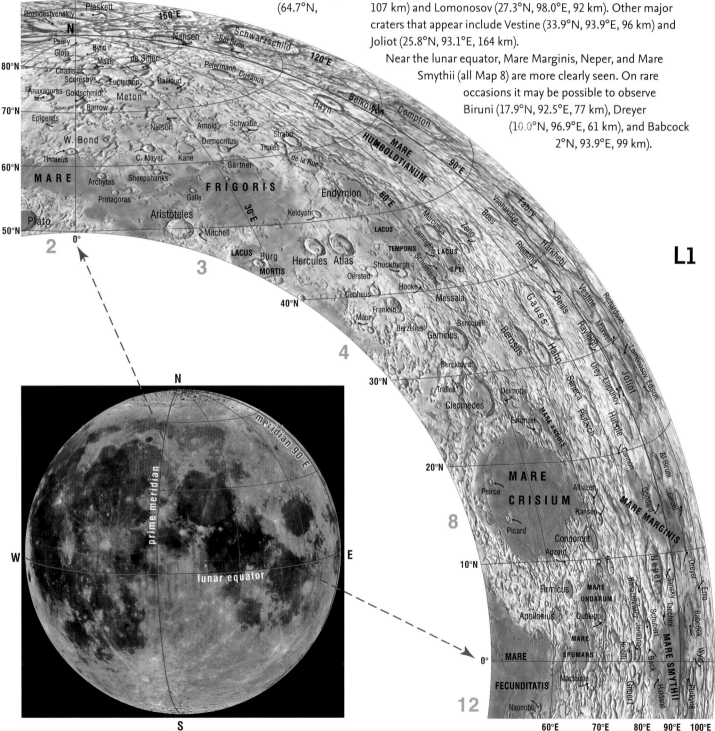

L1

SW (L3) & SE (L4) sectors

In the southwestern sector, favourable libration makes a major difference to the visiblity of the imposing feature of Mare Orientale (Map 9). Not only are the mountain chains of Montes Cordillera and Montes Rook shifted onto the visible disk, but the central region, flooded with lavas, becomes visible, together with the minor dark areas of Lacus Autumni and Lacus Veris.

Farther south, three valley systems: Vallis Bouvard, Vallis Inghirami, and Vallis Baade become fully visible. The major craters

Lagrange and Inghirami, and the unique, flooded crater Wargentin (all Map 13) are more fully revealed.

The size of the giant crater Bailly (Map 14) becomes easier to appreciate. Beyond it lies another large crater, Hausen (65.0°S, 88.1°W, 167 km), with terraced walls and a central peak. To the south lie the degraded crater Le Gentil (74.6°S, 75.7°W, 128 km) and Drygalski (79.3°S, 84.9°W, 149 km).

Near the South Pole, features such as Newton (Map 14) are more readily examined, and major craters like Scott, Demonax, and Helmholtz (Map 15) are revealed. Beyond these, Amundsen

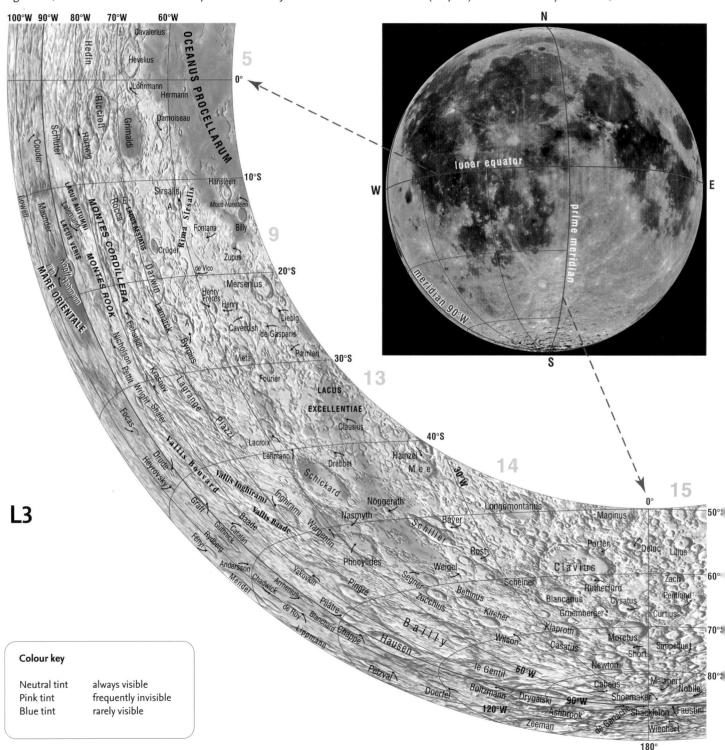

LUNAR MAPS

Colour key

Neutral tint	always visible
Pink tint	frequently invisible
Blue tint	rarely visible

(84.3°S, 85.6°E, 101 km) and even farther onto the far side, the giant crater Schrödinger (75.0°S, 132.4°E, 312 km), which is an impact basin in its own right, may become visible. Slightly farther north, it is possible to glimpse Vallis Schrödinger.

Mare Australe is an irregular maria, but under favourable libration it appears as numerous patches of mare material and lighter intervening areas, around the large, flooded crater Lyot (Map 16). Maximum libration affords a glimpse of the large crater Lebedev (47.3°S, 107.8°E, 102 km).

Towards the northeast, the farther ramparts of the complex crater Hecataeus and Humboldt (Map 12) become visible. Abel (34.5°S, 87.3°E, 122 km) and Barnard (29.5°S, 85.6°E, 105 km) are clearer, and the large craters Curie (22.9°S, 91.0°E, 151 km) and Sklodowska (18.2°S, 95.5°E, 127 km) also appear.

Beyond Kästner and Ansgarius (both Map 12) the crater Kiess (6.4°S, 84.0°E, 63 km) is revealed. Mare Smythii is normally difficult to discern. With full libration it appears as a fairly extensive mare area. Slightly farther towards the limb is the large crater Hirayama (6.1°S, 93.5°E, 132 km).

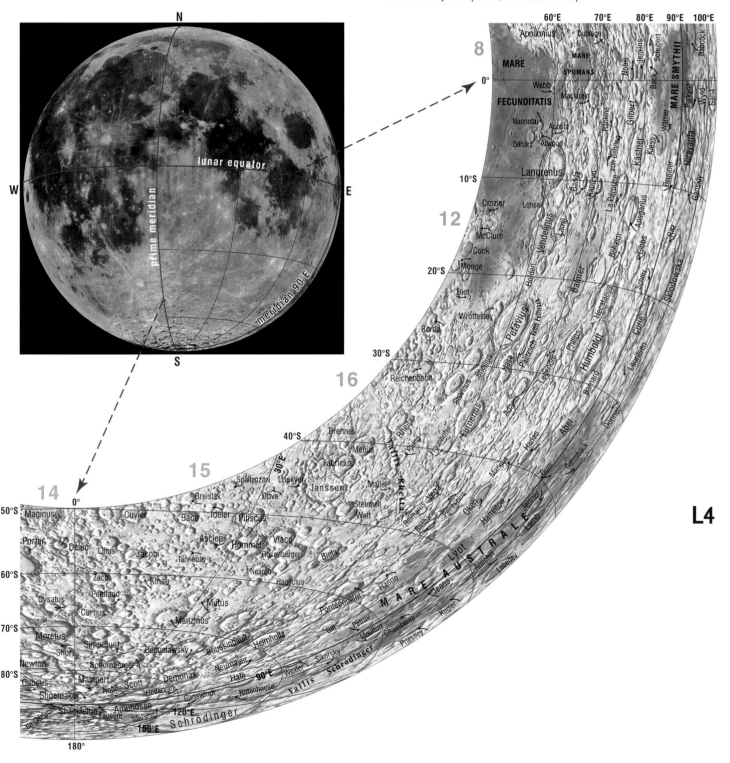

L4

Near and far sides of the Moon

The distribution of mare-type terrain differs greatly between the near and far sides of the Moon. On the near side, 31.2 per cent of the surface is covered by maria, but on the far side maria occupy just 2.5 per cent of the surface: in Mare Orientale, Mare Ingenii, and Mare Moscoviense, as well as parts of Mare Australe, Mare Marginis, and Mare Smythii. Parts of some far side impact basins like Hertzsprung, Apollo, and Poincaré are filled with dark mare material, and the floor of the crater Tsiolkovskiy is exceptionally dark.

The distribution of elevations on the Moon is also distinctly irregular, and the near side and far sides differ in mean elevation

by about 3 km. The heavily cratered far side is generally higher and, as mentioned earlier, the crust is much thicker. As a result, it has been more difficult for molten lava from the Moon's interior to reach the surface and create mare areas.

Impact basins

General outlines and names (in colour) mark 30 confirmed impact basins, together with the outline of the hypothetical Procellarum basin. Basin names are not yet included in the IAU nomenclature system, but those given here are regularly used in the scientific

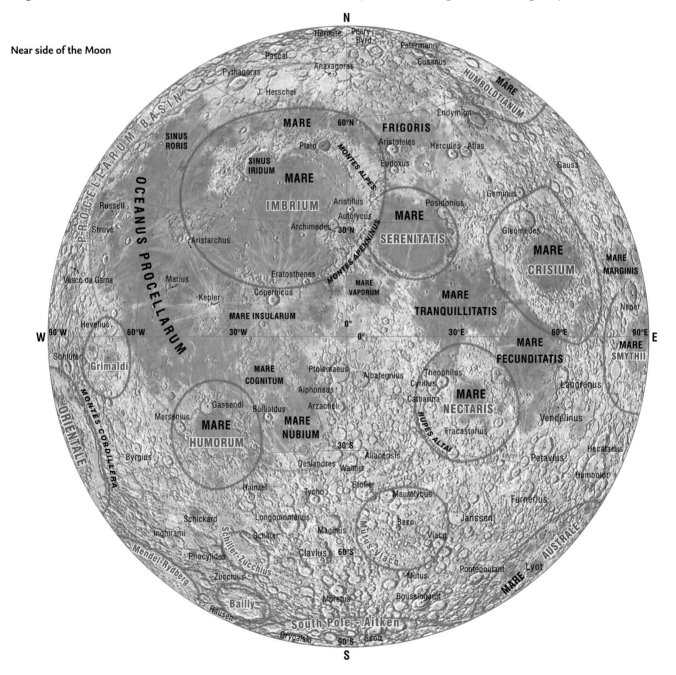

Near side of the Moon

literature. Details of the basins are shown on page 222.

The largest topographic feature on the Moon (not, however, directly visible on photographs) is the South Pole–Aitken Basin. Revealed by the Galileo remote-sensing and the Clementine laser-altimeter measurements, this is the oldest discernible lunar basin. It is 2500 km in diameter, with an average depth of nearly 13 km (rim crest to floor), making it one of the largest and deepest impact basins in the Solar System. The crater Aitken (17°S, 173°E) and the lunar south pole near the basin's rim give the feature its name. The second-largest basin is the Imbrium basin, which is formed by a monumental ring arc that includes Montes Carpatus, Apenninus, and Caucasus.

The Orientale basin on the western limb of the Moon is a magnificent example. Although only partially visible from Earth, it has a nearly complete set of concentric mountainous

rings, parts of which are known as Montes Cordillera and Montes Rook. Another example is the Nectaris basin. Its main rim is well defined by the Rupes Altai. The next time Nectaris is suitably illuminated, readers may like to try to see if they can identify other remnants of its basin.

Name	Translation
Lacus Luxuriae	Lake of Luxury
Mare Australe	Southern Sea
Mare Humboldtianum	Humboldt Sea
Mare Ingenii	Sea of Ingenuity
Mare Moscoviense	Sea of Muscovy
Mare Orientale	Eastern Sea
Mare Smythii	Smyth Sea

Far side of the Moon

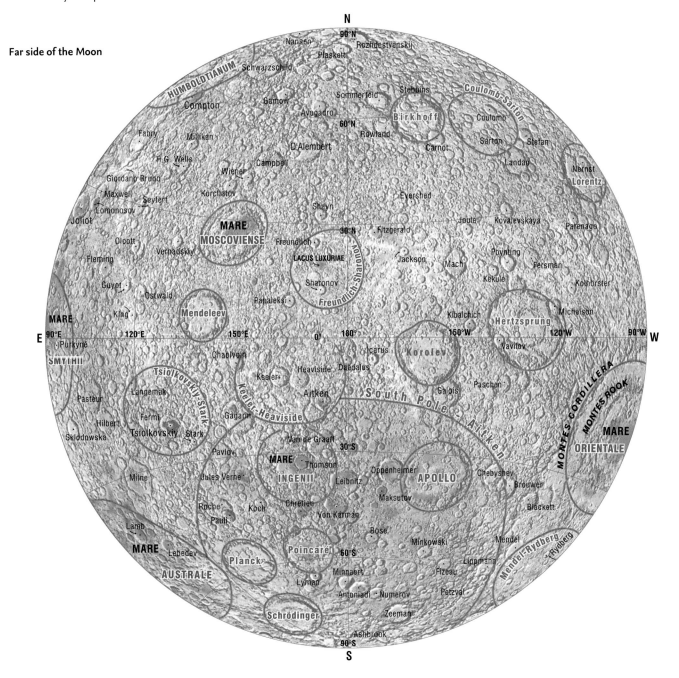

Observing Solar System objects

Sunrise, sunset, and the duration of twilight

The times of sunrise, sunset, and the duration of twilight and full darkness during the night vary dramatically with latitude. At the equator, daylight and darkness have approximately the same duration throughout the year, whereas near the poles there are many months of darkness, followed by a period when the Sun is above the horizon for months on end.

There are three specific periods of twilight. During civil twilight, the centre of the Sun is less than 6° below the horizon. In the evening, this ends at the 'lighting-up time' given for motorists. In general, only the very brightest planets, such as Venus and Jupiter, are visible during civil twilight. Nautical twilight lasts while the centre of the Sun is between 6° and 12° below the horizon. The horizon itself and the bright stars that are used for navigation are visible. Astronomical twilight lasts while the centre of the Sun is between 12° and 18° below the horizon. As darkness falls in the evening, faint stars become visible at the zenith at the beginning of astronomical twilight. When the Sun is more than 18° below the horizon, the faintest stars are visible anywhere in the sky. There are, of course, similar periods of twilight at dawn.

The diagrams on the following pages show the changes in the times of sunrise, sunset, and the length of the three forms of twilight for four different latitudes. Notice how for 50°N it does not become fully dark during the summer, and how at 60°N, nautical twilight persists throughout the night. It is also important to note that these diagrams relate to local time – i.e., they apply at any longitude around the Earth. They do not take account of the various adjustments that are incorporated into civil (clock) time to ensure that one single time applies in each time zone, or for Summer (Daylight Saving) Time corrections.

Date and time

It should be noted that the date and time of astronomical events are normally given in the internationally accepted scientific convention: year, month (in letters), day, hour (24-hour clock), minute, and second. Thus a transit of Venus began on 2004 Jun. 08, 05:15 UT. Note that Universal Time (UT) is generally used for the time of astronomical events, and for reporting observations. It is the time that applies at the Greenwich Meridian, to which no adjustments are made for Summer (Daylight Saving) Time. On occasions, for specific purposes, time may be specified as decimal fraction of a day or minute.

The motion of the Moon

As mentioned earlier, the Moon and planets always lie near the ecliptic, generally within the band of zodiacal constellations. Quite apart from the rotation of the Earth, which carries all celestial bodies across the sky from east to west during the course of a day, the Moon and planets have their own individual motion. The Moon slowly moves eastwards against the stars, by about its diameter in one hour, completing one circuit in one sidereal month (27.32166 days). The Moon's phase, however, depends upon its position relative to the Sun, and this month, New Moon to New Moon, is known as a synodic month (29.53059 days). The dates of New Moon and Full Moon are shown on the diagrams given later.

The motion of the Moon is extremely complex – too complex to be discussed in detail here. Its distance above or below the ecliptic (its ecliptic latitude) oscillates in a very complicated manner over a period of many years. In addition, the position of the ecliptic in the sky varies with the observer's latitude, introducing yet another complication. Luckily, except around the time of New Moon, the Moon is relatively bright and may be located without much trouble.

Solar eclipses occur when the Moon passes directly between the Sun and the Earth. Such events are relatively infrequent, and do not occur every month at New Moon because, as the Moon orbits the Earth, it usually passes above or below the line joining the centres of the Sun and Earth. The Moon's shadow cone consists of an inner umbra, where light from the Sun is completely absent (giving complete shadow), and an outer penumbra, in which light from a portion of the Sun's disk is present (giving partial shadow). If the umbral cone touches the surface of the Earth, there is a total eclipse, along a very narrow central line. The theoretical maximum duration for a total eclipse is 7^m31^s, but it is usually much shorter. If, because of the relative distances and apparent sizes of the Moon and Sun, the Moon does not completely cover the Sun's disk, there is an annular eclipse. Occasionally, an extremely short total eclipse may occur in the middle of an otherwise annular eclipse. In many cases, the Moon does not completely cover the Sun, giving rise to a partial eclipse. Unless a partial eclipse exceeds 70 per cent – i.e., more than 70 per cent of the Sun's disk is covered – partial eclipses are normally unnoticed by the general public. For completeness, a list of forthcoming solar eclipses is given in Table 6.

Note that when viewing solar eclipses, looking for sunspots, or observing transits of Mercury and Venus across the Sun's disk, it is essential to take proper precautions to prevent damage to one's eyesight. Invisible infrared radiation is present even when the Sun is low on the horizon, so no ordinary optical equipment (including

Table 6 Solar eclipses

Year	Date	Type	Mid-eclipse (UT)	Duration	Location
2005	Apr. 08	Annular/total	20:36	0^{m}42^s	New Zealand, mid-Pacific, Venezuela
	Oct. 03	Annular	10:32	4^{m}31^s	Spain, N. Africa, Sudan, Kenya, Indian Ocean
2006	Mar. 29	Total	10:11	4^{m}07^s	W. & N. Africa, Turkey, Central Asia
2006	Sep. 22	Annular	11:40	7^{m}09^s	Northern S. America, South Atlantic
2007	Mar. 19	Partial	02:32		E. Asia
	Sep. 11	Partial	12:31		S. America, Antarctica
2008	Feb. 07	Annular	03:55	2^{m}12^s	Southern-Pacific Ocean, Antarctica
	Aug. 01	Total	10:21	2^{m}27^s	N. Canada, Greenland, Novaya Zemlya, Siberia, China
2009	Jan. 26	Annular	07:58	7^{m}56^s	S. Atlantic, Indian Ocean, Sumatra, Borneo
	Jly. 22	Total	02:35	6^{m}40^s	Asia, Pacific Ocean

binoculars) should ever be used. The only safe methods are viewing the image by projection, or the use of specially coated filters that reject most of the light and heat from the Sun. (Note that the so-called 'solar filters' supplied with cheap telescopes are unsafe, and should never be used.)

Lunar eclipses, when the Moon passes through the Earth's shadow, are visible from a large portion of the Earth. As with solar eclipses, there are both penumbral and umbral cones of shadow. Again, there are total and partial eclipses, where the whole or part of the Moon passes through the central umbra. The maximum duration for a total lunar eclipse, where the Moon passes through the very centre of the umbra, is 1^{h}47^m. A list of forthcoming lunar eclipses is given in Table 7. Penumbral eclipses, where the Moon enters the weak penumbra, are not readily visible and have been omitted.

Table 7 Lunar Eclipses

Year	Date	Type	Mid-eclipse (UT)	Location
2005	Oct. 17	Partial	12:03	North America, Asia (not visible in Europe)
2006	Sep. 07	Partial	18:51	W. Asia, India, E. Africa
2007	Mar. 03	Total	23:21	Europe, Africa
	Aug. 28	Total	10:37	Pacific, E. Australia
2008	Feb. 21	Total	03:26	W. Europe & Africa, S. America, N. America, (except W. coast)
	Aug. 16	Partial	21:10	India, Africa, E. Europe
2009	Dec. 31	Partial	19:23	Europe, Africa, S. America

The motion of the planets

The planets have their own distinctive patterns of motion against the background stars, and their behaviour depends on whether their orbits lie inside or outside that of the Earth. The inner (or inferior) planets, Mercury and Venus, never move far from the Sun in the sky. Four positions relative to the Earth are particularly important: inferior and superior conjunction, and eastern and western elongation (Fig. 10). The planets are easiest to see when at eastern or western elongation, although visibility depends on their position above or below the ecliptic and the observer's position on Earth. Mercury may reach magnitude -1.7, slightly brighter than Sirius, but Venus may become as bright at magnitude -4.3.

Mercury and Venus disappear from view when near inferior or superior conjunction, except on the infrequent occasions when, at inferior conjunction, they appear to cross (transit) the face of the Sun. This occurs more frequently for Mercury than Venus. Future transits of Mercury are 2006 November 8, 2016 May 9, and 2019 November 11. Transits of Venus occur in pairs, separated by about 8 years, with much longer intervals between pairs. The current transits are 2004 June 8 and 2012 June 5–6. (The previous pair were 1874 December 9 and 1882 December 6.)

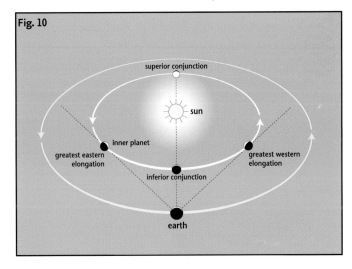

Fig. 10

Similar positions apply to the outer (or superior) planets, Mars, Jupiter, Saturn, Uranus, Neptune (and Pluto), but here the planets are best seen when at opposition, opposite the Sun in the sky (Fig. 11). In the case of Mars, which has an eccentric orbit, the distance at opposition may vary widely. The planet appears largest when opposition occurs near perihelion (the closest point of a body's orbit to the Sun), and particularly large when Mars is near perihelion and the Earth is reasonably close to aphelion (the point farthest from the Sun). In 2003 (August) such a situation occurred and Mars was at its closest to Earth for about 60,000 years.

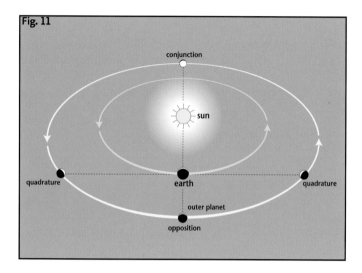

Fig. 11

Generally the planets move from west to east against the sky (like the Moon). This is known as direct motion. At times the combined motions of the Earth and of the planet concerned, cause the planet to appear to move backwards (or retrograde) against the sky for some time, before it returns to direct motion (Fig. 12). Depending on the circumstances, the paths may form loops, or open 'S' or 'Z' shapes. Opposition occurs during the period of retrograde motion, when the Earth is 'overtaking' the outer planet.

Because of the length of its orbital period, Mars reaches opposition in alternate years, although there is generally a period

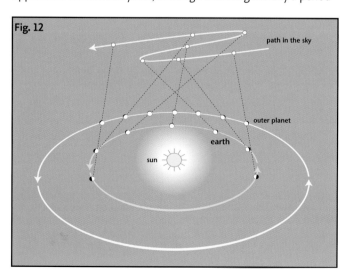

Fig. 12

each year when it is bright and readily visible. Although the other planets normally come to opposition each year, occasionally (as with Saturn in 2004), a year may pass without opposition.

The positions of the planets

The positions of the outer planets – Mars, Jupiter, Saturn, Uranus, and Neptune – and of minor planets may be shown on charts that apply anywhere in the world. Unfortunately this is not the case for Mercury and Venus, because their altitude above the horizon varies greatly with the latitude of the observer. For this reason, their positions, relative to the Sun, are shown on the twilight diagrams; Venus as a continuous line, and Mercury as a broken one. When a planet appears on the left-hand side of the diagram it is visible after sunset, and when on the right, before sunrise. The diagrams show how visibility of these two planets varies greatly at different apparitions during the year.

The inner planets

Observation of Mercury is always difficult, because it is never more than 28° from the Sun, and immediately after sunset or before sunrise, few stars are visible to act as guides. In the northern hemisphere, conditions are best at eastern elongations in the spring, and western elongations in the autumn, when the planet is highest in the sky, although it is never more than 18° from the Sun. In the southern hemisphere, conditions are much more favourable and the planet may even reach its maximum elongation. Observations are best at western (morning) elongation in the autumn (April), and eastern (evening) elongation in the spring (September). Observers in the tropics are often able to observe the planet at any elongation. Forthcoming elongations are given in Table 8. Few details are visible on Mercury's surface, except with advanced CCD equipment, but it does show phases.

Venus, however, is brighter, may reach an elongation of 47°, and is visible for longer. In some years it may be seen for months at a time. Few details are apparent on the dense cloud layer, but its phases are clearly visible. It may be observed in the daylight sky as it passes inferior conjunction, when refraction of sunlight through the atmosphere produces a ring of light around the dark body of the planet. Forthcoming conjunctions and elongations of Venus are given in Table 9.

The outer planets

Although the complex motions of the inferior planets may be plotted on star charts, such diagrams are of little use because so few reference stars are visible in the twilight, when Mercury (in particular) and Venus must be observed. The situation is far better for the outer planets, and individual charts showing the positions of Mars, Jupiter, Saturn, Uranus and Neptune for the next five years are given later. These planets will be brightest and easiest to observe when near opposition.

Table 8 Elongations of Mercury

Year	Eastern elongations				Western elongations			
2005	Mar. 12	18°20'	Jly. 09	26°15'	Apr. 26	27°10'	Aug. 23	18°24'
	Nov. 03	23°31'			Dec. 12	21°05'		
2006	Feb. 24	18°08'	Jun. 20	24°56'	Apr. 08	27°46'	Aug. 07	19°11'
	Oct. 17	24°49'			Nov. 25	19°54'		
2007	Feb. 07	18°14'	Jun. 02	23°22'	Mar. 22	27°44'	Jly. 20	20°19'
	Sep. 29	25°59'			Nov. 08	18°59'		
2008	Jan. 22	18°39'	May. 14	21°48'	Mar. 03	27°09'	Jly. 01	21°47'
	Sep. 11	26°52'			Oct. 22	18°19'		
2009	Jan. 04	19°21'	Apr. 26	20°25'	Feb. 13	26°06'	Jly. 13	23°27'
	Aug. 24	27°22'	Dec. 18	20°18'	Oct. 06	17°57'		
2010	Apr. 08	19°21'	Aug. 07	27°22'	Jan. 27	24°45'	May. 26	25°08'
	Dec. 01	21°27'			Sep. 19	17°52'		
2011	Mar. 23	18°37'	Jly. 20	26°49'	Jan. 09	23°17'	May. 07	26°33'
	Nov. 14	22°45'			Sep. 03	18°07'	Dec. 23	21°51'
2012	Mar. 05	18°13'	Jly. 01	25°45'	Apr. 18	27°30'	Aug. 16	18°42'
	Oct. 26	24°05'			Dec. 04	20°33'		
2013	Feb. 16	18°08'	Jun. 12	24°17'	Mar. 31	27°50'	Jly. 30	19°38'
	Oct. 09	25°20'			Nov. 18	19°29'		
2014	Jan. 31	18°22'	May. 25	22°41'	Mar. 14	27°33'	Jly. 12	20°55'
	Sep. 21	26°24'			Nov. 01	18°40'		

Mars

As mentioned earlier, some oppositions of Mars are far more favourable for observation than others. Forthcoming oppositions are listed in Table 10, where the exceptionally fine opposition of 2003 is shown for comparison purposes. The best oppositions occur in August and September when Mars is near perihelion and has a southern declination, which favours observers in the southern hemisphere. At these times the south polar region is visible. It is also around perihelion that the maximum heating occurs, which may give rise to major dust storms.

The small disk of Mars means that observations really require an aperture of at least 100 mm, and preferably much more. Although, unlike Mercury and Venus, Mars never displays crescent phases, it often presents a gibbous phase (less than a full disk), and this must be taken into account when making observations,

particularly drawings. The polar caps are normally clearly visible, though they are sometimes masked by a polar hood that may extend over 50° of latitude. The surface itself presents a multitude of dark markings. These tend to change with time, but the most prominent, essentially permanent markings are shown on the map (Fig. 13). Note that, unlike all the other charts and photographs in this atlas, the images of Mars, Saturn and Jupiter show south at the top. A surprising amount of detail may be detected through patient observation and taking advantage of moments of best seeing. Dust storms may cover a large portion of the planet and there are also white hazes, seen at the morning terminator, where clouds that have formed during the night do not disappear immediately at sunrise. Blue hazes may cover a considerable portion of the disk. Naturally, no amateur can hope to detect as many details as those shown by large professional telescopes or the Hubble Space Telescope (Fig. 14).

Table 9 Conjunctions and elongations of Venus

Superior conjunction	Eastern elongation		Inferior conjunction	Western elongation	
2005 Mar. 31	2005 Nov. 03	47°	2006 Jan. 13	2006 Mar. 25	47°
2006 Oct. 27	2007 Jun. 09	45°	2007 Aug. 18	2007 Oct. 28	46°
2008 Jun. 09	2009 Jan. 14	47°	2009 Mar. 27	2009 Jun. 05	46°
2010 Jan. 11	2010 Aug. 20	46°	2010 Oct. 29	2011 Jan. 08	47°
2011 Aug. 16	2012 Mar. 27	46°	2012 Jun. 06	2012 Aug. 15	46°
2013 Mar. 28	2013 Nov. 01	47°	2014 Jan. 11	2014 Mar. 22	47°
2014 Oct. 25	2015 Jun. 06	45°	2015 Aug. 15	2015 Oct. 26	46°

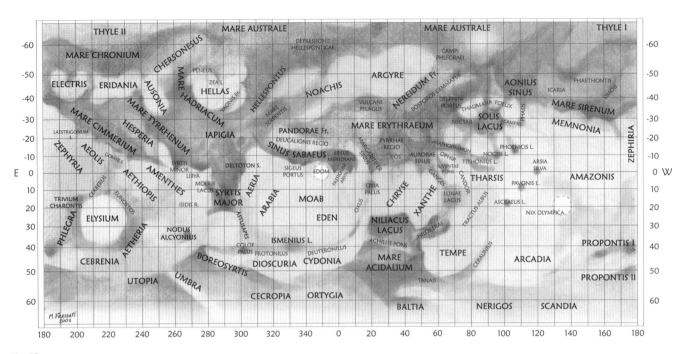

Fig. 13

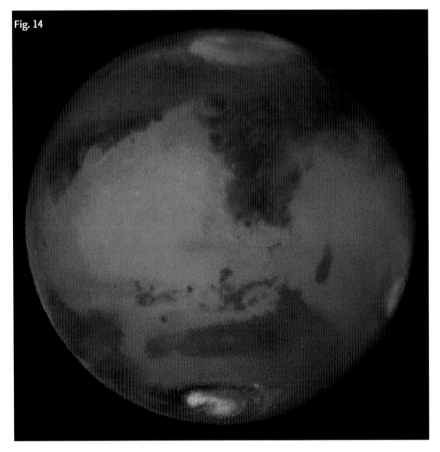

Fig. 14

Figs. 15 & 17 Key to the atmospheres of Jupiter and Saturn

B	Belt	**E**	Equatorial	**P**	Polar	**S**	South	**Tr**	Tropical
Ba	Band	**N**	North	**R**	Region	**T**	Temperate	**Z**	Zone

SOLAR SYSTEM OBJECTS

Table 10	Oppositions of Mars		
Date	Declination	Diameter	Magnitude
2003 Aug. 28	-15 49	25"	-2.7
2005 Nov. 07	+15 54	20"	-2.1
2007 Dec. 24	+26 46	16"	-1.4
2010 Jan. 29	+22 09	14"	-1.1
2012 Mar. 03	+10 17	14"	-1.0
2014 Apr. 08	-05 08	15"	-1.3

Table 11	Oppositions of Jupiter	
Date	Declination	Magnitude
2005 Apr. 03	-04°03'	-2.0
2006 May. 04	-14°46'	-2.0
2007 Jun. 05	-21°54'	-2.1
2008 Jly. 09	-22°29'	-2.3
2009 Aug. 14	-15°10'	-2.4
2010 Sep. 21	-02°06'	-2.5
2011 Oct. 29	+11°53'	-2.5
2012 Dec. 03	+21°21'	-2.4
2014 Jan. 05	+22°40'	-2.2

Jupiter

Even a small telescope of 50–75 mm aperture will suffice to show the dark belts and bright zones on Jupiter. These names of these features are shown in the diagram (Fig. 15), which also shows where the Great Red Spot occupies the Hollow in the South

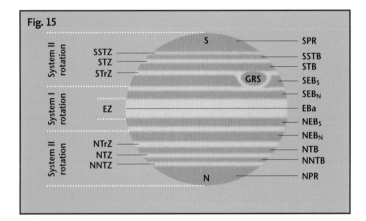

Fig. 15

Fig. 16

Equatorial Belt. Larger apertures will enable many individual dark and light spots and streaks to be seen, together with the occasional, more prominent white ovals. All these features change with time, and move at different rates in the atmosphere. Jupiter's atmosphere does, in fact, rotate at different rates from the deep interior. There are two rates: System I ($9^h50^m30^s$) applies to the equatorial regions; and System II ($9^h55^m40^s$) covers the rest of the planet. The belts and zones within each system are shown in the diagram, which may be compared with the Hubble Space Telescope image in Fig. 16.

Table 12	Satellite phenomena
Transit	Satellite passes in front of planet
Shadow transit	Satellite's shadow is cast on planet
Eclipse	Satellite is eclipsed by planet's shadow
Occultation	Satellite is hidden by planet's disk

Oppositions of Jupiter occur at intervals of approximately 13 months (Table 11), so it is readily visible at some time during a year. Unlike Mars, there is only a slight phase effect. The four brightest satellites, Io, Europa, Ganymede, and Callisto are readily visible, even in binoculars. They frequently cross (transit) Jupiter's disk, on which their shadows may be seen, as well as being eclipsed by Jupiter's shadow, or occulted by its disk. The various phenomena, which may be observed with small telescopes (50–75 mm aperture) are listed in Table 12.

Saturn

With its system of rings, Saturn is a striking object for observation. Oppositions occur at intervals of about 378 days, so occasionally a year may pass without an opposition, but the planet will nevertheless be visible for some time at the beginning and end of that year. Oppositions of Saturn are given in Table 13. The structure of its atmosphere is very similar to that of Jupiter (Fig. 16), although the belts and zones are more subdued, being veiled by an upper-atmosphere haze. Only occasionally is any detail visible within the belts and zones, although single, large,

Table 13 Oppositions of Saturn

Date	Declination	Magnitude
2005 Jan. 13	+21°20'	-0.2
2006 Jan. 27	+18°58'	-0.0
2007 Feb. 10	+15°32'	+0.2
2008 Feb. 24	+11°20'	+0.4
2009 Mar. 08	+06°41'	+0.7
2010 Mar. 22	+01°51'	+0.7
2011 Apr. 03	-02°57'	+0.6
2012 Apr. 15	-07°31'	+0.4
2013 Apr. 28	-11°42'	+0.3
2014 May. 10	-15°21'	+0.3

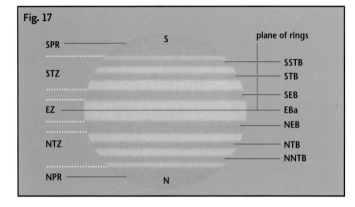

Fig. 17

white spots sometimes form when the planet is near perihelion.

Saturn's rings have a very complex structure, but amateur telescopes are normally able to show Rings A and B, both of which are bright, with B the brighter of the two, and separated by the Cassini Division. The inner, C ring, is more difficult to detect, because it is thin and faint. It sometimes appears against the disk of the planet, looking like a faint dark belt. The other rings, D to G, are narrow, and not readily detectable with amateur equipment.

Passes through the ring plane occur twice per Saturnian year – i.e., once every 15 years. At present the southern hemisphere of the planet is visible, and the next passage through the ring plane will occur in 2010, after which the northern hemisphere will be tilted towards us. The rings are extremely thin – generally thought to have an average thickness of about 100 metres – and when edge-on often disappear temporarily. As they come into view, however, they hide more and more of one hemisphere, and the area around the opposite pole comes into view.

Saturn has a large satellite system, with at least 30 satellites, eight of which may be seen with amateur equipment, including Titan, the largest, and Iapetus, which shows striking changes in magnitude, always appearing brighter at western elongation.

Uranus and Neptune

Both of these planets are too distant and appear too small to offer any details for observation. (We know, in fact, from Voyager spaceprobe observations that Uranus is essentially featureless, but

Fig. 18

that Neptune does show some cloud features.) Uranus is just bright enough (pproximately mag. 5.7 at opposition) for it to be detectable with the naked eye, provided one knows where to look, but is never an easy object. Neptune reaches approximately mag. 7.8 at opposition, and therefore always requires some form of optical equipment. Advanced amateurs are able to record the satellites of Uranus and Neptune, but these are generally beyond the capabilities of most amateurs. Oppositions of Uranus are shown in Table 14, and those of Neptune in Table 15.

Minor bodies: asteroids, comets, and meteors

Of the many thousands of minor planets (asteroids), the majority of which orbit between the orbits of Mars and Jupiter, four are detectable with binoculars or small telescopes when near opposition. These are Ceres, Pallas, Juno, and Vesta. Vesta may, in fact, reach mag. 5.9, just within naked-eye visibility.

Bright comets are, by their very nature, largely unpredictable. Those with short orbital periods are generally faint, only Comet Halley, with a period of 76 years, is normally bright enough to be seen easily. Most bright comets, such as Comet Hyakutake in 1996 and Comet Hale-Bopp in 1997, arrive unexpectedly, and details of their positions are made available either through circulars issued by various astronomical organisations, or through the Internet.

Comets consist of ices and dust particles, and as they are warmed by the Sun, gases and dust are released into interplanetary space. The dust particles are the primary source of the meteors that are observed in the Earth's atmosphere on any clear night. The general population of dust, in more-or-less random orbits, gives rise to what are known as sporadic meteors, which may appear at any time, and in any direction. More important are the streams of dust particles released by comets, and which follow paths along the cometary orbits. At certain times of the year, the Earth intercepts some of these streams, producing predictable meteor showers. The meteors in a particular shower appear to arise from a particular point on the sky (known as the radiant), and are known by the constellation in which the radiant lies. Shower members also tend to have specific characteristics, with colours, speeds, magnitudes, and numbers that are typical for each shower. Brief details of a number of major showers are given in Table 16, and more specific information is given under the entries for the individual constellations. (Note that details of the Quadrantid shower may be found under Boötes.)

Table 14 Oppositions of Uranus

Date	Declination	Diameter	Magnitude
2005 Sep. 01	-9°02'	3.60	6.06
2006 Sep. 05	-7°32'	3.59	6.07
2007 Sep. 09	-6°00'	3.59	6.07
2008 Sep. 13	-4°26'	3.59	6.07
2009 Sep. 17	-2°52'	3.59	6.07
2010 Sep. 21	-1°17'	3.59	6.07
2011 Sep. 26	+0°19'	3.59	6.07
2012 Sep. 29	+1°55'	3.60	6.06
2013 Oct. 03	+3^30'	3.60	6.06
2014 Oct. 07	+5°04'	3.61	6.05

Table 15 Oppositions of Neptune

Date	Declination	Diameter	Magnitude
2005 Aug. 08	-16°07'	2.52	7.66
2006 Aug. 11	-15°30'	2.52	7.65
2007 Aug. 13	-14°53'	2.52	7.65
2008 Aug. 15	-14°14'	2.52	7.65
2009 Aug. 17	-13°33'	2.52	7.65
2010 Aug. 20	-12°52'	2.52	7.65
2011 Aug. 22	-12°09'	2.52	7.65
2012 Aug. 24	-11°26'	2.52	7.65
2013 Aug. 27	-10°42'	2.52	7.64
2014 Aug. 29	-09°56'	2.52	7.64

Table 16 Meteor showers

Shower	Maximum	Normal Limits
Quadrantids	Jan. 04	Jan. 01–06
Virginids	Apr. 10	Mar.–Apr. Apr. 07–18
Lyrids	Apr. 22	Apr. 19–25
η-Aquarids	May. 05	Apr. 24–May 20
α-Scorpids	Apr. 27 May. 12	Apr. 20–May 19
Ophiuchids	Jun. 09 Jun. 19	May 19–Jly.
α-Cygnids	Jly. 21 Aug. 21	Jly.–Aug.
Capricornids	Jly. 08 Jly. 15 Jly. 26	Jly.–Aug.
δ-Aquarids	Jly. 28 Aug. 06	Jly. 15–Aug. 20
Piscis Australids	Jly. 31	Jly. 15–Aug. 20
α-Capricornids	Aug. 02	Jly. 15–Aug. 20
ι-Aquarids	Aug. 06	Jly.–Aug.
Perseids	Aug. 12	Jly. 23–Aug. 20
Piscids	Sep. 08 Sep. 31 Oct. 13	Sep.–Oct.
Orionids	Oct. 21	Oct. 16–26
Taurids	Nov. 03	Oct. 20–Nov. 30
Leonids	Nov. 17	Nov. 15–20
Puppids-Velids	Dec. 08 Dec. 25	Nov. 27–Jan.
Geminids	Dec. 13	Dec. 07–15
Ursids	Dec. 22	Dec. 17–25

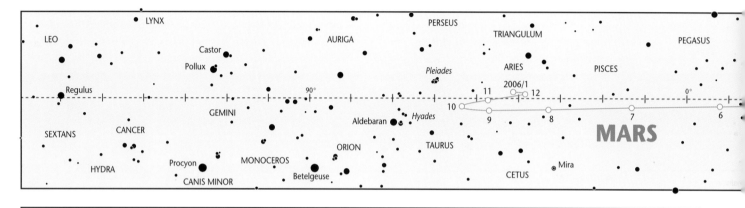

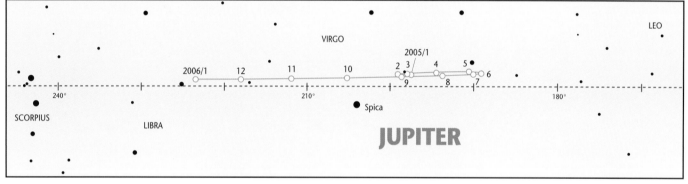

Key

- civil twilight
- nautical twilight
- astronomical twilight
- full darkness

—— sunrise/sunset time

○ exact time of Full Moon

● exact time of New Moon

visible times within
twilight/darkness
for :-

—— Venus

—— Mercury

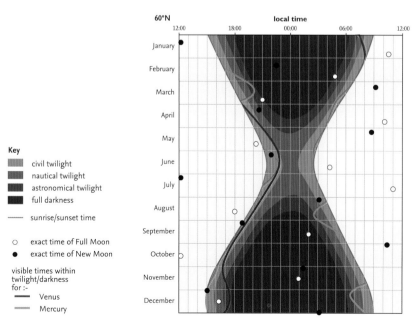

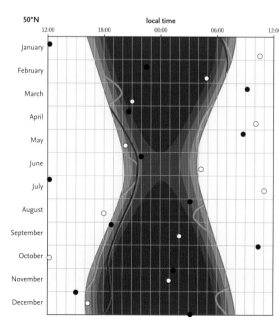

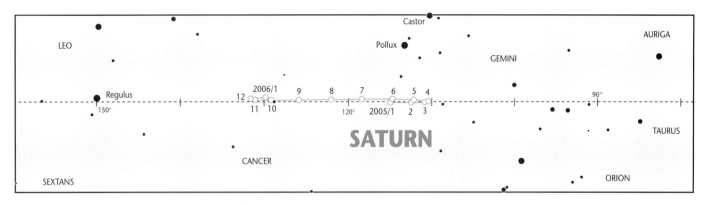

SATURN

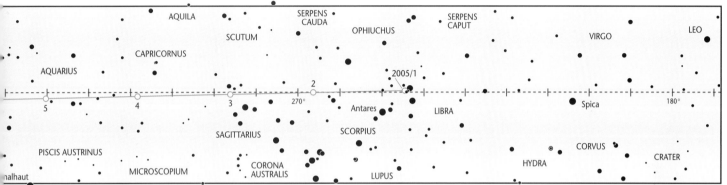

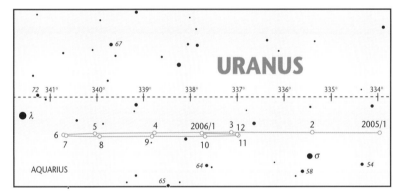

URANUS

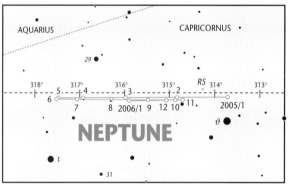

NEPTUNE

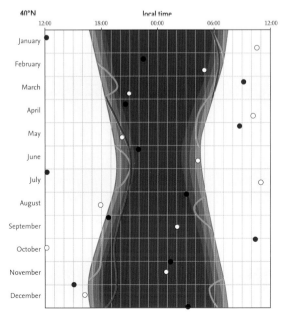

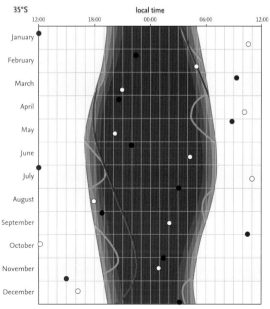

SOLAR SYSTEM OBJECTS

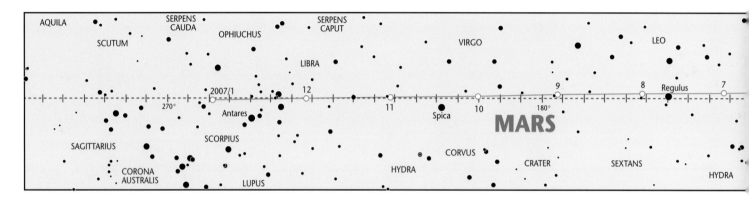

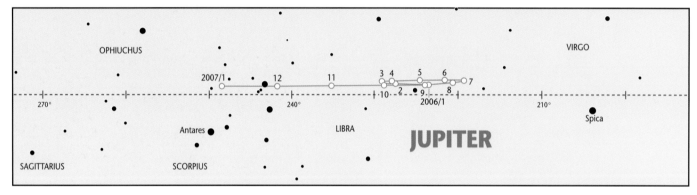

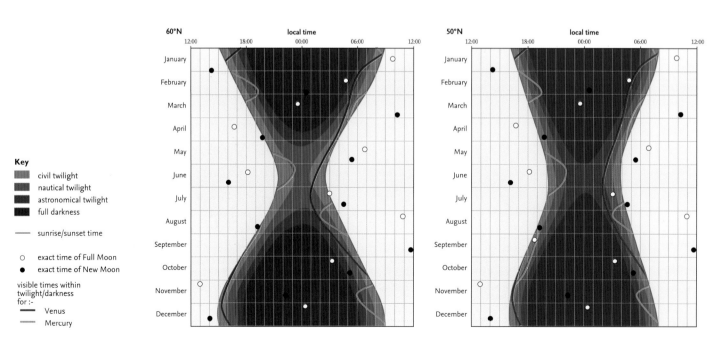

Key

civil twilight
nautical twilight
astronomical twilight
full darkness

—— sunrise/sunset time

○ exact time of Full Moon
● exact time of New Moon

visible times within
twilight/darkness
for :-
—— Venus
—— Mercury

SOLAR SYSTEM OBJECTS

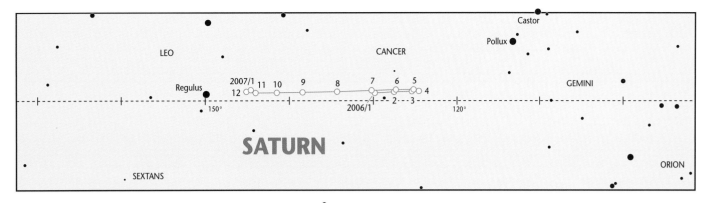

SATURN

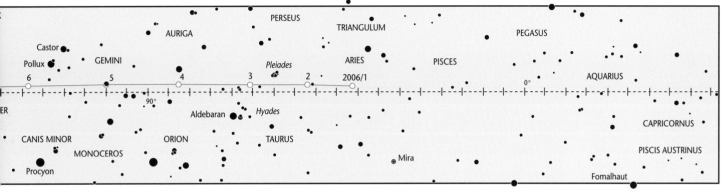

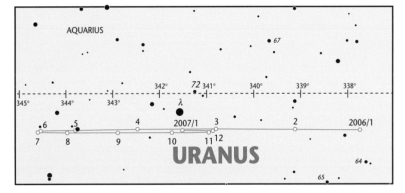

URANUS

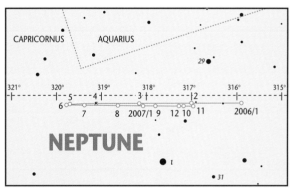

NEPTUNE

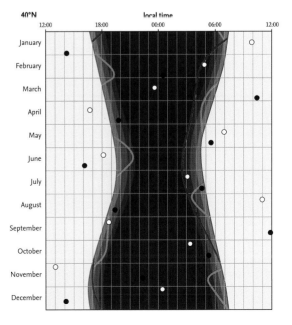

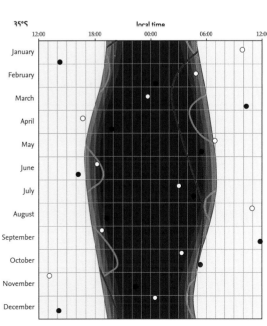

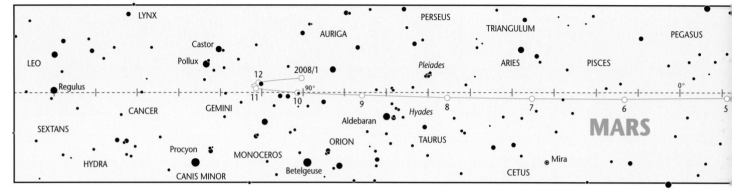

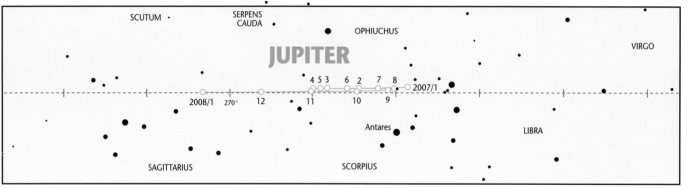

Key

- civil twilight
- nautical twilight
- astronomical twilight
- full darkness
- —— sunrise/sunset time

- ○ exact time of Full Moon
- ● exact time of New Moon

visible times within
twilight/darkness
for :-
- —— Venus
- —— Mercury

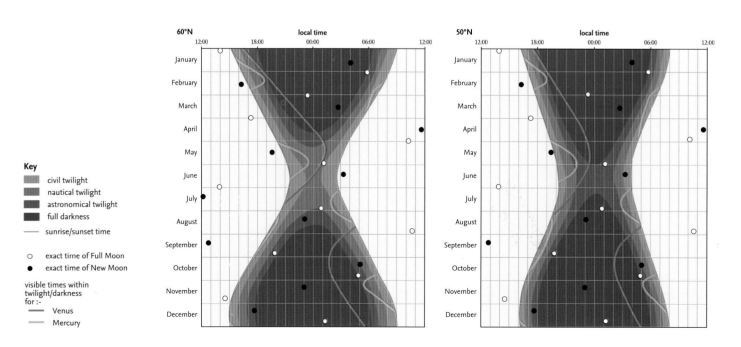

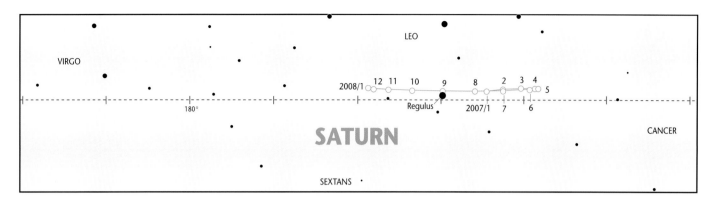

SATURN

LEO
VIRGO
2008/1 12 11 10 9 8 2 3 4 5
180°   Regulus   2007/1 7 6
CANCER
SEXTANS

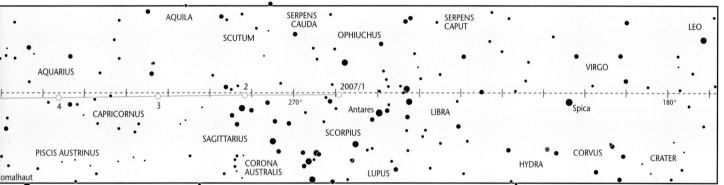

AQUILA SERPENS CAUDA SERPENS CAPUT LEO
SCUTUM OPHIUCHUS VIRGO
AQUARIUS 2 2007/1 180°
4 3 270° Antares LIBRA Spica
CAPRICORNUS SCORPIUS
SAGITTARIUS CORVUS CRATER
PISCIS AUSTRINUS CORONA AUSTRALIS LUPUS HYDRA
omalhaut

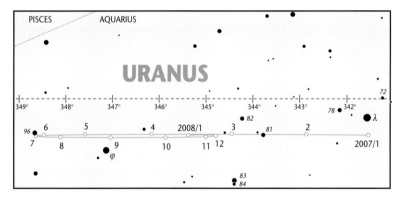

PISCES AQUARIUS

URANUS

72
349° 348° 347° 346° 345° 344° 343° 342°
78 λ
96 6 5 4 2008/1 3 2
7 8 9 10 11 12 2007/1
φ
83
84

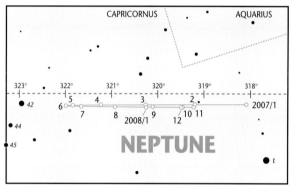

CAPRICORNUS AQUARIUS

323° 322° 321° 320° 319° 318°
5 4 3 2
42 6 2007/1
7 8 2008/1 9 10 11
44 12
NEPTUNE
45 ι

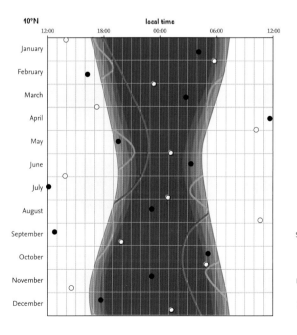

10°N
local time
12:00 18:00 00:00 06:00 12:00
January
February
March
April
May
June
July
August
September
October
November
December

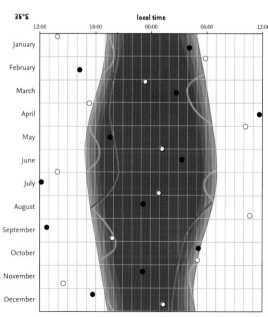

35°S
local time
12:00 18:00 00:00 06:00 12:00
January
February
March
April
May
June
July
August
September
October
November
December

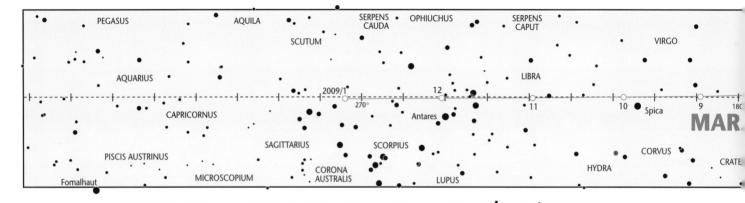

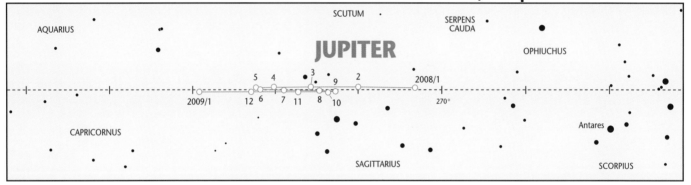

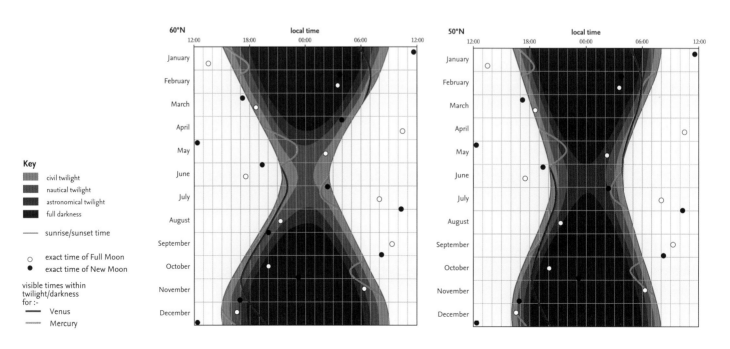

Key

civil twilight

nautical twilight

astronomical twilight

full darkness

—— sunrise/sunset time

○ exact time of Full Moon

● exact time of New Moon

visible times within
twilight/darkness
for :-

—— Venus

—— Mercury

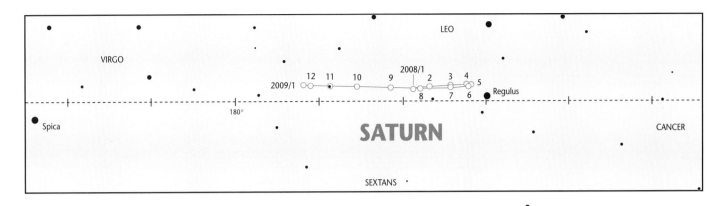

SATURN

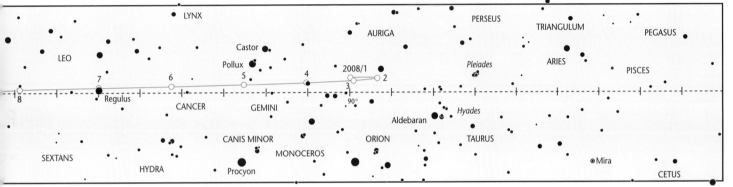

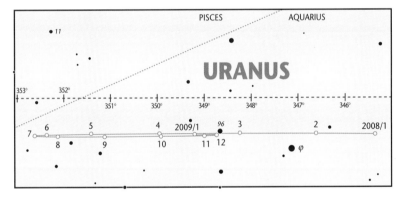

URANUS

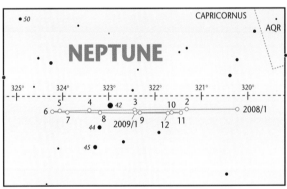

NEPTUNE

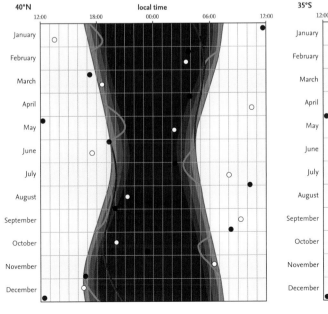

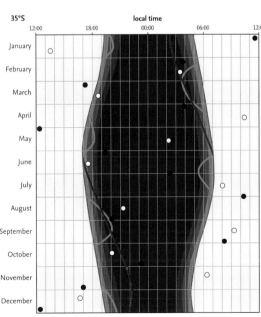

2009

SOLAR SYSTEM OBJECTS

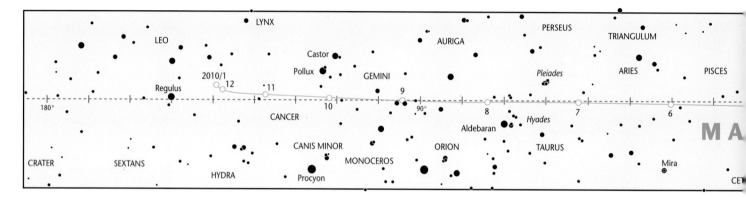

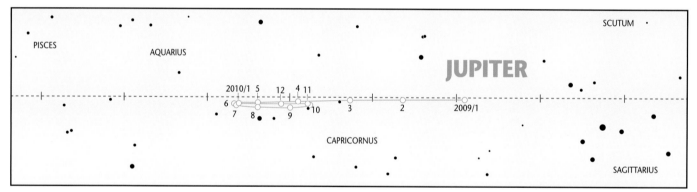

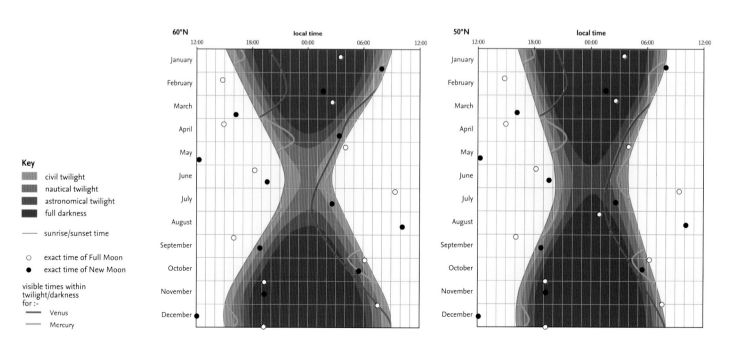

Key

- civil twilight
- nautical twilight
- astronomical twilight
- full darkness

—— sunrise/sunset time

○ exact time of Full Moon
● exact time of New Moon

visible times within
twilight/darkness
for :-
—— Venus
—— Mercury

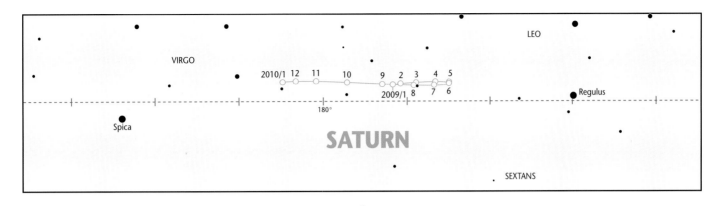

SATURN

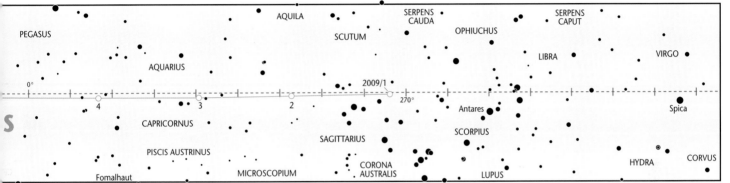

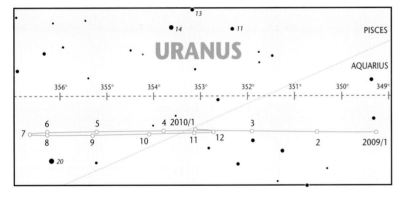

URANUS

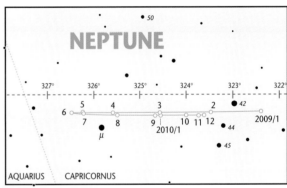

NEPTUNE

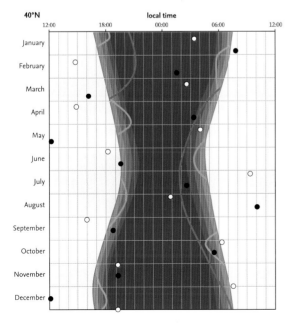

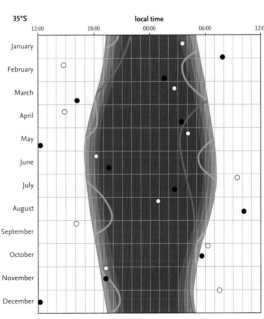

SOLAR SYSTEM OBJECTS

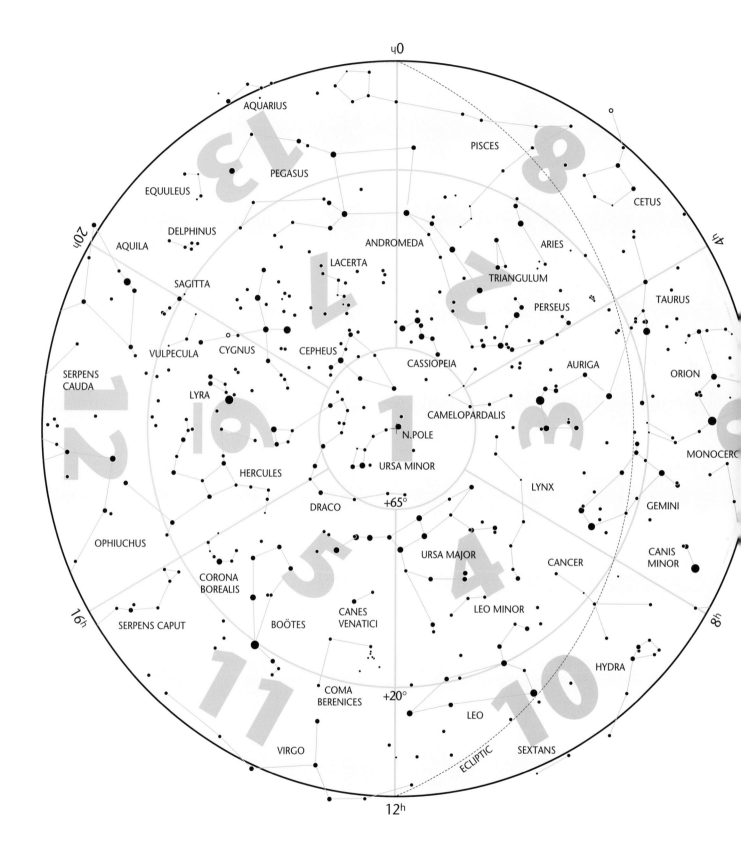

Northern Hemisphere

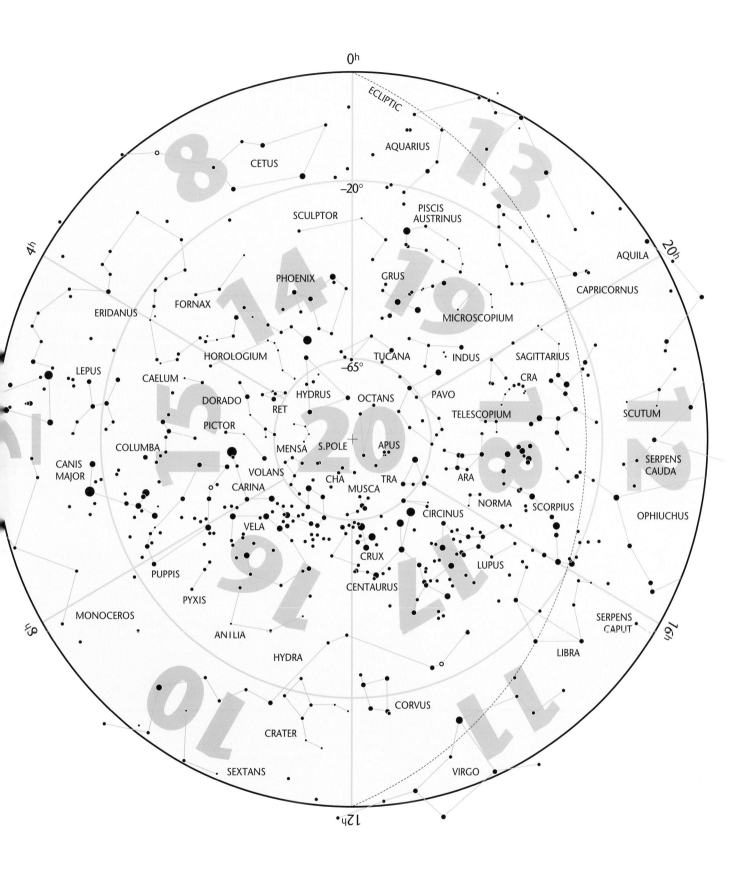

Southern Hemisphere

Index of lunar features

INDEX

Index of constellations

Bold indicates main entry. Subsequent page numbers refer to the main star chart(s) on which the constellation may be found.

INDEX

INDEX

Table L2 - Lunar Basins	Map	Latitude	Longtitude	Diameter (km)	
				D1	D2
Apollo	FS	36°S	151°W	505	250
Australe	NS, FS	51.5°S	94.5°W	880	550
Bailly	NS	67°S	68°W	300	150
Birkhoff	FS	59°N	147°W	330	150
Coulomb-Sarton	FS	52°N	123°W	530	400, 180
Crisium	NS	17.5°N	58.5°E	1060	635,500,380
Freundlich-Sharonov	FS	18.5°N	175°E	600	–
Grimaldi	NS	5°S	68°W	430	230
Hertzsprung	FS	1.5°N	128.5°W	570	265, 140
Humboldtianum	NS, FS	61°N	84°E	600	275
Humorum	NS	24°S	39.5°W	820?	440, 325
Imbrium	NS	33°N	18°W	1160	670
Ingenii	FS	34°S	163°E	560?	325
Keeler-Heaviside	FS	10°S	162°E	780?	–
Korolev	FS	4.5°S	157°W	440	220
Lorentz	FS	34°N	97°W	360	185
Mendel-Rydberg	NS, FS	50°S	94°W	630?	460, 200
Mendeleev	FS	6°N	141°E	330	140
Moscoviense	FS	26°N	147°E	445	210
Mutus-Vlacq	NS, FS	51.5°S	21°E	690	–
Nectaris	NS	16°S	34°E	860	600, 450, 35
Orientale	NS, FS	20°S	95°W	930	620, 480, 320
Planck	FS	57.5°S	135.5°E	325	175
Poincaré	FS	57.5°S	162°E	340	175
Serenitatis	NS	27°N	19°E	740	420
Schiller-Zucchius	NS, FS	56°S	44.5°W	325	165
Schrödinger	FS	75°S	134°E	320	155
Smythii	NS, FS	2°S	87°E	840	360
South Pole-Aitken	NS, FS	56°S	180°	2500	1800
Tsiolkovskiy-Stark	FS	15°S	128°E	700	–

The latitude and longitude are for the centre, diameter D1 (km) is for the main or outer ring, diameter(s) D2 for the inner ring(s), if observed, queried where uncertain. NS = nearside map (P. 196), FS = farside map (P. 197).

Further information

Bone, Neil (1993), *Philip's Observer's Handbook: Meteors*, George Philip, London.

Burnham, Robert (1978), *Burnham's Celestial Handbook*, 3 vols, Dover Publications, NY.

Cook, J., ed. (1999), *The Hatfield Photographic Lunar Atlas*, Springer-Verlag, Heidelberg.

Dunlop, Storm (2003), *Practical Astronomy*, Philip's, London.

Dunlop, Storm & Tirion, Wil (2004), *How to Identify Night Sky*, 2nd edn, HarperCollins.

Dunlop, Storm & Tirion, Wil (2003), *Firefly Planisphere Deluxe*, Firefly Books, Buffalo, NY & Toronto.

ESA (1997), *The Hipparcos and Tycho Catalogues*, ESA SP-1200, European Space Agency, Noordwijk.

Good, Gerry A. (2003), *Observing Variable Stars*, Springer-Verlag, London.

Harrington, Philip S. (1990), *Touring the Universe through Binoculars*, Wiley, New York.

Hirschfeld, A., Sinnott, R.W. & Ochsenbein, F. (1991), *Sky Catalogue 2000.0, Volume 1, Stars to Magnitude 8.0*, 2nd edn, Sky Publ. Corp., Cambridge, Mass., & Cambridge University Press, Cambridge.

Hirschfeld, A. & Sinnott, R.W. (1985), *Sky Catalogue 2000.0, Volume 2, Double Stars, Variable Stars and Nonstellar Objects*, Sky Publ. Corp., Cambridge, Mass., & Cambridge University Press, Cambridge.

Illingworth, Valerie & Clark, John O.E., ed. (2000), *Collins Dictionary of Astronomy*, 2nd edn, HarperCollins, London & *Facts on File Dictionary of Astronomy*, 4th edn, Facts-on-File, New York

Inglis, Mike (2003), *Observer's Guide to Stellar Evolution*, Springer-Verlag, London.

Karkoschka, E. (1999), *The Observer's Sky Atlas*, 2nd edn, Springer-Verlag, New York.

Malin, David & Frew, David, eds (1995), *Hartung's Astronomical Objects for Southern Telescopes*, 2nd edn, Cambridge University Press, Cambridge.

Moore, Patrick, (2000), *Exploring the night sky with binoculars*, 4th edn, Cambridge University Press, Cambridge.

Moore, Patrick, ed. (1995), *The Observational Amateur Astronomer*, Springer-Verlag, London.

O'Meara, Stephen (1998), *The Messier Objects*, Sky Publ. Corp. & Cambridge University Press, Cambridge.

O'Meara, Stephen (1998), *The Caldwell Objects*, Sky Publ. Corp. & Cambridge University Press, Cambridge.

Ridpath, Ian & Tirion, Wil (2000), *Collins Pocket Guide: Stars & Planets*, 3rd edn, HarperCollins, London.

Ridpath, Ian & Tirion, Wil (2003), *Monthly Sky Guide*, 6th edn, Cambridge University Press, Cambridge.

Ridpath, Ian, ed. (2003), *Dictionary of Astronomy*, 2nd edn, Oxford University Press, Oxford.

Rükl, Antonín (1991), *Hamlyn Atlas of the Moon*, Paul Hamlyn, London (new edition in press, Sky Publ. Corp.).

Sinnott, Roger (ed.) (1988), *NGC 2000.0*, Sky Publ. Corp., Cambridge, Mass., & Cambridge University Press, Cambridge.

Sinnott, Roger & Perryman, Michael (1997), *Millennium Star Atlas*, Sky Publ. Corp., Cambridge, Mass. & European Space Agency, Noordwijk.

Tirion, Wil & Skiff, Brian (2001), *Bright Star Atlas*, 2nd edn, Willmann-Bell, 2nd edn, Richmond, Virginia.

Tirion, Wil (2001), *Cambridge Star Atlas*, 3rd edn, Cambridge University Press, Cambridge.

Tirion, Wil & Sinnott, Roger (1998), *Sky Atlas 2000.0*, 2nd edn, Sky Publ. Corp. & Cambridge University Press, Cambridge.

Tirion, Wil, Rappaport B. & Remaklus, W. (2001), *Uranometria 2000.0*, 2nd edn, Willmann-Bell, Richmond, Virginia. A major, three-volume work.

Handbooks (Published yearly)

British Astronomical Association, *Handbook*
Royal Astronomical Society of Canada, *Observer's Handbook*

CD-ROMs (Reference)

Douglass, Eric (2003), *Consolidated Lunar Atlas*, Lunar and Planetary Institute

European Space Agency (1998), *Celestia 2000 (The Hipparcos and Tycho Catalgues)*, SP-1220, ESA

Journals

Astronomy, Astro Media Corp., 21027 Crossroads Circle, P.O. Box 1612, Waukesha, WI 53187-1612 USA. www: http://www.astronomy.com

Astronomy Now, Pole Star Publications, PO Box 175, Tonbridge, Kent TN10 4QX UK. www: http://www.astronomynow.com

Sky & Telescope, Sky Publishing Corp., Cambridge, MA 02138-1200, USA. www: http://www.skyandtelescope.com/

Societies

American Association of Variable Star Observers (AAVSO), 25 Birch Street, Cambridge, Mass. 02138-1205, USA. www: http://www.aavso.org/

Astronomical League, Executive Secretary: 11305 King Street, Overland Park, KS 66210-3421. www: http://www.astroleague.org/

British Astronomical Association (BAA), Burlington House, Piccadilly, London W1J 0DU www: http://www.ast.cam.ac.uk/~baa/

New South Wales Branch: P.O. Box 138, Randwick, NSW 2031, Australia.

Federation of Astronomical Societies (FAS), Secretary: Ken Sheldon, Whitehaven, Maytree Road, Lower Moor, Pershore, Worcs. WR10 2NY. www: http://www.ukindex.co.uk/ukastro/fasmain.html

Royal Astronomical Society (RAS), Burlington House, Piccadilly, London W1J 0BQ. www: http://www.ras.org.uk/

Royal Astronomical Society of Canada, 136 Dupont Street, Toronto, Ontario M5R 1V2 Canada. www: http://www.rasc.ca

Royal Astronomical Society of New Zealand (RASNZ), P.O. Box 3181, Wellington, New Zealand. www: http://rasnz@rasnz.org.nz

Society for Popular Astronomy, 36 Fairway, Keyworth, Nottingham NG12 5DU. www: http://www.popastro.com/home.htm

Software

Dark Skies (Twilight and lunar phase freeware program) by Todd Daniels. www: http://www.acretiondisk.org

Planet's Visibility, (Planetary and eclipse freeware): Alcyone Software, Germany. www: http://www.alcyone.de

Starry Night & Starry Night Pro, Sienna Software Inc., Toronto, Canada. www: http://www.starrynight.com

Internet sources

There are a number of sites with information about all aspects of astronomy, and all of those given above have numerous links. Although many amateur sites are excellent, treat any statements and data with caution. The additional sites listed below offer accurate information. Please note that the URLs may change. If so, use a search engine to locate the information source.

Information

Auroral information Michigan Tech: http://www.geo.mtu.edu/weather/aurora/

Comets JPL Comet Home Page: http://encke.jpl.nasa.gov/

Comets & Meteor Showers Gary Kronk's Home Page: http://comets.amsmeteors.org/

Deep sky objects Saguaro Astronomy Club Database: http://www.virtualcolony.com/sac/

Eclipses: Fred Espenak's Eclipse Page: http://planets.gsfc.nasa.gov/eclipse/eclipse.html

Moon (inc. Atlas) Inconstant Moon: http://www.inconstantmoon.com/

Planets Goddard Spaceflight Center: http://planets.gsfc.nasa.gov

Satellites (inc. Space Station) Heavens Above: http://www.heavens-above.com/
Visual Satellite Observer's: http://www.satellite.eu.org/satintro.html

Star Chart National Geographic Chart: http://www.nationalgeographic.com/features/97/stars/chart/index.html

What's Visible Skyhound: http://www.skyhound.com/sh/skyhound.html

Skyview Cafe: http://www.skyviewcafe.com

Stargazer: http://www.outerbody.com/stargazer/ (choose 'New View', click & drag to change)

Institutes and organisations

European Space Agency: http://www.esa.int/

International Dark Sky Association: http://www.darksky.org/

Jet Propulsion Laboratory: http://www.jpl.nasa.gov/

Lunar and Planetary Laboratory: http://cass.jsc.nasa.gov/lpi.html

National Aeronautics and Space Administration: http://www.hq.nasa.gov/

Solar Institute: http://umbra.gsfc.nasa.gov/

Space Telescope Science Institute: http://www.stsci.edu/public.html